Introduction to Engineering

E 10

SAN JOSE STATE UNIVERSITY

Course   Introduction to Engineering
Course Number   **E 10**
                SAN JOSE STATE UNIVERSITY

http://create.mheducation.com

ISBN-10: 1307009174   ISBN-13: 9781307009170

Contents

Credits

CHAPTER **1**

The Engineering Profession

Chapter Objectives

When you complete your study of this chapter, you will be able to:

- Understand the role of engineering in the world
- Understand how to prepare for a meaningful engineering career
- Understand the role of an engineer in the engineering workplace
- Describe the responsibilities and roles of the most common engineering disciplines
- Gain academic career advice from past engineering graduates from various engineering disciplines

1.1 An Engineering Career

The rapidly expanding and developing sphere of science and technology may seem overwhelming to the individual exploring a career in a technological field. A technical specialist today may be called engineer, scientist, technologist, or technician, depending on education, industrial affiliation, and specific work. For example, about 700 colleges and universities in 29 countries offer close to 3 600 engineering programs accredited by ABET, the main accrediting body for engineering and technology programs. Included in these programs are such traditional specialties as aerospace, agricultural, architectural, chemical, civil, computer, construction, electrical, industrial, manufacturing, materials, mechanical, and software engineering—as well as expanding bioengineering, biomedical, biological, electromechanical, environmental, and telecommunications. Programs in engineering, mechanics, mining, nuclear, ceramic, software, and petroleum engineering add to a lengthy list of career options in engineering alone. Coupled with thousands of programs in science and technical training offered at hundreds of universities, colleges, and technical schools, the task of choosing the right field no doubt seems formidable (Figure 1.1).

Since you are reading this book, we assume that you are interested in studying engineering or at least are trying to decide whether to do so. Up to this point in your academic life you probably have had little experience with engineering as a career and have gathered your impressions from advertising materials, counselors, educators, and perhaps a practicing engineer or two. Now you must investigate as many careers as you can as soon as possible to be sure of making the right choice.

The study of engineering requires a strong background in mathematics and the physical sciences. Section 1.5 discusses typical areas of study within an engineering

Figure 1.1

Imagine the number of engineers who were involved in the design of the windmill related to construction, material choices, electrical systems, and mechanical systems.
© David Wasserman/Stockbyte/Getty Images

program that lead to the bachelor's degree. You also should consult with your academic counselor about specific course requirements. If you are enrolled in an engineering program but have not chosen a specific discipline, consult with an adviser or someone on the engineering faculty about particular course requirements in your areas of interest.

When considering a career in engineering or any closely related fields, you should explore the answers to several questions:

- What is engineering?
- What are the career opportunities for engineers?
- What are the engineering disciplines?
- Where does the engineer fit into the technical spectrum?
- How are engineers educated?
- What is meant by professionalism and engineering ethics?
- What have engineers done in the past?
- What are engineers doing now? What will engineers do in the future?
- What are the workplace competencies needed to be a successful engineer?

Finding answers to such questions can be difficult and time consuming, but essential to determining the proper path for you as an individual. To assist you in assessing your educational goals, we have included a number of student profiles. These are students that have recently graduated from an accredited engineering program and selected different career paths. Each student background is unique and each career path is different. We hope you find these helpful.

1.2 The Technology Team

In 1876, 15 men led by Thomas Alva Edison gathered in Menlo Park, New Jersey, to work on "inventions." By 1887, the group had secured over 400 patents, including ones for the electric lightbulb and the phonograph. Edison's approach typified that used for early engineering developments. Usually one person possessed nearly all the knowledge in one field and directed the research, development, design, and manufacture of new products in this field.

Today, however, technology has become so advanced and sophisticated that one person cannot possibly be aware of all the intricacies of a single device or process. The concept of systems engineering thus has evolved; that is, technological problems are studied and solved by a technology team.

Scientists, engineers, technologists, technicians, and craftspersons form the *technology team*. The functions of the team range across what often is called the *technical spectrum*. At one end of the spectrum are functions that involve work with scientific and engineering principles. At the other end of this technical spectrum are functions that bring designs into reality. Successful technology teams use the unique abilities of all team members to bring about a successful solution to a human need.

Each of the technology team members has a specific function in the technical spectrum, and it is of utmost importance that each specialist understands the role of all team members. It is not difficult to find instances where the education and tasks of team members overlap. For any engineering accomplishment, successful team performance requires cooperation that can be realized only through an understanding of the functions of the technology team. The technology team is one part of a larger team that has the overall responsibility for bringing a device, process, or system into reality. This team, frequently called a project or design team, may include managers, sales representatives, field service persons, financial representatives, and purchasing personnel in addition to the technology team members. These project teams meet frequently from the beginning of the project to ensure that schedules and design specifications are met, and that potential problems are diagnosed early. We will now investigate each of the team specialists in more detail.

1.2.1 Scientist

Scientists have as their prime objective increased knowledge of nature (see Figure 1.2). In the quest for new knowledge, the scientist conducts research in a systematic manner. The research steps, referred to as the *scientific method,* are often summarized as follows:

1. Formulate a hypothesis to explain a natural phenomenon.
2. Conceive and execute experiments to test the hypothesis.
3. Analyze test results and state conclusions.
4. Generalize the hypothesis into the form of a law or theory if experimental results are in harmony with the hypothesis.
5. Publish the new knowledge.

An open and inquisitive mind is an obvious characteristic of a scientist. Although the scientist's primary objective is that of obtaining an increased knowledge of nature, many scientists are also engaged in the development of their ideas into new and useful creations. But to differentiate quite simply between the scientist and engineer, we might

Figure 1.2

Scientists use the laboratory for discovery of new knowledge.
© _Corbis_

say that the true scientist seeks to understand more about natural phenomena, whereas the engineer primarily engages in applying new knowledge. Science degree programs include chemistry, physics, agronomy, biology, horticulture, botany, genetics, earth science, geology, meteorology, and many more.

1.2.2   Engineer

The profession of engineering takes the knowledge of mathematics and natural sciences gained through study, experience, and practice and applies this knowledge with judgment to develop ways to utilize the materials and forces of nature for the benefit of all humans.

An engineer is a person who possesses this knowledge of mathematics and natural sciences, and through the principles of analysis and design applies this knowledge to the solution of problems and the development of devices, processes, structures, and systems. Both the engineer and scientist are thoroughly educated in the mathematical and physical sciences, but the scientist primarily uses this knowledge to acquire new knowledge, whereas the engineer applies the knowledge to design and develops usable devices, structures, and processes. In other words, the scientist seeks to know, the engineer aims to do.

You might conclude that the engineer is totally dependent on the scientist for the knowledge to develop ideas for human benefit. Such is not always the case. Scientists learn a great deal from the work of engineers. For example, the science of thermodynamics was developed by a physicist from studies of practical steam engines built by engineers who had no science to guide them. On the other hand, engineers have applied the principles of nuclear fission discovered by scientists to develop nuclear power plants and numerous other devices and systems requiring nuclear reactions for their operation. The scientist's and engineer's functions frequently overlap, leading at times to a somewhat blurred image of the engineer. What distinguishes the engineer from the scientist in broad terms, however, is that the engineer often conducts research but does so for the purpose of solving a problem.

The end result of an engineering effort—generally referred to as *design*—is a device, structure, system, or process that satisfies a need. A successful design is achieved when a logical procedure is followed to meet a specific need. The procedure, called the *design process,* is similar to the scientific method with respect to a step-by-step routine, but it differs in objectives and end results. The design process encompasses the following activities (all of which must be completed):

1. Define the problem to be solved.
2. Acquire and assemble pertinent data.
3. Identify solution constraints and criteria.
4. Develop alternative solutions.
5. Select a solution based on analysis of alternatives.
6. Communicate the results.

As the designer proceeds through each step, new information may be discovered and new objectives may be specified for the design. If so, the designer must backtrack and repeat steps. For example, if none of the alternatives appears to be economically feasible when the final solution is to be selected, the designer must redefine the problem or possibly relax some of the constraints to admit less expensive alternatives. Thus, because decisions must frequently be made at each step as a result of new developments or unexpected outcomes, the design process becomes iterative.

As you progress through your engineering education, you will solve problems and learn the design process using the techniques of analysis and synthesis. Analysis is the act of separating a system into its constituent parts, whereas synthesis is the act of combining parts into a useful system. In the design process you will observe how analysis and synthesis are utilized to generate a solution to a human need.

1.2.3 Technologist and Technician

Much of the actual work of converting the ideas of scientists and engineers into tangible results is performed by technologists and technicians (see Figure 1.3). A technologist generally possesses a bachelor's degree and a technician an associate's degree. Technologists are involved in the direct application of their education and experience to make appropriate modifications in designs as the need arises. Technicians primarily perform computations and experiments and prepare design drawings as requested by engineers and scientists. Thus technicians (typically) are educated in mathematics and science but not to the depth required of scientists and engineers. Technologists and technicians obtain a basic knowledge of engineering and scientific principles in a specific field and develop certain manual skills that enable them to communicate technically with all members of the technology team. Some tasks commonly performed by technologists and technicians include drafting, estimating, model building, data recording and reduction, troubleshooting,

Figure 1.3

A technician makes sound measurements in an acoustics laboratory.
© _Fuse/Getty Images_

servicing, and specification. Often they are the vital link between the idea on paper and the idea in practice.

1.2.4 Skilled Tradespersons/Craftspersons

Members of the skilled trades possess the skills necessary to produce parts specified by scientists, engineers, technologists, and technicians. Craftspersons do not need to have an indepth knowledge of the principles of science and engineering incorporated in a design (see Figure 1.4). They often are trained on the job, serving an apprenticeship during which the skills and abilities to build and operate specialized equipment are developed. Specialized positions include welder, machinist, electrician, carpenter, plumber, and mason.

1.3 The Engineering Profession

Engineering is an exciting profession. Engineers don't just sit in a cubicle and solve mathematical equations; they work in teams to solve challenging engineering problems to make life safer, easier, and more efficient for the world we live in. Engineers must demonstrate competence in initiative, professionalism, engineering knowledge, teamwork, innovation, communication, cultural adaptability, safety awareness, customer focus, general knowledge, continuous learning, planning, analysis and judgment, quality orientation, and integrity. In addition, engineers are expected to be leaders. Engineers help to shape government policies, international development, and education at all levels. Engineering is fun and challenging, and it provides for a meaningful career.

Figure 1.4

Skilled craftspersons are key elements in a manufacturing process.
© *Kim Steele/Getty Images*

1.4   The Engineering Functions

As we alluded to in Section 1.2, engineering feats dating from earliest recorded history up to the Industrial Revolution could best be described as individual accomplishments. The various pyramids of Egypt were usually designed by one individual, who directed tens of thousands of laborers during construction. The person in charge called every move, made every decision, and took the credit if the project was successful or accepted the consequences if the project failed.

The Industrial Revolution brought a rapid increase in scientific findings and technological advances. One-person engineering teams were no longer practical or desirable. Today, no single aerospace engineer is responsible for a jumbo jet and no one civil engineer completely designs a bridge. Automobile manufacturers assign several thousand engineers to the design of a new model. So we not only have the technology team as described earlier, but we have engineers from many disciplines who are working together on single projects.

One approach to explaining an engineer's role in the technology spectrum is to describe the different types of work that engineers do. For example, agricultural, biological, civil, electrical, mechanical, and other engineers become involved in design, which is an engineering function. The *engineering functions,* which are discussed briefly in this section, are research, development, design, production, testing, construction, operations, sales, management, consulting, and teaching. Several of the *engineering disciplines* will be discussed later in the chapter.

To avoid confusion between "engineering disciplines" and "engineering functions," let us consider the following. Normally a student selects a curriculum (e.g., aerospace, chemical, mechanical) either before or soon after admission to an engineering program. When and how the choice is made varies with each school. The point is, the student does not choose a function but rather a discipline. To illustrate further, consider a student who has chosen mechanical engineering. This student will, during an undergraduate education, learn how mechanical engineers are involved in the engineering functions of research, development, design, and so on. Some program options allow a student to pursue an interest in a specific subdivision within the curriculum, such as energy conversion in a mechanical engineering program. Most other curricula have similar options.

Upon graduation, when you accept a job with a company, you will be assigned to a functional team performing in a specific area such as research, design, or sales. Within some companies, particularly smaller ones, you may become involved in more than one function—design *and* testing, for example. It is important to realize that regardless of your choice of discipline, you may become involved in one or more of the functions discussed in the following paragraphs:

Space Exploration: Where Do We Go From Here?

Clayton Anderson

NASA

Clayton Anderson received his undergraduate degree in Physics from Hastings College, Nebraska, and an MS in Aerospace Engineering from Iowa State University. He joined the Johnson Space Center (JSC) in 1983 in Mission Planning and Analysis, before moving to the Missions Operations Directorate and leading the trajectory design team for the Galileo planetary mission. He became supervisor of the Ascent Flight Design Section in 1992, which was then reorganized into the Flight Design Engineering Group. In 1993 he was named chief of the Flight Design Branch and in 1996 he assumed the role of manager of the Emergency Operations Center at JSC.

His broad expertise in space operations at JSC led to his selection as a NASA Mission Specialist astronaut in 1998. Intensive training for missions to the International Space Station (ISS) included physiological aspects and flight training in a T-38 aircraft, as well as underwater training and wilderness survival techniques. In 2007, Anderson embarked on his first space adventure aboard the Space Shuttle *Atlantis* to the ISS. Aboard the ISS he served as the Flight Engineer and Science Officer. During the 152-day stay, he performed three EVAs (extravehicular activity or spacewalks) totaling 18 hours. His second mission came in 2010 when he rode Space Shuttle *Discovery* on a resupply mission to the ISS. During this short 15-day stay, he performed three more EVAs totaling 20 hours, 17 minutes.

Anderson retired from NASA in 2013 very proud of his accomplishments and filled with a strong desire to educate the public on the knowledge, research, and training necessary to conduct continued space exploration in a logical and safe manner. To this end, he has traveled extensively around the country giving keynote presentations on his experiences and visions for future space endeavors. Recently there have been efforts to develop commercial launching rockets to transport travelers into space (and the ISS), to the moon, and possibly to Mars. Anderson asks, "What capabilities does the commercial space industry need to have in order to transport spacefaring neophytes safely? Will passengers need three years of intensive astronaut training? How could engineers design controls and user interfaces to better serve inexperienced space travelers?"

Anderson believes we must take measured steps in educating and training the public for space travel and he believes the first step is using our Moon. ". . . Theoreticians claim that the surface of Mars or the Moon may provide on-site (in situ) resources that could be used. They tout our ability to concoct fuel, extract water, and create oxygen, simply by living off the land. While this may be true, *how* do we do this? What technologies are needed?

It does not seem completely practical to commit to Mars before we have answers to these fundamental questions. We can use our 35 years of space experience with moon missions and space station operations to develop the foundation for longer missions. A mission to Mars and its 20-minute communication lapses introduce new psychological implications within an 18-month trip requiring sufficient fuel, food, water, spare parts, clothing, etc. Planning and training for such a mission is a huge and, as yet, not completely defined task."

In 2014, Anderson was named an Iowa State University Distinguished Faculty Fellow in Aerospace Engineering. He has developed a prototype workshop in space flight operations intended to expose students to training events similar to those completed by astronauts. For example, scuba diving certification will help students learn how to work in a hazardous environment while following distinctly operational procedures. Wilderness survival training uniquely introduces students to the basic concepts of mission planning, expeditionary behavior, and teamwork. Aircraft flight simulation training reinforces procedural concepts while introducing more "big picture" and anticipatory thinking. Further, in an effort to provide ISU graduating students with a new and different thought process, the workshop attempts to address the needs of the emerging commercial spaceflight companies, by providing students whose decision analysis and leadership capabilities reflect this more operational background. Supplemented with general training in spacecraft subsystems, space physiology, and space suits, the workshop experience is coupled with virtual reality spaceflight scenarios using the C6 virtual reality room in the Virtual Reality Applications Center at Iowa State University. Anderson is collaborating with Dr. Nir Keren, Associate Professor in the Department of Agricultural and BioSystems Engineering and a Graduate Faculty member at the Virtual Reality Applications Center. Dr. Keren utilizes VirtuTrace, a powerful simulation engine he developed with his research team, to simulate the main U.S. living section of the ISS and the exterior of the station in full scale three-dimension in exquisite detail. Students experience the space station environment and the inherent stressors associated with combating an in-flight emergency situation.

1.4.1 Research

Successful research is one catalyst for starting the activities of a technology team or, in many cases, the activities of an entire industry. The research engineer seeks new findings, as does the scientist; but keep in mind that the research engineer also seeks a way to use the discovery.

Key qualities of a successful research engineer are perceptiveness, patience, and self-confidence. Most students interested in research will pursue the master's and doctor's degrees in order to develop their intellectual abilities and the necessary research skills. An alert and perceptive mind is needed to recognize nature's truths when they are encountered. When attempting to reproduce natural phenomena in the laboratory, cleverness and patience are prime attributes. Research often involves tests, failures, retests, and so on for long periods of time (see Figure 1.5). Research engineers therefore are often discouraged and frustrated and must strain their abilities and rely on their self-confidence in order to sustain their efforts to a successful conclusion.

Billions of dollars are spent each year on research at colleges and universities, industrial research laboratories, government installations, and independent research institutes. The team approach to research is predominant today primarily because of the need to incorporate a vast amount of technical information into the research effort. Individual research also is carried out but not to the extent it was several years ago. A large share of research monies are channeled into the areas of energy, environment, health, defense, and space exploration. A fast growing research area is nanotechnology. The Royal Academy of Engineering describes it this way: "Nanotechnology is the application of nanoscale science, engineering and technology to produce novel materials and devices, including biological and medical applications." Research funding from

Figure 1.5

Research requires high-cost, sophisticated equipment.
© *Gary Gladstone/Stockbyte/Getty Images*

federal agencies is very sensitive to national and international priorities. During a career as a research engineer you might expect to work in many diverse, seemingly unrelated areas, but your qualifications will allow you to adapt to many different research efforts.

1.4.2   Development

Using existing knowledge and new discoveries from research, the development engineer attempts to produce a functional device, structure, or process (see Figure 1.6). Building and testing scale or pilot models is the primary means by which the development engineer evaluates ideas. This has been made easier to accomplish with 3-D modeling software, rapid prototyping equipment, and virtual reality software and visualization tools. A major portion of development work requires use of well-known devices and processes in conjunction with established theories. Thus reading available literature and having a solid background in the sciences and in engineering principles are necessary for the engineer's success.

Many people who suffer from heart irregularities are able to function normally today because of the pacemaker, an electronic device that maintains a regular heartbeat. The pacemaker is an excellent example of the work of development engineers. The first pacemakers developed in the 1950s were externally AC powered units that sent pulses of energy through an implanted lead wire to the heart. However, the power requirement for heart stimulus was so great that patients suffered severe burns on their chests. As improvements were studied, research in surgery and electronics enabled development engineers to devise a battery-powered external pacemaker that eliminated concerns about chest burns and allowed the patients more mobility. Although more efficient from the standpoint of

Figure 1.6

Development engineers take an idea and produce a concept of a functional product or system. The result of this activity is passed on to the design engineers for completing necessary details for production.
© Corbis

Conducting Engineering Research
Julie Friend

© *Suwit Ngaoka/Shutterstock*

Julie Friend received her undergraduate degrees in chemical engineering and French and her PhD in chemical engineering. She is currently a senior research engineer with DuPont. DuPont, headquartered in Wilmington, Delaware, with over 60 000 employees in 70 countries worldwide, offers a wide range of innovative products and services for markets including agriculture, nutrition, electronics, communications, safety and protection, home and construction, transportation, and apparel.

Dr. Friend works in research and development for DuPont and focuses on early-stage work, meaning that she determines the appropriate combination and quantity of chemicals as well as the steps required to make a desired compound. Her work can involve lab experiments, modeling, and economic evaluations. Her goal is to come up with a method to take through development and scale up to a safe and cost-effective commercial process. To do this, Dr. Friend works in teams with other chemists, biologists, and engineers.

Dr. Friend was in a marching band and participated in various campus groups while pursuing her undergraduate degree, but her other main "activity" was studying abroad in Switzerland during her junior year. She felt it was very important while in school to have something to do that was completely different than engineering to take her mind off the engineering coursework.

Dr. Friend has found that a degree in engineering can take a person in many different directions, something she didn't fully appreciate as an undergrad. She knows engineers who work in the more traditional areas of manufacturing, consulting, and research, but also engineers who work in law, medicine, marketing, regulatory affairs, and human resources. As for her future, who knows! The last five years have been nothing like she had expected, she says, and she doesn't expect the next five to be any different in that respect.

power requirements, the devices were uncomfortable, and patients frequently suffered infection where the wires entered the chest. Finally, two independent teams developed the first internal pacemaker, eight years after the original pacemaker had been tested. Their experience and research with tiny pulse generators for spacecraft led to this achievement. But the very fine wire used in these early models proved to be inadequate and quite often failed, forcing patients to have the entire pacemaker replaced. A team of engineers at General Electric developed a pacemaker that incorporated a new wire, called a *helicable*. The helicable consisted of 49 strands of wire coiled together and then wound into a spring. The spring diameter was about 46 μm, one-half the diameter of a human hair. Thus, with doctors and development engineers working together, an effective, comfortable device was perfected that has enabled many heart patients to enjoy a more active life.

To illustrate how important technological changes can arise from the work of development engineers, here's what's become of the pacemaker. Today pacemakers have been developed by engineers and doctors to operate at more than one speed, enabling the patient to speed up or slow down heart rate depending on physical activity. Motion sensors are used to detect breathing rate and can be programmed by the doctor for individual needs. The new pager-sized pacemakers are also now programmed to act as sensors to detect problems with intermittent atrial fibrillation and switch the pacemaker to a different mode that paces the lower heart chamber only. For those with damage to the heart muscles and the heart's electrical systems, the new biventricular pacemaker can pace both of the lower heart chambers so that they beat at the same rate. In addition to the advances in pacemakers, medical research has evolved many other procedures for correcting heart deficiencies. The field of electrophysiology, combining cardiology with electrical and computer engineering, is enabling thousands of persons with heart irregularities to live productive and happy lives.

We have discussed the pacemaker in detail to point out that important changes in technology can arise from the work of development engineers. That it took only 13 years to develop an efficient, dependable pacemaker, five years to develop the transistor, and 25 years to develop the digital computer indicates that modern engineering methods generate and improve products nearly as fast as research generates new knowledge.

Successful development engineers are ingenious and creative. Astute judgment often is required in devising models that can be used to determine whether a project will be successful in performance and economical in production. Obtaining an advanced degree is helpful, but not as important as it is for an engineer who will be working in research. Practical experience more than anything else produces the qualities necessary for a career as a development engineer.

Development engineers frequently are asked to demonstrate that an idea will work. Within certain limits they do not work out the exact specifications that a final product should possess. Such matters are usually left to the design engineer if the idea is deemed feasible.

1.4.3 Design

The development engineer produces a concept or model that is passed on to the design engineer for converting into a device, process, or structure (see Figure 1.7). The designer relies on education and experience to evaluate many possible design options, keeping in mind the cost of manufacture, ease of production, availability of materials, and performance requirements. Usually several designs and redesigns will be undertaken before the product is brought before the general public.

Figure 1.7

A team of design engineers review a proposed design solution.
© *Fuse/Getty Images*

To illustrate the role that the design engineer plays, we will discuss the development of the side air bags for added safety in automobiles. Side air bags created something of a design problem, as designers had to decide where and how the air bags would be fastened to the car body. They had to determine what standard parts could be used and what parts had to be designed from scratch. Consideration was given to how to hide the air bags so not to take away from the aesthetics of the interior of the car while still providing maximum impact safety. Materials to be used for attaching the air bags to the frame and for the air bag itself had to be selected. An inflation device had to be designed that would give flawless performance.

The 12 000 or so other parts that form the modern automobile also demand numerous considerations: Optimum placement of engine accessories, comfortable design of seats, maximization of trunk space, and aesthetically pleasing body design all require thousands of engineering hours if the model is to be successful in a highly competitive industry.

Like the development engineer, the designer is creative. But where the development engineer is usually concerned only with a prototype or model, the designer is restricted by the state of the art in engineering materials, production facilities, and, perhaps most important, economic considerations. An excellent design from the standpoint of performance may be completely impractical from a monetary point of view. To make the necessary decisions, the designer must have a fundamental knowledge of many engineering specialty subjects as well as an understanding of economics and people.

1.4.4   Production and Testing

When research, development, and design have created a device for use by the public, the production and testing facilities are geared for mass production (see Figures 1.8 and 1.9). The first step in production is to devise a schedule that will

Figure 1.8

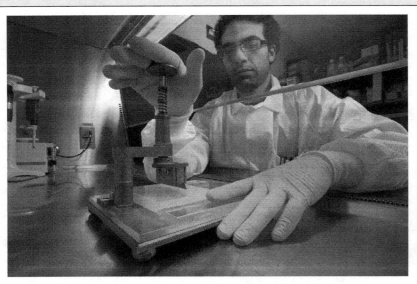

Test engineering is a major component in the development of new products.
James Gathany/CDC

Figure 1.9

Mass production of projects takes careful planning by the engineers who oversee facilities planning and layout.
© *DreamPictures/Shannon Faulk/Blend Images LLC*

efficiently coordinate materials and personnel. The production engineer is responsible for such tasks as ordering raw materials at the optimum times, setting up the assembly line, and handling and shipping the finished product. The individual who chooses this field must be able to visualize the overall operation of a particular project as well as know each step of the production effort. Knowledge of design, economics, ergonomics, and psychology is of particular importance for production engineers.

Test engineers work with a product from the time it is conceived by the development engineer until such time as it may no longer be manufactured. Some testing can be conducted prior to the creation of an actual physical model through the use of 3-D modeling and analysis software. Finite element analyses allow the test engineer to evaluate load changes, temperature changes, pressure change, and many other physical variations prior to building a prototype for testing. In the automobile industry, for example, test engineers evaluate new devices and materials that may not appear in automobiles for several years. At the same time, they test component parts and completed cars currently coming off the assembly line. Test engineers are usually responsible for quality control of the manufacturing process. In addition to the education requirements of the design and production engineers, a fundamental knowledge of statistics is beneficial to the test engineer.

1.4.5 Construction

The counterpart of the production engineer in manufacturing is the construction engineer in the building industry (see Figure 1.10). When an organization bids on a competitive construction project, the construction engineer begins the process by estimating material, labor, and overhead costs. If the bid is successful, a construction engineer assumes the responsibility of coordinating the project. On large projects, a team of construction engineers may supervise the individual segments of construction such as

Figure 1.10

Numerous engineers from many disciplines are involved in the design and construction of massive structures such as this hydroelectric plant.
© Corbis

Figure 1.11

Operations engineers help to lay out manufacturing facilities for optimum efficiency.
© *Corbis*

mechanical (plumbing), electrical (lighting), and civil (building). In addition to a strong background in engineering fundamentals, the construction engineer needs on-the-job experience and an understanding of labor relations. With the increased regulation of energy and sustainability, the construction engineer must also be familiar with LEED, an internationally "green" building certification system. LEED certification assesses building design for energy savings, improved indoor environmental quality, CO_2 emissions reduction, water efficiency, and stewardship of resources.

1.4.6 Operations

Up to this point, discussion has centered on the results of engineering efforts to discover, develop, design, and produce products that are of benefit to humans. For such work engineers obviously must have offices, laboratories, and production facilities in which to accomplish it. The major responsibility for supplying such facilities falls on the operations engineer (see Figure 1.11). Sometimes called a plant engineer, this individual selects sites for facilities, specifies the layout for all facets of the operation, and selects the fixed equipment for climate control, lighting, and communication. Once the facility is in operation, the plant engineer is responsible for maintenance and modifications as requirements demand. Because this phase of engineering comes under the economic category of overhead, the operations engineer must be very conscious of cost and keep up with new developments in equipment so that overhead is maintained at the lowest possible level. Knowledge of basic engineering, industrial engineering principles, economics, and law are prime educational requirements of the operations engineer. Operation engineers also are trained in total quality improvement methods and lean manufacturing production products that help to provide "value" to the process and final product.

1.4.7 Sales

In many respects all engineers are involved in selling. To the research, development, design, production, construction, and operations engineers, selling means convincing management that money should be allocated for development of particular concepts or expansion of facilities. This is, in essence, selling one's own ideas. Sales engineering, however, means finding or creating a market for a product. The complexity of today's products requires an individual who is thoroughly familiar with materials in and operational procedures for consumer products to demonstrate to the consumer in layperson's terms how the products can be of benefit. The sales engineer is thus the liaison between the company and the consumer, a very important part of influencing a company's reputation. Therefore, excellent communication and teamwork skills are important to becoming a successful sales engineer. Some engineering schools are now providing a sales engineering major or minor.

An engineering background plus a sincere interest in people and a desire to be helpful are the primary attributes of a sales engineer. The sales engineer usually spends a great deal of time in the plant learning about the product to be sold. After a customer purchases a product, the sales engineer is responsible for coordinating service and maintaining customer satisfaction. As important as sales engineering is to a company, it still has not received the interest from new engineering graduates that other engineering functions have. (See Figure 1.12.)

Figure 1.12

Sales engineers interact with people around the world using many forms of communications media.
© *John Fedele/Blend Images LLC*

Figure 1.13

Managers often must balance design projects, staff, and finances.
© *John Fedele/Blend Images LLC*

1.4.8 Management

Traditionally management has consisted of individuals who are trained in business and groomed to assume positions leading to the top of the corporate ladder (Figure 1.13). However, with the influx of scientific and technological data being used in business plans and decisions, and hence the increasing need for managers with knowledge and experience in engineering and science, a growing percentage of management positions are being assumed by engineers and scientists. Inasmuch as one of the principal functions of management is to use company facilities to produce an economically feasible product, and decisions often must be made that may affect thousands of people and involve millions of dollars over periods of several years, a balanced education of engineering or science and business seems to produce the best managerial potential. Engineering programs are now partnering with business programs to offer undergraduates the opportunity to obtain an undergraduate engineering degree and a master of business administration degree at the same time, with as little as one year added onto the undergraduate degree program time.

1.4.9 Consulting

For someone interested in self-employment, a consulting position may be an attractive one (see Figure 1.14). Consulting engineers operate alone or in partnership furnishing specialized help to clients who request it. Of course, as in any business, risks must be taken. Moreover, as in all engineering disciplines, a sense of integrity and a knack for correct engineering judgment are primary necessities in consulting.

Figure 1.14

Consulting engineers often partner with clients in a team setting to provide engineering expertise and guidance.
© Corbis/Superstock

A consulting engineer must possess a professional engineer's license before beginning practice. Consultants usually spend many years in the private, corporate, or government world gaining experience in a specific area before going on their own. A successful consulting engineer maintains a business primarily by being able to solve unique problems for which other companies have neither the time nor capacity. In many cases large consulting firms maintain a staff of engineers of diverse backgrounds so that a wide range of engineering problems can be contracted.

1.4.10 Teaching

Individuals interested in helping others to become engineers will find teaching very rewarding (see Figure 1.15). The engineering teacher must possess an ability to communicate abstract principles and engineering experiences in a manner that students can understand and appreciate. Teachers must follow general guidelines but are usually free to develop their own method of teaching and means of evaluating its effectiveness. In addition to teaching, the engineering educator can become involved in student advising, extension, and research. At research universities, faculty members rarely have a 100 percent teaching load. They usually split their time between teaching, research, and extension (off-campus instruction often for engineering professionals). These faculty members are rewarded and promoted based on peer-reviewed scholarly work related to their appointments, the ability to obtain external funds for research, and national recognition for their contribution to their profession.

Figure 1.15

Teaching provides opportunities for student coaching, mentoring, and research collaboration.
© *BananaStock/PictureQuest*

Engineering teachers today must have a mastery of fundamental engineering and science principles and knowledge of applications. Customarily, they must obtain an advanced degree in order to improve their understanding of basic principles, to perform research in a specialized area, and perhaps to gain teaching experience on a part-time basis.

The emphasis in the classrooms today is moving from teaching to learning. Methods of presenting material and involving students in the learning process to meet designed outcomes follow the sound educational principles developed by our education colleagues. You as a student will benefit greatly by these learning processes, which empower you to take control of your education through teamwork, active participation, and hands-on learning.

If you are interested in a teaching career in engineering or engineering technology, you should observe your teachers carefully as you pursue your degrees. Note how they approach the teaching process, the methodologies they use to stimulate learning, and their evaluation methods. Your initial teaching methods likely will be based on the best methods you observe as a student.

1.5 The Engineering Disciplines

There are over 25 specific disciplines of engineering that can be pursued for the baccalaureate degree. The opportunities to work in any of these areas are numerous. Most engineering colleges offer some combination of the disciplines, primarily as four-year programs. In some schools two or more disciplines, such as industrial, management, and manufacturing engineering, are combined within one department that may offer separate degrees, or include one discipline as a specialty within another discipline. In this case a degree in the area of specialty is not offered. Other common combinations of engineering disciplines include civil/construction/environmental, mechanical/aerospace, and electrical/computer.

Figure 1.16 gives a breakdown of the number of engineering degrees in seven categories for 2014. Note that each category represents combined disciplines and does not provide information about a specific discipline within that category. The "other" category includes, among others, agricultural, biological, ceramic, materials, metallurgical, mining, nuclear, safety, and ocean engineering. The percentage of bachelor's degrees awarded to women was 19.5 percent of the total number of engineering graduates.

Seven of the individual disciplines will be discussed in this section. Engineering disciplines which pique your interest may be investigated in more detail by contacting the appropriate department, checking the library at your institution, and searching the Internet.

Developing Technical Skills

Sarah Campie

Courtesy of Sarah Campie

Sarah Campie received her BS in Engineering from University of Iowa and MBA from the University of Nebraska at Omaha and is now Director of Network Design, Voice Engineering, and Voice Automation at Union Pacific Railroad in Omaha, Nebraska. Union Pacific provides freight transportation that helps American businesses compete in the global marketplace. They operate in 23 states, mainly west of the Mississippi River and serve, or run through more than 7 000 communities.

Campie's teams are responsible for the architecture of Union Pacific's mission critical IP network, which supports the communication backbone for Union Pacific's train control operations. Her team also designs and supports Union Pacific's phone network, voicemail, and audio conferencing platforms, in addition to handling voice application development and call center design and consulting. Supporting these highly visible applications requires proactive communication with call centers, suppliers, customers, and business partners to understand and implement end user requirements. The engineers and software developers on the team must be good project managers, as well as technical experts, to deliver projects on time and maintain high availability. She enjoys the diversity of projects that come her way and is motivated by a positive environment where team members share ideas and learn from one another.

Under her parents' encouragement, she pursued engineering at the University of Iowa, which provided her with critical thinking and time-management skills that have been fundamental in her career development. As an undergraduate student, Campie placed a high value on her two summer engineering internship experiences, and she recommends students apply for internships or pursue research positions early in their academic program to get hands-on experience to guide their career choices.

Campie is grateful that she pursued engineering because the curriculum not only taught her necessary skills but also offered her a lot of options to explore during her graduation. "Technical problem-solving skills are extremely valuable, and technology will only become more critical to businesses in the future. With an engineering degree, graduates can stay in academia, pursue professional degrees, or decide to branch out into any business career. I know from experience: engineering is hard work, but stay the course, give your best, and exciting opportunities await you!"

Figure 1.16

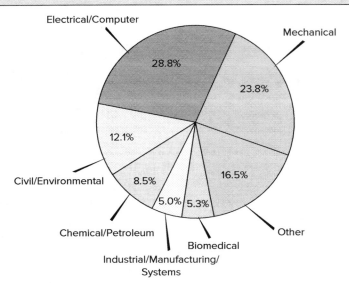

Engineering degrees by discipline. Total engineering degrees awarded in 2014–2015 were 106,658. (ASEE Profiles of Engineering & Technology Colleges, 2015 Edition.)

1.5.1 Aerospace Engineering

Aerospace engineers study the motion and control of all types of vehicles, including aircraft weighing upward of one million pounds and spacecraft flying at 17 000 miles per hour. Aerospace engineers must understand many flight environments, from turbulent air in Earth's atmosphere to the winds and sandstorms on Mars. They design, develop, and test aircraft, missiles, space vehicles, helicopters, hydrofoils, ships, and submerging ocean vehicles (see Figure 1.17). Areas of specialty include aerodynamics, propulsion, orbital mechanics, stability and control, structures, design, testing, and supervision of the manufacturing of aerospace vehicles. Aerospace engineers work for private aviation companies, government defense contractors, and research organizations.

Aerodynamics is the study of the effects of moving a vehicle through the Earth's atmosphere. The air produces forces that have both a positive effect on a properly designed vehicle (lift) and a negative effect (drag). In addition, at very high speeds (e.g., reentry velocities of spacecraft), the air generates heat on the vehicle that must be dissipated to protect crews, passengers, and cargo. Aerospace engineering students learn to determine such things as optimum wing and body shapes, vehicle performance, and environmental impact.

The operation and construction of turboprops, turbo and fan jets, rockets, ram and pulse jets, and nuclear and ion propulsion are part of the aerospace engineering student's study of propulsion. Such constraints as efficiency, noise levels, and flight distance enter into the selection of a propulsion system for a flight vehicle.

The aerospace engineer develops plans for interplanetary missions based on knowledge of orbital mechanics. The problems encountered include determination of trajectories, stabilization, rendezvous with other vehicles, changes in orbit, and interception.

Figure 1.17

Many aerospace engineers work in avionics and design for new aircraft.
NASA

Stability and control involves the study of techniques for maintaining stability and establishing guidance and control of vehicles operating in the atmosphere or in space. Automatic control systems for autopilots and unmanned vehicles are part of the study of stability and control.

The study of structures is primarily involved with thin-shelled, flexible structures that can withstand high stresses and extreme temperature ranges. The structural engineer works closely with the aerodynamics engineer to determine the geometry of wings, fuselages, and control surfaces. The study of structures also involves thick-shelled structures that must withstand extreme pressures at ocean depths and lightweight composite structural materials for high-performance vehicles.

The aerospace design engineer combines all the aspects of aerodynamics, propulsion, orbital mechanics, stability and control, and structures into the optimum vehicle. Design engineers work in a team and must learn to compromise in order to determine the best design satisfying all criteria and constraints.

The final proofing of a design involves the physical testing of a prototype. Aerospace test engineers use testing devices such as wind tunnels, lasers, and data acquisition systems. They may work on the flight line for aircraft testing, at a launch facility for spacecraft, or for organizations that build and test component parts such as automatic control systems, engines, landing gear, and control surface operating mechanisms.

New and exciting areas for aerospace development evolve continually. The construction and utilization of the international space station is stimulating new developments in service vehicles making round-trips from Earth. Perhaps you may someday participate in a commercial venture to add the space station or the Moon as an exotic vacation destination. Other areas of development include the unmanned drone aircraft for defense activity, hypersonic vehicles for suborbital flights between points on the Earth, innovative methods to improve the safety of aircraft through nondestructive structural testing, new engine designs that significantly reduce noise levels, and turbulence detection.

1.5.2 Chemical Engineering

Chemical engineers deal with the chemical and physical principles that allow us to maintain a suitable environment. They create, design, and operate processes that produce useful materials, including fuels, plastics, structural materials, food products, health products, fibers, and fertilizers (Figure 1.18). As our natural resources become scarce, chemical engineers are finding ways to extend them or creating substitutes.

Graduates of chemical engineering programs have a strong background in basic chemistry and advanced chemistry (such as organic, inorganic, physical, analytical, materials chemistry, and biochemistry). They also need working knowledge of occupational safety, material and energy balance, thermodynamics, heat transfer, chemical reaction engineering, separation operations, process design and modern experimental and computing techniques.

Figure 1.18

Chemical engineers design processing plants for many of the products on which we depend in our daily lives.
© Corbis

The chemical engineer, in the development of new products, in designing processes, and in operating plants, may work in a laboratory, pilot plant, or full-scale plant. In the laboratory the chemical engineer searches for new products and materials that benefit humankind and the environment. This laboratory work would be classified as research engineering.

In a pilot plant the chemical engineer is trying to determine the feasibility of carrying on a process on a large scale. There is a great deal of difference between a process working in a test tube in the laboratory and a process working in a production facility. The pilot plant is constructed to develop the necessary unit operations to carry out the process. Unit operations are fundamental chemical and physical processes that are uniquely combined by the chemical engineer to produce the desired product. A unit operation may involve separation of components by mechanical means, such as filtering, settling, and floating. Separation also may take place by changing the form of a component—for example, through evaporation, absorption, or crystallization. Unit operations also involve chemical reactions such as oxidation and reduction. Certain chemical processes require the addition or removal of heat or the transfer of mass. The chemical engineer thus works with heat exchanges, furnaces, evaporators, condensers, and refrigeration units in developing large-scale processes.

In a full-scale plant the chemical engineer will continue to fine-tune the unit operations to produce the optimum process based on the lowest cost. The day-by-day operations problems in a chemical plant, such as piping, storage, and material handling, are the responsibility of chemical engineers.

Many chemical engineering degree programs are also active in biological engineering education and research. This might include working in the areas of biomedical engineering, bioinformatics, biomaterial engineering, biobased products, metabolic and tissue engineering, or biocatalyst and separation engineering.

1.5.3   Civil Engineering

Civil engineering is the oldest branch of the engineering profession. The term "civil" was used to distinguish this field from military engineers. Military engineers originated in Napoleon's army. The first engineers trained in this country were military engineers at West Point. Civil engineering involves application of the laws, forces, and materials of nature to the design, construction, operation, and maintenance of facilities that serve our needs in an efficient, economical manner. Civil engineers work for consulting firms engaged in private practice, for manufacturing firms, and for federal, state, and local governments. Civil engineers, more than any other specialists, work outdoors at least some of the time. Thus persons who enjoy working outside may find civil engineering attractive.

Because of the nature of their work, civil engineers assume a great deal of responsibility, which means that professional registration is a vital goal for the civil engineer who is beginning to practice. Typical specialties within civil engineering include structures, transportation, environmental (including water/wastewater treatment and water resources), geotechnical, surveying, and construction.

Structural engineers design bridges, buildings, dams, tunnels, and supporting structures (building structures, for example). The designs include consideration of loads, winds, temperature extremes, and other natural phenomena such as earthquakes and hurricanes. Advanced technology such as mathematical modeling and computer simulation is used extensively in this specialty. Civil engineers with a strong structural background often are found in aerospace and manufacturing firms, playing an integral role in the design of vehicular structures.

Civil engineers in transportation plan, design, construct, operate, and maintain facilities that move people and goods throughout the world, whether by land, sea, or air. For example, civil engineers decide where a freeway system should be located and describe the economic impact of the system on the affected public (Figure 1.19). They plan for growth of residential and industrial sectors of the nation. The modern rapid transit systems are another example of a public need satisfied by transportation engineers. Transportation specialists often work for public agencies or consulting firms that support public agencies.

Environmental and water/wastewater treatment engineers are concerned with maintaining a healthful environment by proper treatment and distribution of drinking water, treatment of wastewater, and control of all forms of pollution. The water resources engineer specializes in the evaluation of potential sources of new water for increasing or shifting populations, irrigation, and industrial needs and in the prevention and control of flooding.

Before any structure can be erected, geotechnical engineers carefully study the soil, rock, and groundwater conditions to ensure stability of pavements and structures. Foundations must be designed to support all structures. The geotechnical engineer also plans portland cement and asphaltic concrete mixes for all types of construction.

Chemical Engineering Consultant/ Project Manager
David Shallberg

David Shallberg received his BS degree in chemical engineering and his MBA in finance. He is currently a senior consultant/project manager for Black & Veatch. Black & Veatch has headquarters in Kansas City, Missouri, and employs over 8 000 people at 90 sites. It is one of the largest and most diversified engineering and construction firms in the world, having completed more than 35 000 projects for over 6 500 clients worldwide.

Shallberg is a registered professional engineer and member of the Enterprise Management Solutions division of Black & Veatch. Currently, he is responsible for performing independent engineering assessments, strategic planning, and economic analysis for owners, developers, and project lenders of electric power generation assets. These reviews provide technical, financial, and economic analysis of projects across the spectrum of the power industry. Prior to his current assignment, Shallberg served in a variety of roles including power project development, business development, and detailed engineering assignments.

Shallberg estimates that at least 90 percent of his work involves interaction with coworkers, clients, suppliers, and others. Involvement in extracurricular activities and organizations (including Tau Beta Phi and Omega Chi Epsilon honor societies, residence hall governance, clubs, and intramural sports) while he was an undergraduate student provided opportunities for personal and professional development in areas such as interpersonal communication and leadership skills. Participation also provided a convenient way to demonstrate these skills to potential employers at graduation.

Analysis and problem-solving skills are highly valued in most endeavors, and in Shallberg's experience, an engineering degree, while being very specific in its studies, serves as a springboard to a wide variety of career opportunities. The photo shows Shallberg in Albania while he was doing some work related to power-plant siting.

Figure 1.19

Civil engineers had a major role in the design of the route of this new highway. The terrain had to be prepared to support the highway and care had to be taken to protect the local environment.
© *Digital Vision/PunchStock*

Surveying engineers develop maps for any type of engineering project. For example, if a road is to be built through a mountain range, the surveyors will determine the exact route and develop the topographical survey, which is then used by the transportation engineer to lay out the roadway. Global positioning systems (GPS) and geographic information systems (GIS) make surveying projects easier to complete and more accurate and are helpful in making complex decisions.

Construction engineering is a significant portion of civil engineering, and many engineering colleges offer a separate degree in this area. Often construction engineers will work outside at the actual construction site. They are involved with the initial estimating of construction costs for surveying, excavation, and construction. They supervise the construction, start-up, and initial operation of the facility until the client is ready to assume operational responsibility. Construction engineers work around the world on many construction projects such as highways, skyscrapers, and power plants.

Figure 1.20

Electrical engineers work with new electronics and control systems.
© *Brand X Pictures/PunchStock*

1.5.4 Electrical Engineering

Electrical Engineering is one of the largest branch of engineering. Because of the rapid advances in technology associated with electronics and computers, this branch of engineering also is the fastest growing. Areas of specialty include communications, power systems, analog/digital electronics, controls, signals and systems, power systems, computing and networking systems, security and reliable computing, semiconductor devices, linear systems, software systems, and electromagnetic fields, antennas, and propagation (Figure 1.20).

Almost every minute of our lives, we depend on communication equipment developed by electrical engineers. Telephones, television, radio, and radar are common communications devices that we often take for granted. Our national defense system depends heavily on the communications engineer and on the hardware used for our early warning and detection systems.

The power engineer is responsible for producing and distributing the electricity demanded by residential, business, and industrial users throughout the world. The production of electricity requires a generating source such as fossil fuels, nuclear reactions, or hydroelectric dams. The power engineer may be involved with research and development of alternative generation sources, such as sun, wind, and fuel cells. Transmission of electricity involves conductors and insulating materials. On the receiving end, appliances are designed by power engineers to be highly efficient in order to reduce both electrical demand and costs.

1.5.5 Computer Engineering

Computer engineers deal with both hardware and software problems in the design and application of computer systems. The design, construction, and operation of computer systems are the tasks of computer engineers. The areas of application include research, education, design engineering, scheduling, accounting, control of manufacturing operations, process control, and home computing needs. No single development in history has had as great an impact on our lives in such a short time span as has the computer. Computer engineers typical specialized in areas such as computer architecture, control systems, information security, VLSI, and embedded systems.

The area of digital electronics is one the fastest-growing specialty in software engineering. The development of solid-state circuits (functional electronic circuits manufactured as one part rather than wired together) has produced high reliability in electronic devices. Microelectronics has revolutionized the computer industry and electronic controls. Circuit components that are much smaller than one micrometer in width enable reduced costs and higher electronic speeds to be attained in circuitry. The microprocessor, the principal component of a digital computer, is a major result of solid-state circuitry and microelectronics technology. Home computers, cellular telephones, automobile control systems, and a multitude of electrical application devices conceived, designed, and produced by electronic engineers have greatly improved our standard of living.

Great strides have also been made in the control and measurement of phenomena that occur in all types of processes. Physical quantities such as temperature, flow rate, stress, voltage, and acceleration are detected and displayed rapidly and accurately for optimal control of processes. In some cases, the data must be sensed at a remote location and accurately transmitted long distances to receiving stations. The determination of radiation levels is an example of the electrical process called *telemetry*. The impact of microelectronics on the computer industry has created a multibillion-dollar annual business that in turn has enhanced all other industries.

Software engineering is a fairly new degree program. Software engineering combines computer science and computer engineering knowledge, skills, and abilities to design, develop, and evaluate software for industries who specialize in installing new computer systems or in reconfiguring old computer systems.

1.5.6 Environmental Engineering

Environmental engineering deals with the appropriate use of our natural resources and the protection of our environment (Figure 1.21). For the most part, environmental engineering curricula are relatively new and in many instances reside as a specialty within other disciplines, such as civil, chemical, and agricultural engineering. Environmental engineers focus on at least one of the following environmental issues areas: air, land, water, or environmental health.

The construction, operation, and maintenance of the facilities in which we live and work have a significant impact on the environment. Environmental engineers with a civil engineering background are instrumental in the design of water and wastewater

Figure 1.21

When engineers design a new product or system, such as an offshore drilling rig, the design must minimize the impact on the environment.
© *Corbis*

treatment plants, facilities that resist natural disasters such as earthquakes and floods, and facilities that use no hazardous or toxic materials. The design and layout of large cities and urban areas must include protective measures for the disturbed environment.

Environmental engineers with a chemical engineering background are interested in air and water quality, which is affected by many by-products of chemical and biological processes. Products that are slow to biodegrade are studied for recycling possibilities. Other products that may contaminate or be hazardous are being studied to develop either better storage or replacement products that are less dangerous to the environment. With the concerns of energy conservation, environmental engineers consider the use of energy and resources such that the rate of use does not compromise the environment. This is often called sustainable engineering. Sustainable engineering minimizes waste in the design process and also considers the material used in the design process to ensure that the product will not be detrimental to the environment or can be recycled after its useful life.

With an agricultural engineering background, environmental engineers study air and water quality that is affected by animal production facilities, chemical runoff from agricultural fertilizers, and weed control chemicals. As we become more environmentally conscious, the demand for designs, processes, and structures that protect the environment will create an increasing demand for environmental engineers. They will provide the leadership for protecting our resources and environment for generations to come.

1.5.7   Industrial Engineering

Industrial engineering covers a broad spectrum of activities in organizations of all sizes. A primary objective of this engineering specialty is to improve the competitiveness and vitality of industry, government, and nonprofit institutions through the application of theory to human endeavors. Industrial engineering education requires a balanced understanding of mathematics, physical, and engineering sciences, as well as laboratory and industrial experiences. The principal efforts of industrial engineers are directed to the

Agricultural/Civil Engineer Emphasizes Goal Setting

Kyle D. Riley, P.E., CFM

Kyle Riley received his undergraduate degree in Agricultural Engineering and his master's in Agricultural and Civil Engineering. He currently works as a water resources engineer for Snyder & Associates, Inc. Snyder & Associates, Inc. provides public agencies and private business interests with comprehensive civil engineering and planning support. Their core services include civil and structural engineering, planning, survey, landscape architecture, environmental and water resources, and construction observation. As a water resources engineer, Kyle manages clients and projects, as well as, works on projects such as floodplain mapping, watershed management plans, bridge/culvert design and replacement projects, urban stormwater design and management studies, stream rehabilitation/restoration, hydrologic and hydraulic modeling, rural drainage management, and dam breach analyses.

Courtesy of Kyle Riley

Kyle didn't study or become a water resources engineer to design things, necessarily. He knew that he would be able to bring a different element to the profession by being able to work and understand people and their needs. So, the ability to work with people on a solution that works best for them is where he gets most of his pleasure. This can be challenging at times due to budgetary constraints. However, he enjoys sitting down with the client, or owner, to best understand what their needs are for each individual project. This ensures that each solution, or service, that is provided to that client is tailored to what will benefit them the most when the project is complete.

Kyle has learned many valuable lessons from his college, workplace and life experiences. First, sitting in your dorm room or apartment all the time is not healthy. On the flipside, never being there studying or working on homework is not good either. Being active outside of the classroom was vital for his success. For Kyle, life is a delicate balance between church, family, career, and pleasure. The balance has allowed him to juggle various aspects of his life that he needed to do, had to do, and wanted to do early on. Second, each individual experience brings a new perspective to your life that you might not have thought about before. This will allow you to understand someone you work with, or for, a little better throughout your life and career. For instance, he has officiated high school football and still does to this day. When you choose to do something like that, although it is tremendously enjoyable, you learn to deal with conflict and stay calm in stressful situations very quickly. He would not get that kind of experience if he did not desire to be a well-rounded person.

Here is Kyle's advice for undergraduate students for success. First and foremost, be humble in whatever you do. Although you have been given a gift, and probably worked very hard to get where you are, you should not act any different than anyone else. They have worked hard to get where they are as well and deserve your respect and compassion. Second, you should never sit idle and always strive to become better in everything you are involved in with life. Whether you are setting goals physically, for your career, financially, intellectually, or for your family, make sure these goals have the following attributes:

1. Be Specific—Goals should be very specific and not vague, or you will never achieve them. Saying you want to get better grades does not necessarily pinpoint the problem, let alone any possible solutions on how you are going to achieve better grades.

2. Measurable—Goals should be easily measured for success. Do not just say you want to lose weight. Be specific about how much weight you wish to lose. "I want to lose 10 pounds."

3. Yours—You need to have ownership of your goals. Do not try to accomplish something that someone else wants you to do. When was the last time you were happy about having to do something because your parents wanted you to do it? Really contemplate what you want out of a situation or experience and set the goal you want to achieve.

4. Time Limit—If you set a goal with no time limit, it will never get done. Wanting to have a certain amount of money saved up for a car, house, kids' college, or retirement is a great goal. However, if you don't set a time-frame for when you want that goal accomplished, you will always find something else to spend your money on.

5. Write it down—Always write you goals down and I do not mean type it in an e-mail or on your phone somewhere. Physically write your goal down on and post it in a very visible location for yourself and others. This will keep you accountable to yourself, but also allow others to help you in check and moving toward your goal.

Figure 1.22

Industrial engineers design the assembly lines for production of products such as new electronics units.
© Corbis

design of production systems for goods and services (Figure 1.22). Most departments allow for specialization in at least one of three areas:

Manufacturing: Industrial engineers must understand the fundamentals of modern and economic manufacturing; use product specifications as the keystone of part interchangeability; verify a product's conformance to its specifications; apply manufacturing principles to a manufacturing process; program flexible manufacturing equipment and system controllers; design logical manufacturing layouts; and implement contemporary systems issues such as lean manufacturing.

Human Factors: Industrial engineers analyze and design both the job and the worksite in a cost-effective manner using time studies, as well as measure the resulting output; they also design, implement, and evaluate human-computer interfaces according to principles outlined in foundational human-computer interaction readings.

Management and Information Systems: Industrial engineers apply time value of money to make financial decisions; use probability concepts to solve engineering problems; estimate parameters; conduct tests of hypotheses and create regression models; apply statistical quality control methods such as process capability, control charts, and tolerance allocation; design experiments; optimize and solve mathematical models of real problems using linear programming, dynamic programming, networking, Markov chains, queuing, and inventory models; and create simulation models of manufacturing and service systems and analyze simulation output; understand object-oriented programming foundations; and develop applications of information technology in industrial engineering.

1.5.8 Mechanical Engineering

Mechanical engineers are involved with all forms of energy generation, distribution, utilization and conversion, the design and development of machines, the control of automated systems, manufacturing and processing of materials, and the creative solutions to environmental problems (Figure 1.23). Practicing mechanical engineers are typically associated with research, manufacturing, operations, testing, marketing, administration, and teaching.

A typical undergraduate curriculum includes required and elective courses in the following areas:

Design	Noise and vibration control
Fluid mechanics and	Modeling and simulation
propulsion	Acoustics
Heat transfer	Robotics
Solid mechanics	HVAC (heating, ventilation,
	thermodynamics
	and air-conditioning)
Combustion and energy	Mechatronics
utilization	Measurements and
Manufacturing and materials	instrumentation
processing	Automatic controls

The energy crisis and environmental challenges in the current decade have reprioritized a need for new sources of energy as well as new and improved methods of energy conversion. Mechanical engineers are involved in the research and development of solar, geothermal, biomass, and wind energy sources, along with research to increase the efficiency of producing electricity from fossil fuel, hydroelectric, and nuclear sources.

Figure 1.23

Here a mechanical engineer is involved with the design of alternative energy solar panels.
© *Brand X Pictures/PunchStock*

Machines and mechanisms that are used daily in all forms of manufacturing and transportation have been designed and developed by mechanical engineers. Automobiles, airplanes, and trains combine a source of power with an aerodynamically designed enclosure to provide modern transportation. Tractors and other farm implements aid the agricultural community. Automated machinery and robotics are rapidly growing areas for mechanical engineers. Machine design requires a strong mechanical engineering background and a vivid imagination.

In order to drive modern machinery, a source of power is needed. The mechanical engineer is involved with the generation of electricity by converting chemical energy in fuels to thermal energy in the form of steam, then to mechanical energy through a

Industrial Engineering Focused on Food Quality
Kara Hobart

Courtesy of Kara Hobart

Kara Hobart received her bachelor's degree in Industrial Engineering from Iowa State, her master's degree also in Industrial Engineering from Pennsylvania State University, and is currently a Senior R&D Engineer for General Mills in Minneapolis, MN. General Mills is the maker of well-known food products such as Cheerios, Nature Valley, and Yoplait, to name a few. Kara develops global baking products. You may find her running a DOE to test new ingredients in the pilot plant, analyzing data to create manufacturing efficiencies across plant locations, or interacting with consumers about all kinds of baking products. Prior to her current role, Kara held positions supporting the quality and regulatory organization in General Mills' Grain Lab in Minneapolis, MN, and plant operations in Lodi, CA, and Cedar Rapids, IA. Kara's favorite aspect to all the roles she has had so far with General Mills is that she has been able to "play"—to test, to tinker, to create, to analyze, to troubleshoot. Common to most other engineering-related professions, no two days are completely alike. Manufacturing is a passion of Kara's and her ability to apply the skills developed during undergraduate and graduate studies provides her with immense satisfaction.

During her time at Iowa State, she was very active with several organizations on campus including IIE, Alpha Pi Mu, Tau Beta Pi, First Lego League, and Ballroom Dance Club. Benefits of this involvement included resource management skills (time, money, people, organization), but more importantly, developing a refined sense of self—she never knew how much she loved dancing until she tried it!

In addition to R&D work at General Mills, Kara spends much of her time supporting Partners in Food Solutions (PFS), which is a nonprofit organization that "Connects Expertise with Opportunity." PFS connects small and growing businesses in Africa to learn from experts around the world to create improved business models and processing efficiencies. Kara is the country lead for Ethiopia, supporting 10 different businesses on 22 projects. She is incredibly motivated by the simplicity of transferring her engineering skills and knowledge to someone looking for just those skills to improve their business.

Advice to Undergraduate Students:

- Use your degree to think, adapt, and be flexible—the minutia of facts and formulas matter, but only in how they are applied. Application takes thinking, creativity, and flexibility to create the solutions for the present and future.
- Take a class (or join a club) JUST for fun—give yourself a broad perspective of what this world has to offer. You're only in college for a few short years and it's one of the best places to tap world-renown subject-matter experts so take advantage of it!
- Be intentional—as long as you can clearly communicate your thought process for your decisions, you will likely find success.

turbine to drive the electric generator. Internal combustion devices such as gasoline, turbine, and diesel engines are designed for use in most areas of transportation. The mechanical engineer studies engine cycles, fuel requirements, ignition performance, power output, cooling systems, engine geometry, and lubrication in order to develop high-performance, low-energy-consuming engines.

Mechanical engineers work on engineering teams that are responsible for design and development of products and systems. Virtually any machine or process you can imagine has benefited from the influence of a mechanical engineer.

Mechanical Engineer Performance Analyst
Sheela Rajendran

Sheela Rajendran received her BS degree in mechanical engineering. She is currently a senior associate engineer with Caterpillar's Global Engine Development—North America Division. Rajendran is a performance analyst for engine development in Caterpillar's Engine Systems Technology & Solutions division, which provides comprehensive engine testing and development services to designers, manufacturers, and other customers. The division applies a variety of analytical and developmental techniques to ensure that engines meet high standards for performance, durability, and emission standards. Rajendran's responsibilities require working in a lab environment that focuses on the testing and development of diesel engines. The goal is to ensure that Caterpillar's diesel engines comply with increasingly stringent emissions standards, while maintaining high performance.

Rajendran's five-year plan is to continue developing a sound technical engineering foundation and eventually transition into management. She also plans to pursue a master's degree in engineering or business.

Rajendran honed many necessary job skills (including communication, networking, and coordinating/planning) through her involvement in the Society of Women Engineers and through working at the Industrial Assessment Center while pursuing her undergraduate studies. She uses many of these skills in her job on a daily basis.

1.6 Conclusion

We have touched only briefly on the possibilities for exciting and rewarding work in all engineering areas. The first step is to obtain the knowledge during your college education that is necessary for your first technical position. After that you must continue your education, either formally by seeking an advanced degree or degrees or informally through continuing education courses or appropriate reading to maintain pace with the technology, an absolute necessity for a professional. Many challenges await you. Prepare to meet them well.

Problems

1.1 Describe which engineering roles best fit your long-term career goals.

1.2 Compare the definitions of an engineer and a technologist from at least two sources.

1.3 When considering the engineering functions of research, development, design, production, testing, construction, operations, sales, management, consulting, and teaching, which two best fit your personality and long-term goals? Explain why.

1.4 Find the name of a prominent engineer in the field of your choice and write a brief paper on the accomplishments of this individual.

1.5 Select a specific discipline of engineering and list at least 10 different companies and/or government agencies that utilize engineers from this field.

1.6 For the discipline selected in Exercise 1.5, choose a function such as design. Select one of the 10 industrial organizations utilizing engineers in this discipline and write a brief report on some typical activities that are undertaken by the engineers who perform that function in this organization. Be specific in your discussion of the activities. For example: A mechanical engineer for Company X designs the steering linkage for a garden tractor, specifies all the parts, and conducts prototype tests.

1.7 Read through each of the personal profiles of engineering graduates from this chapter. List and describe five lessons you learned from their advice.

1.8 Locate a full-time job description for an engineering major that interests you. You can find this on the Internet or on your campus's career services job posting website. What knowledge, skills, and abilities does the job require? Include the job description along with your answer.

1.9 After learning about the different types of engineering programs, select a program that is offered at your school and read the catalog descriptions for courses offered in this major. Find two courses that best fit your personal interest in this major and describe why they interest you.

1.10 Prepare a brief paper on the engineering degree that you are most interested in. Explain why this degree program best fits your academic and professional goals.

1.11 Prepare a five-minute talk to present to your class describing one of the engineering disciplines that most interests you.

1.12 Choose one of the following topics (or one suggested by your instructor) and write a paper that discusses technological changes that have occurred in this area in the past 15 years. Include commentary on the social and environmental impact of the changes and on new problems that may have arisen because of the changes.

(_a_) passenger automobiles
(_b_) electric power-generating plants
(_c_) phones
(_d_) heart surgery
(_e_) heating systems (furnaces)
(_f_) microprocessors
(_g_) water treatment
(_h_) road paving (both concrete and asphalt)
(_i_) composite materials
(_j_) robotics
(_k_) air-conditioning

CHAPTER **2**

Education for Engineering

Chapter Objectives

When you complete your study of this chapter, you will be able to:

- Understand the skills and abilities needed to pursue an engineering degree
- Understand how to prepare for a meaningful engineering career workplace
- Understand the importance of obtaining an internship/cooperative education experience
- Realize the importance of the engineering profession and the steps to becoming a professional engineer

2.1   Education for Engineering

The amount of information coming from the academic and business world is increasing exponentially. More than any other group, engineers are using this knowledge to shape civilization. To keep pace with a changing world, engineers must be educated to solve problems that are as yet unheard of. A large share of the responsibility for this mammoth education task falls on the engineering colleges and universities. But the completion of an engineering program is only the first step toward a lifetime of education. The engineer, with the assistance of the employer, professional society, and the university, must continue to study. (See Figure 2.1.)

Logically, then, an engineering education should provide a broad base in scientific and engineering principles, some study in the humanities and social sciences, and specialized studies in a chosen engineering curriculum. But specific questions concerning engineering education still arise. We will deal here with the questions that are frequently asked by students. What are the desirable characteristics for success in an engineering program? What knowledge, skills, and abilities should be acquired in college? What is meant by continuing education with respect to an engineering career?

2.1.1   Desirable Characteristics

Years of experience have enabled engineering educators to analyze the performance of students in relation to the abilities and interests they possess when entering college. The most important characteristics for an engineering student can be summarized as follows:

1. A strong interest in and ability to work with mathematics and science taken in high school.
2. An ability to think through a problem in a logical manner.

Figure 2.1

Engineering education takes place at colleges and universities, as well as within industry, and through continuing education programs supported by professional engineering societies.
© *Ariel Skelley/Blend Images LLC*

3. A knack for organizing and carrying through to conclusion the solution to a problem.
4. An unusual curiosity about how and why things work.
5. The desire to design new and innovative products, processes, or systems to solve everyday problems.
6. A passion for helping solve modern-day challenges (e.g., renewable, nonpolluting energy; abundant clean water; modern health care; sustainable agriculture and manufacturing; safe roads and bridges; designs for natural and man-made disasters).

Although such attributes are desirable, having them is no guarantee of success in an engineering program. Simply a strong desire for the job has made successful engineers of some individuals who did not possess any of these characteristics; and, conversely, many who possessed them did not complete an engineering degree. Moreover, an engineering education is not easy, but it can offer a rewarding career to anyone who accepts the challenge. To succeed, it is important to choose an engineering field of study that best matches your personal passions and interests.

Developing into a professional engineer (PE) takes more than just taking the classes required for an engineering degree. Undergraduate engineers also need to develop their knowledge, skills, and abilities outside the classroom. There are many opportunities for students to become leaders through professional and nonprofessional student club experiences, internship or cooperative education experiences with industries closely associated with the student's chosen engineering field, community or service learning projects, international study abroad experiences and participation in many other academic and nonacademic related activities.

Engineering Is More Than Just Taking Courses

Abhinaya Raghothaman

Abhinaya Raghothaman received her bachelor of science degree in Aerospace Engineering. She is currently working for the Boeing Company in Everett, Washington, DC. Boeing is one of the largest aircraft manufacturers in the world. Boeing designs and manufactures commercial and military aircraft, space systems, rockets, and rotorcraft. Abhinaya works as an aerodynamics engineer for Boeing Commercial Airplanes (BCA), which is one of the five main divisions of Boeing. More specifically, she evaluates the airplane's performance (both high-speed and low-speed aero performance). Her primary responsibility includes doing mission analysis for the 777X to quantify essential performance metrics of the airplane such as fuel burn, range, payload, and field performance. Her group

Courtesy of Abhinaya Raghothaman

works with other engineers such as weights, configuration, and propulsion engineers in order to evaluate and optimize the airplane's performance. Her group is also heavily involved in every step of the airplane design process – from concept to the airplane's entry into service. Abhinaya really appreciates getting an integrated and high-level view of the airplane as an airplane performance engineer. It also gives her a chance to interact with other groups at Boeing and expand her knowledge of engineering.

As an undergraduate, Abhinaya participated in a variety of activities, many of which involved mentoring. Being a peer mentor for the Program for Women in Science and Engineering helped her develop excellent interpersonal and communication skills. She also co-led the Iowa State student chapter of the American Institute of Aeronautics and Astronautics (AIAA) where she learned about what it means to be a professional engineer (PE). She organized and led the executive meetings where the teams brainstormed ideas to provide aerospace engineering students at Iowa State more opportunities to interact with the university's faculty and also with engineers from major aerospace companies (i.e., Boeing, Lockheed Martin, SpaceX) and NASA. During her senior year as an undergraduate, she also volunteered to mentor a freshman aerospace engineer through AIAA's mentoring program. These leadership experiences gave her the chance to work with very diverse groups of people and tactfully solve problems with group dynamics. The skills that she developed from being actively involved, along with her strong engineering foundation, act as a toolset to tackle problems as an engineer.

What advice does she have for undergraduate engineers? Having a strong and thorough understanding of engineering fundamentals is extremely important. However, the ability to *communicate* your critical thinking, logic, and ideas clearly and concisely is the most valuable skill of all. Investing time and effort in becoming a better communicator is essential as an undergraduate. Companies will almost always train you further on the technical skills directly related to your job, but they expect you to have a solid and vibrant palette of "soft skills" such as communication, collaboration, and leadership when you join their team. Communication is a soft skill that is important in all aspects of life, whether it is work, family, or friends. The rewards of devoting time to develop these soft skills can be noticed every day, at work and at home.

2.1.2 Course of Study

The quality control of engineering programs is effected through the accreditation process. The engineering profession, through ABET and CEAB, has developed standards and criteria for the education of engineers entering the profession.

Through visitations, evaluations, and reports, the written criteria and standards are compared with the engineering curricula at a university. For ABET, individual degree-granting programs complete a self-study report that must address several criteria in areas related to students, program educational objectives, program outcomes and assessment, the professional or technical component of the curriculum, faculty, facilities, institutional support and financial resources, and program criteria. Each program, if operating according to the standards and criteria, may receive up to six years of accreditation. If some discrepancies appear, accreditations may be granted for a shorter time period or may not be granted at all until appropriate improvements are made.

It is safe to say that for any given engineering discipline, no two schools will have identical offerings. However, close scrutiny will show a framework within which most courses can be placed, with differences occurring only in textbooks used, topics emphasized, and sequences followed. Figure 2.2 depicts this framework and some of the courses that fall within each of the areas. The approximate percentage of time spent on each course grouping is indicated.

Figure 2.2

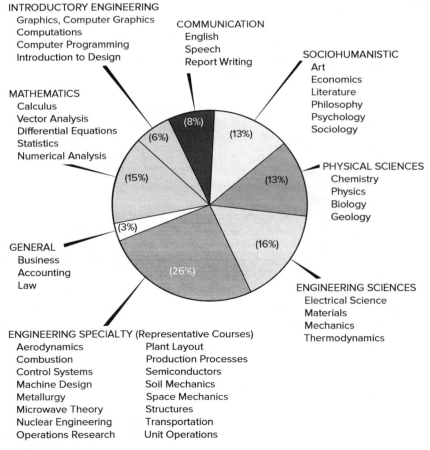

Elements of engineering curricula.

The general education block is a small portion of most engineering curricula, but it is important because it helps the engineering student to understand and develop an appreciation for the potential impact of engineering to undertakings on the environment and general society. When the location of an ethanol plant is being considered, the engineers involved in this decision must respect the concerns and feelings of all individuals who might be affected by the location. Discussions of the interaction between engineers and the general public take place in few engineering courses; general education courses (sociology, economics, history, management, etc.) thus are needed to furnish engineering students with an insight into the needs and aspirations of society.

Chemistry and physics are almost universally required in engineering. They are fundamental to the study of engineering science. The mathematics normally required for college chemistry and physics is more advanced than that for the corresponding high school courses. Higher-level chemistry and physics also may be required, depending on departmental structure. Finally, other physical science, biological, or business courses may be required in some programs or taken as electives.

An engineer cannot be successful without the ability to communicate ideas and the results of work efforts. The research engineer writes reports and orally presents ideas to management. The production engineer must be able to converse with craftspersons in understandable terms. And all engineers have dealings with the public and must be able to communicate on a nontechnical level. Engineers must become proficient in written, oral, visual, and electronic communication. For some, this may mean taking communication courses above and beyond the required communication courses, becoming involved in extracurricular activities, or obtaining an internship that will develop communication competence.

Mathematics is the engineer's most powerful problem-solving tool. The amount of class time spent in this area is indicative of its importance. Courses in calculus, vector analysis, and differential equations are common to all degree programs. Statistics, numerical analysis, and other mathematics courses support some engineering specialty areas. Students desiring an advanced degree may want to take mathematics courses beyond the baccalaureate-level requirements.

In the early stages of an engineering education, introductory courses in graphical communication, computational techniques, design, and computer programming are often required. Engineering schools vary somewhat in their emphasis on these areas, but the general intent is to develop skills in the application of theory to practical problem solving and familiarity with engineering terminology. Design is presented from a conceptual point of view to aid the student in creative thinking. Graphics develops the visualization capability and assists the student in transferring mental thoughts into well-defined concepts on paper. The tremendous potential of the computer to assist the engineer has led to the requirement of computer programming in all curricula. Use of the computer to perform many tedious calculations has increased the efficiency of the engineer and has allowed more time for creative thinking. Computer graphics is also an important part for many engineering curricula. Its ability to enhance the visualization of geometry and to depict engineering quantities graphically has increased productivity in the design process.

With a strong background in mathematics and physical sciences, you can begin to study engineering sciences, courses that are fundamental to all engineering specialties. Electrical science includes study of charges, fields, circuits, and electronics. Materials science courses involve study of the properties and chemical compositions of metallic and nonmetallic substances (see Figure 2.3). Mechanics includes study of statics, dynamics, fluids, and mechanics of materials. Thermodynamics is the science of heat

Figure 2.3

Engineers select appropriate materials for designing solar panels that will endure extreme conditions.
© Henglein and Steets/Cultura RF/Getty Images

and is the basis for study of all types of energy and energy transfer. A sound understanding of the engineering sciences is most important for anyone interested in pursuing postgraduate work and research.

Figure 2.2 shows only a few examples of the many specialized engineering courses given. Scanning course descriptions in a college general bulletin or catalog will provide a more detailed insight into the specialized courses required in the various engineering disciplines.

Most curricula allow students flexibility in selecting a few outside courses. For example, a student interested in management may take some courses in business and accounting. Another may desire some background in law or medicine, with the intent of entering a professional school in one of these areas upon graduation from engineering. Many new curricula are integrating biological sciences into their programs to meet industry demand for those who can design systems or products that have a biological twist. Other new programs are integrating entrepreneurship and leadership into their curricula.

2.1.3 Preparation for an Engineering Work Environment

As an engineering student, you must prepare yourself for the engineering workplace by gaining key knowledge and by developing core skills and abilities/competencies. The ABET, the organization that accredits engineering programs in the United States and abroad, validates that engineering programs have documented student outcomes that prepare graduates to attain the program educational objective. The educational objectives need to be consistent with the mission of the institution, the needs of the program's various constituents, and the accreditation criteria. In ABET's 2016–2017 Criteria for Accrediting Engineering Programs document, they identify the following student outcomes:

(a) *an ability to apply knowledge of mathematics, science, and engineering*

(b) *an ability to design and conduct experiments, as well as to analyze and interpret data*

(c) *an ability to design a system, component, or process to meet desired needs within realistic constraints such as economic, environmental, social, political, ethical, health and safety, manufacturability, and sustainability*

(d) *an ability to function on multidisciplinary teams*

(e) *an ability to identify, formulate, and solve engineering problems*

(f) *an understanding of professional and ethical responsibility*

(g) *an ability to communicate effectively*

(h) *the broad education necessary to understand the impact of engineering solutions in a global, economic, environmental, and societal context*

(i) *a recognition of the need for, and an ability to engage in life-long learning*

(j) *a knowledge of contemporary issues*

(k) *an ability to use the techniques, skills, and modern engineering tools necessary for engineering practice.*

Note that seven of these outcomes start with "an ability to . . .", one requires "an understanding of . . .", one requires "a knowledge of . . .", and another calls for "the broad education necessary to . . .". All of these are difficult to measure. So where are the best settings and what are the best activities to participate in to develop these "a–k" student learning outcomes? In the past, it was expected that most if not all of these should be addressed in the college classroom during the pursuit of an undergraduate degree. Today, faculty and industry representatives realize that these outcomes can only be met through active participation in a combination of curricular, co-curricular, and extra-curricular activities. The curricular activities would include the traditional classroom experiences (e.g., lecture, laboratory, and capstone design courses) and participation in an academic engineering cooperative education/internship program. We will talk about cooperative education/internship programs in the next section. Co-curricular activities might include participation in an engineering study abroad program, an engineering service learning project, or an engineering student club. Extracurricular activities could include participation in a non-engineering club, intramural sports, college sports, community service, or volunteer programs.

Industries are interested in what you will contribute to their company to help make them successful. They determine future behavior of potential employees by evaluating past behavior. When interviewing engineering undergraduates for cooperative education/internship programs or full-time employment, many companies today use behavioral-based interviewing. Instead of asking you an interview question like, "How well do you think you would work in a team within our company?" they would instead ask, "Can you tell us of a time when you worked on an engineering design project, where you contributed significantly to the success of the final design?" Did you notice the difference between these two questions? The first question allows you to make up a story about how you would work on a team, whereas with the second question you have to reflect on a specific time when you contributed to a team's success either in a class project or during your internship.

To best determine which workplace competencies a company is looking for, conduct a key word or phrase analysis of a job posting from an engineering company that you are interested in working for. The most common competencies that a company is looking for include communication (oral, written, visual, and electronic), teamwork, initiative, engineering knowledge, and analysis and judgment. Other competencies might include innovation, safety awareness, general knowledge, cultural adaptability, planning, professional impact, quality orientation, customer focus, inclusion, and integrity.

As you plan out your engineering academic program, make sure that you have a well-balanced program that includes key curricular, co-curricular, and extra-curricular activities. When companies evaluate your resume, they will typically rank your engineering work experience as the most important, followed by your grade point average (GPA), leadership experiences, and useful skills learned in class, on a job, or through other activities. When you first start your degree program, take a course load that helps you to be successful in the classroom. Establishing a good grade point average is critical to obtaining a cooperative education/internship experience. As you establish good study and time management skills and a strong GPA, start to integrate co-curricular and extra-curricular activities that will help to strengthen your resume. Don't forget to have some fun along the way.

2.1.4 Cooperative Education/Internship Programs

Almost all engineering degree programs offer their students the opportunity to obtain meaningful industry work experience through some sort of engineering experiential education. The three basic forms of engineering experiential education are cooperative education, an engineering internship, and an engineering summer work experience. Although the definitions given below are fairly common across engineering programs, there are variations. Check the website information from your local engineering career services office for the definitions at your institution. Also note that for some engineering programs, an engineering experiential education experience may be required, while for other programs it may be voluntary.

Cooperative Education

Cooperative education is typically defined as alternating periods of full-time academic college training with periods of full-time work experience of approximately equal length. At least one calendar year equivalent of institutionally supervised work experience is typically required (e.g., a minimum of two semesters and one summer).

Internship

An internship is most often defined as a single work period of institutionally supervised full-time employment of at least one semester. This experience would typically not include two semesters in the same academic year, but instead one semester, or one semester plus one summer. A summer internship is defined as a single work period of institutionally supervised, engineering-related, full-time employment of typically 8–10 weeks.

Obtaining a Cooperative Education or Internship Experience

If you are interested in pursuing one of these experiences, it is important to establish a strong GPA, obtain meaningful non-engineering or technical work experience, and develop competencies required for the engineering field you are interested in. Some campuses hold career fairs that you can attend in order to interact with industrial representatives interested in hiring coops, interns, or summer hires. If this is not the case at your institution, you may have to pursue these opportunities by sending your resume to human resources personnel at the company you are interested in. Also check for career fairs that you can attend at your professional society meetings or at another school within driving distance. There are also numerous online career websites that can be helpful in finding a position. Many companies will only accept resumes through a link on their website, so ask a company representative what route you should take to get your resume looked at. Your academic advisor is a great resource for determining the best options for you.

2.1.5 Continuing Education

Once you have received a bachelor of science degree in engineering, it would be a mistake to think the learning process has been completed. On the contrary, it has just begun. Continued education can take many forms. It may involve preparation for a professional license, and it certainly will include seminars, short courses, and professional conferences to maintain an up-to-date understanding of your selected area of expertise. Many students elect to continue their undergraduate studies with a master of science (MS) or even a PhD in their discipline. Numerous online continuing education opportunities are available today, making it easy to learn from home, your office, or where ever you may be.

Another common area for engineering grads to consider is a master of business administration (MBA). A few students will pursue law and occasionally medicine as a path toward continued professional development.

2.2 The Engineer as a Professional

Engineering is a learned vocation, demanding an individual with high standards of ethics and sound moral character. When making judgments, which may create controversy and affect many people, the engineer must keep foremost in mind a dedication to the betterment of humanity.

2.2.1 Professionalism

Professionalism is a way of life. A professional person is one who engages in an activity that requires a specialized and comprehensive education and is motivated by a strong desire to serve humanity. A professional thinks and acts in a manner that brings favor upon the individual and the entire profession. Developing a professional frame of mind begins with your engineering education.

The PE can be said to have the following:

1. Specialized knowledge and skills used for the benefit of humanity.
2. Honesty and impartiality in engineering service.
3. Constant interest in improving the profession.
4. Support of professional and technical societies that represent the PE.

It is clear that these characteristics include not only technical competence but also a positive attitude toward life that is continually reinforced by educational accomplishments and professional service.

2.2.2 Professional Registration

The power to license engineers rests with each of the 50 states. Since the first registration law in Wyoming in 1907, all states have developed legislation specifying requirements for engineering practice. The purpose of registration laws is to protect the public. Just as one would expect a physician to provide competent medical service, an engineer can be expected to provide competent technical service. However, the laws of registration for engineers are quite different from those for lawyers or physicians. An engineer does not have to be registered to practice engineering. Legally, only the chief engineer of a firm needs to be registered for that firm to perform engineering services. Individuals testifying as expert engineering witnesses in court and those offering engineering consulting services need to be registered. In some instances the practice of engineering is allowed as long as the individual does not advertise as an engineer.

The legal process for becoming a licensed PE consists of four parts, two of which entail examinations. The parts include

1. An engineering degree from an acceptable institution as defined by the state board for registration. Graduation from an ABET-accredited institution satisfies the degree requirement automatically.
2. Successful completion of the Fundamentals of Engineering (FE) exam is the first step in preparing to become a professional engineer. This six-hour computer-based examination may be taken during the last term of an undergraduate program that is ABET-accredited. The 110 multiple-choice exam covers fundamentals in the areas of mathematics, chemistry, physics, engineering mechanics, electrical science, thermal science, economics, and ethics. Currently, the FE exam is offered in seven disciplines including: chemical, civil, electrical and computer, environmental, industrial, mechanical, and other disciplines (agricultural, architectural, biolocial, civil, general engineering, mechanical, mining/mineral, naval architecture and marine, petroleum, structural). The passing grade is determined by the National Council of Examiners for Engineering and Surveying (NCEES).
3. Completion of at least four years of post-college work experience in chosen engineering discipline under the supervision of an engineer who is already licensed.
4. Successful completion of the PE exam completes the licensing process. This eight-hour examination covers problems normally encountered in the area of specialty such as mechanical or chemical engineering.

It should be noted that once the license is received, it is permanent although there is an annual renewal fee. In addition, the trend is toward specific requirements in continuing education each year in order to maintain the license. Licensed engineers in some states may attend professional meetings in their specialty, take classes, and write professional papers or books to accumulate sufficient professional development activities beyond their job responsibilities to maintain their licenses. This trend is a reflection of the rapidly changing technology and the need for engineers to remain current in their area.

Figure 2.4

Preamble to the NSPE Code of Ethics for Engineers *(National Society of Professional Engineers).*

NSPE Code of Ethics for Engineers

PREAMBLE

Engineering is an important and learned profession. As members of this profession, engineers are expected to exhibit the highest standards of honesty and integrity. Engineering has a direct and vital impact on the quality of life for all people. Accordingly, the services provided by engineers require honesty, impartiality, fairness, and equity, and must be dedicated to the protection of the public health, safety, and welfare. Engineers must perform under a standard of professional behavior that requires adherence to the highest principles of ethical conduct.

Registration does have many advantages. Most public employment positions, all expert witness roles in court cases, and some high-level company positions require the PE's license. However, less than one-half of the eligible candidates are currently registered. You should give serious consideration to becoming registered as soon as you qualify. Satisfying the requirements for registration can be started even before graduation from an ABET-accredited curriculum.

2.2.3 Professional Ethics

Ethics is the guide to personal conduct of a professional. Most technical societies have a written code of ethics for their members. The preamble for the NSPE Code of Ethics for Engineers is shown in Figure 2.4. Figure 2.5 is the "Engineers' Creed" as published by the NSPE.

Figure 2.5

Engineers' Creed *(National Society of Professional Engineers)*

Engineers' Creed

As a Professional Engineer, I dedicate my professional knowledge and skill to the advancement and betterment of human welfare.

I pledge:

- To give the utmost of performance;
- To participate in none but honest enterprise;
- To live and work according to the laws of man and the highest standards of professional conduct;
- To place service before profit, the honor and standing of the profession before personal advantage, and the public welfare above all other considerations.

In humility and with need for Divine Guidance, I make this pledge.

Adopted by National Society of Professional Engineers, June 1954.

2.2.4 Professional Societies

Over 550 colleges and universities offer programs in engineering that are accredited by ABET or CEAB. These boards have as their purpose the quality control of engineering and technology programs offered in the United States and Canada. The basis of the boards is the engineering profession, which is represented through the participating professional groups.

Table 2.1 is a partial listing of the numerous engineering societies that support the engineering disciplines and functions. These technical societies are linked because of their support of the accreditation process. Over 60 other societies exist for the purpose of supporting the professional status of engineers. Among these are the Society of Women Engineers (SWE), the National Society of Black Engineers (NSBE), the Society of Hispanic Professional Engineers (SHPE), the Acoustical Society of America (ASA), the Society of Plastics Engineers (SPE), and the American Society for Quality Control (ASQC).

A primary reason for the rapid development in science and engineering is the work of technical societies. The fundamental service provided by a society is the sharing of ideas, which means that technical specialists can publicize their efforts and assist others in promoting excellence in the profession. When information is distributed to other society members, new ideas evolve and duplicated efforts are minimized. The societies conduct meetings on international, national, and local bases. Students of engineering will find a technical society in their specialty that may operate as a branch of the regular society or as a student chapter on campus. The student organization is an important link with professional workers, providing motivation and the opportunity to make acquaintances that will help students to formulate career objectives.

Table 2.1 Participating Bodies in the Accreditation Process

Organization	Abbreviation
American Academy of Environmental Engineers and Scientists	AAEES
American Institute of Aeronautics and Astronautics, Inc.	AIAA
American Institute of Chemical Engineers	AICHE
American Nuclear Society	ANS
American Society of Agricultural and Biological Engineers	ASABE
American Society of Civil Engineers	ASCE
American Society for Engineers Education	ASEE
ASHRAE	ASHRAE
ASME	ASME
American Society of Safety Engineers	ASSE
Biomedical Engineering Society	BMES
Institute of Biological Engineering	IBE
The Institute of Electrical and Electronics Engineers, Inc.	IEEE
Institute of Industrial Engineers	IIE
National Council of Examiners for Engineering and Surveying	NCEES
National Society of Professional Engineers	NSPE
SAE International	SAE International
SME	SME
Society of Petroleum Engineers	SPE
Society of Women Engineers	SWE

Source: www.abet.org, 2016

2.3   Conclusion

Pursuing an engineering degree will be both challenging and rewarding as you make your way through your degree program. Your undergraduate program will provide many challenges, regardless of whether your studies are in mathematics, physical sciences, engineering sciences, engineering specialties, communication, or social and human sciences. It is important that you develop the overall knowledge, skills, and abilities needed for a successful engineering career through a well-designed academics program, including experiential education and co-curricular and extra-curricular experiences. Engage with others in your chosen profession of study by joining your local professional student club. This is a great way to meet graduates from your degree program who are currently working in the industry. Finally, start to build strong relationships with other engineering students who are serious about their academic success.

Problems

2.1   For a particular discipline of engineering, such as electrical engineering, find the program of study for the first two years and compare it with the program offered at your school approximately 20 years ago. Comment on the major differences.

2.2   Compare the knowledge, skills, abilities, and competencies of a job description for a cooperative education/internship position versus that of a full-time position for a company that you would like to work with. What differences do you see?

2.3   List five of your own personal characteristics and compare that list with the one in Section 2.1.1.

2.4   Prepare a brief paper on the requirements for professional registration in your state. Include the type and content of the required examinations.

2.5   Prepare a five-minute talk to present to your class describing one of the technical societies listed in Table 2.1 and how it can benefit you as a student.

2.6   Go to your engineering career service website and locate the description for cooperative education, internships, and summer work experiences. What are the requirements for each of these programs for your degree program? What are the key differences between a cooperative education experience and an internship experience?

2.7   Compare the Engineers' Creed with that of another profession. What similarities and differences do you see? Explain why they are different.

2.8   Discuss why accreditation from an organization like ABET is important to becoming a PE.

2.9   Which of the abilities listed in ABET's (a) through (k) student learning outcomes most align with the first year course you are taking for your engineering degree? Which ones are more aligned with the last year of study?

CHAPTER 3

Introduction to Engineering Design

Chapter Objectives

When you complete your study of this chapter, you will be able to:

- Identify and explain the key steps in the design process
- Explain the importance of the customer's role in the design process
- Apply the design process to solving an open-ended problem
- Understand the importance of the engineering design process in development of engineering solutions to society's needs

3.1 An Introduction to Engineering Design

What do you say when asked why you are planning to be an engineer? One possible response is, "I want to become an engineer to design . . ." It might be to design a water-quality system for a developing country, a new spacecraft for NASA, the tallest building in the world, an auto-guidance device for automobiles, new and improved sports equipment, or even synthetic blood. The key is that engineers design devices, systems, or processes to help humankind.

So what is engineering design? Engineering design is a systematic process by which solutions to the needs of humankind are obtained. Design is the essence of engineering. The design process is applied to problems (needs) of varying complexity. For example, mechanical engineers will apply the design process to develop an effective, efficient vehicle suspension system; electrical engineers will apply the process to design lightweight, compact wireless communication devices; and materials engineers will apply the process to design strong, lightweight composites for aircraft structures.

The vast majority of complex problems in today's high technology society do not depend for solutions on a single engineering discipline; rather, they depend on teams of engineers, scientists, environmentalists, economists, sociologists, legal personnel, and others. Solutions are dependent not only on the appropriate applications of technology but also on public sentiment as executed through government regulations and political influence. As engineers we are empowered with the technical expertise to develop new and improved products and systems; however, at the same time we must be increasingly aware of the impact of our actions on society and the environment in general and work conscientiously toward the best solution in view of all relevant factors.

The systematic design process can be conveniently represented by the six steps introduced in Section 3.2.

1. Define the problem to be solved.
2. Acquire and assemble pertinent data.
3. Identify solution constraints and criteria.
4. Develop alternative solutions.
5. Select a solution based on analysis of alternatives.
6. Communicate the results.

Building on an Engineering Degree

Nick Mohr

Nick Mohr received his BS in mechanical engineering and then went on to obtain his medical degree. He is currently a resident physician in emergency medicine, caring for patients in the emergency departments of two trauma centers and on a helicopter transport service in Indianapolis, Indiana.

Once he finishes his residency, he plans then either to look for a faculty appointment at a university or to pursue further training, perhaps in a postgraduate aerospace medicine program offered by Johnson Space Center (JSC) in conjunction with the University of Texas. Recently, he spent some time at JSC working with the flight surgeons in space medicine, which he found to be "incredible."

Dr. Mohr was involved with numerous student organizations and activities while pursuing his engineering degree, including Team PrISUm (Iowa State University's solar car team), the Cosmic Ray Observation Project, and the Ames (Iowa) Free Clinic. He feels that his involvement outside the classroom was one of the most important aspects of his undergraduate training. It provided him experience in learning how (1) to solve novel problems and make decisions without knowing the right answers; (2) to succeed and fail when the stakes for failure are high; and (3) to identify what consequences are worth fearing, and using those consequences to choose risks worth taking.

Dr. Mohr recalls that as a student, he had no idea how many doors an engineering degree could open and offers the following advice to students just beginning their engineering education:

"There is no harm in being uncertain about what path your career may take, and in fact, many people change their direction along the way—that's not bad. The important part is to have dreams, and to follow them wholeheartedly until they change. If we do that, we will solve some very interesting problems in our lives and can improve the world in which we live. A strong and diverse educational foundation in engineering has opened doors that I never could have imagined when I was in college."

A formal definition of engineering design is found in the curriculum guidelines ABET. ABET accredits curricula in engineering schools and derives its membership from the various engineering professional societies. Each accredited curriculum has a well-defined design component that falls within the ABET guidelines. The ABET statement on design reads as follows:

Engineering design is the process of devising a system, component, or process to meet desired needs (Figure 3.1). It is a decision-making process (often iterative), in which the basic sciences, mathematics, and engineering sciences are applied to convert resources optimally to meet a stated objective. Among the fundamental elements of the design process are the establishment of objectives and criteria, synthesis, analysis, construction, testing, and evaluation. The engineering design component of a curriculum must include most of the following features: development of student creativity, use of open-ended problems, development and use of modern design theory and methodology, formulation of design problem statements and specifications, consideration of alternative solutions, feasibility considerations, production processes, concurrent engineering design, and detailed system descriptions. Further, it is essential to include a variety of realistic constraints such as economic factors, safety, reliability, aesthetics, ethics, and social impact.

Figure 3.1

The engineering design process was very critical in the design of the international space station.
© *Purestock/SuperStock*

3.2 The Design Process

A simple definition of design is "a structured problem-solving activity." A process, on the other hand, is a phenomenon identified through step-by-step changes that lead toward a required result. Both these definitions suggest the idea of an orderly, systematic approach to a desired end. The design process, however, is not linear. That is, one does not necessarily achieve the best solution by simply proceeding from one step in the process to the next. New discoveries, additional data, and previous experience with similar problems generally will result in several iterations through some or all the steps of the process (Figure 3.2).

It is important to recognize that any project will have time and cost constraints. Normally before a project is approved a time schedule and a budget will be approved by management.

For your initial introduction to the design process, we will explain in more detail what is involved at each of the earlier six steps. Simply memorizing the steps will not give you the needed understanding of design. We suggest that you take one or more of the suggested design problems at the end of the chapter, organize a team of two to four students, and develop a workable solution for each problem selected. By working as a team you will generate more and better solution ideas and develop a deeper understanding of the process.

Figure 3.2

Engineers can use the engineering design process to maximize the efficiency of this recycling system without causing damage to the environment.
© *David Tring/SuperStock*

The process begins with a definition of the problem (Step 1) to be solved. In many cases the engineering design team does not identify or define the problem. Instead customers, field representatives for the company, and management will provide the initial request. The team must be careful not to define a solution at this step. If it does, it has not satisfied the design process. For example, assume company management asks a team to design a cart to transport ingots of metal from one building to another, the buildings approximately 200 meters apart. The solution to this problem is already known: a cart. It is a matter of seeing what is available on the market for handling the required load. It may be to the company's benefit to find a "new system" that effectively and efficiently moves heavy loads over a short distance. This would open up the possibility for a rail system, conveyor, or other creative solution. Usually a simple problem definition allows the most flexibility for the design team. For example, the initial problem could be defined as simply "Currently there are ingots of metal stored in building one. We need a way to get the ingots from that building to building two."

The team next acquires and assembles all pertinent information on the problem (Step 2). Internal company documents, available systems, Internet searches, and other engineers are all possible sources of information. Once all team members are up to speed on the available information, the solution constraints and criteria are identified (Step 3). A constraint is a physical or practical limitation on possible solutions; for example, the system must operate with 220-volt electricity. Criteria are desirable characteristics of a solution; for example, the solution must be reliable, must be easy to operate, must have an acceptable cost, and must be durable. You might think of a constraint as a requirement—all possible solutions must meet it—while a criterion is a relative consideration, in that one solution is better than another ("durable" is a criterion, for example).

Now the team is ready for the creative part of the process, developing alternative solutions (Step 4). This is where experience and knowledge, combined with group activities such as brainstorming, yield a variety of possible solutions (Figure 3.3). Each of the alternatives is now analyzed using the constraints and comparing each to the specified criteria. In many cases prototypes are built and tested to see if they meet constraints and criteria. Computer modeling and analysis are used heavily during this step. Then, using a device such as a decision matrix, a solution is selected (Step 5).

The last step of the design process often involves the most time and requires resources outside the original design team. Communicating the results (Step 6) involves developing all the details and reports necessary for the design to be built or manufactured as well as presentations for management and customers.

Although the systematic design process appears to end at Step 6, it really remains open throughout the product life cycle. Field testing, customer feedback, and new developments in materials, manufacturing processes, and so on may require redesign any time during the life cycle. Today many products are required to have a disposal plan prior to marketing. In these cases the original design needs to include disposal as a constraint on the solution. Although a six-step design

Figure 3.3

The brainstorming of new ideas for solving an engineering problem is important in the design process.
© Tom Merton/age fotostock

Figure 3.4

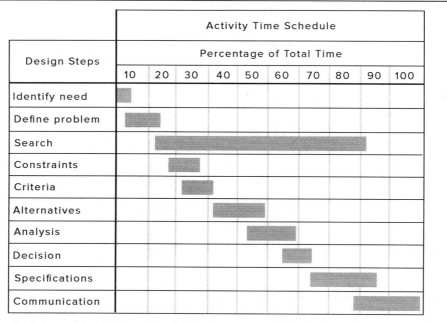

Design Steps	Activity Time Schedule									
	Percentage of Total Time									
	10	20	30	40	50	60	70	80	90	100
Identify need	▨									
Define problem	▨	▨								
Search		▨	▨	▨	▨	▨	▨	▨		
Constraints			▨							
Criteria			▨							
Alternatives				▨						
Analysis					▨					
Decision						▨				
Specifications							▨	▨		
Communication									▨	▨

A time schedule must be developed early in order to control the design process.

process is outlined earlier, other more expanded steps are in common use. For example, Figure 3.4 illustrates a ten-step design process.

To further illustrate the iterative nature of the design process, study Figure 3.5 for a typical industrial activity. The process begins with a conceptual design and proceeds to preliminary design, detailed design, prototype design, and the final design. Note that design evaluation is conducted frequently during the process. Also note that the design

Figure 3.5

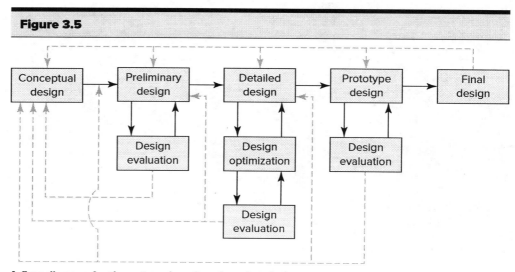

A flow diagram for the categories of engineering design.

is optimized at the detailed design stage. Optimization is beyond the scope of this introduction, but suffice it to say that it occurs after the solution is determined and is based on the analysis of alternatives (Step 5).

3.3 Design and the Customer

Often customer requirements are not well defined. The design team must determine, in consultation with the customer, the expectations of the solution. The customer therefore must be kept informed of the design status at all times during the process. It is likely that compromises will have to be made. Both the design team and customer may have to modify their requirements in order to meet deadlines, cost limits, manufacturing constraints, and performance requirements. Figure 3.6 is a simple illustration of the Kano model showing the relationship between degree of achievement (horizontal axis) and customer satisfaction (vertical axis). Customer requirements are categorized in three areas: basic, performance related, and exciting.

Basic customer requirements are simply expected by the customer and assumed to be available. For example, if the customer desires a new solar-powered barbeque grill, the customer assumes that the design team and the company have proven their ability, with existing successful products, to design and manufacture solar-powered barbeque grills.

Performance-related customer requirements are the basis for requesting the new product. In the example of the barbeque grill, cooking time, cooking effectiveness, ease of setting the controls, and ease of cleaning are among the many possible performance-related items that a customer may specify. As time goes by and more solar powered grills reach the marketplace, these requirements may become basic.

Exciting customer requirements are generally suggested by the design team. The customer is unlikely to request these features because they are often outside the range of customer knowledge or vision. The exciting requirements are often a strong

Figure 3.6

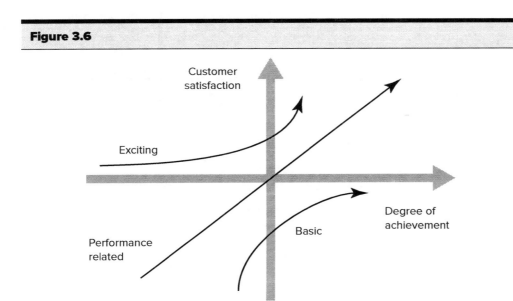

Factors in generating customer satisfaction.

selling point in the design because they give the customer an unexpected bonus in the solution. Perhaps the capability of programming a cooking cycle to vary the temperature during the cooking process would be a unique (but perhaps costly) addition to the solution.

Figure 3.6 indicates that the basic requirements are a must for customer satisfaction. The customer will be satisfied once a significant level of performance-related requirements is met. The exciting requirements always add to customer satisfaction, so the more of these features that can be added, the greater is the satisfaction.

3.4 The Nature of Engineering Design

In the first half of the 20th century, engineering design was considered by many to be a creative, ad hoc process that did not have a significant scientific basis. Design was considered an art, with successful designs emanating from a few talented individuals in the same manner as great artwork is produced by talented artists. However, there are now a wealth of convincing arguments that engineering design is a cognitive process that requires a broad knowledge base, intelligent use of information, and logical thinking. Today successful designs are generated by design teams, comprised of engineers, marketing personnel, economists, management, customers, and so on, working in a structured environment and following a systematic strategy. Utilizing tools such as the Internet, company design documentation, brainstorming, and the synergy of the design team, information is gathered, analyzed, and synthesized with the design process yielding a final solution that meets the design criteria.

What do we mean by a cognitive process? In the 1950s Benjamin Bloom developed a classification scheme for cognitive ability that is called Bloom's taxonomy. Figure 3.7 shows the six levels of complexity of cognitive thinking and provides an insight into how the design process is an effective method of producing successful products, processes, and systems. The least complex level, knowledge, is simply the

Figure 3.7

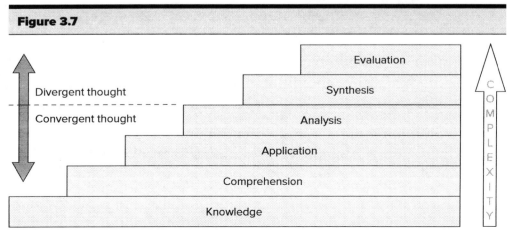

Bloom's taxonomy on learning aligns with the engineering design process.

ability to recall information, facts, or theories. [What was the date of the Columbia space shuttle accident?]

The next level is comprehension, which describes the ability to make sense of (understand) the material. [Explain the cause of the Columbia accident.] The third level is application, which is the ability to use knowledge and comprehension in a new situation and to generalize the knowledge. [What would you have done to prevent the Columbia accident?]

The fourth level is analysis, which is the ability to break learned material into its component parts so that the overall structure may be understood. It includes part identification, relationships of the parts to each other and to the whole, and recognition of the organizational principles involved. The individual must understand both the content and structure of the material. Figure 3.7 shows that analysis is the highest level of convergent thinking, whereby the individual recalls and focuses on what is known and comprehended to solve a problem through application and analysis. [What lessons did we learn about the space program from the Columbia accident?]

The fifth and sixth level on Bloom's taxonomy represent divergent thinking, in which the individual processes information and produces new insights and discoveries that were not part of the original information (thinking outside the box). Synthesis refers to the ability to put parts together to form a new plan or idea. Everyone synthesizes in a different manner. Some accomplish synthesis by quiet mental musing; others must use pencil and paper to doodle, sketch, outline ideas, and so on. [Propose an alternative to the Columbia fuel tank insulation design that would perform the required functions.]

Evaluation is the highest level of thinking. It is the ability to judge the value of material based on specific criteria. Usually the individual is responsible for formulating the criteria to be used in the evaluation. [Assess the impact of the Columbia accident on the U.S. space program.]

To help your understanding of the levels of cognitive thinking, review several exams you have taken in college in mathematics, chemistry, physics, and general education courses (e.g., economics, sociology, history, etc). For each question, decide which level of thinking was required to obtain a successful result. You will find while moving along in your engineering curriculum that exam questions, homework problems, and projects will reflect higher and higher levels of thinking.

3.5   Experiencing the Design Process in Education

The design process, although structured, is an iterative process with flexibility to make necessary adjustments as the design progresses. The emphasis in this chapter is on conceptual design. At this stage of your engineering education it is important that you undergo the experience of applying the design process to a need with which you can identify based on your personal experiences. As you approach the baccalaureate degree, you will have acquired the technical capability to conduct the necessary analyses and to make the appropriate technical decisions required for complex products, systems, and processes. Most engineering seniors will participate in a capstone design experience that will test their ability to apply knowledge toward solving a complicated design problem in their particular discipline.

3.6 Design Opportunities and Challenges of the Future

The world continues to undergo rapid and sometimes tumultuous change. As a practicing engineer, you will occupy center stage in many of these changes in the near future and will become even more involved in the more distant future. The National Academy of Engineering has identified "Engineering Grand Challenges." These include:

- make solar energy economical;
- provide access to clean water;
- restore and improve urban infrastructure;
- advance health informatics;
- engineer better medicines;
- reverse-engineer the brain;
- secure cyberspace;
- enhance virtual reality;
- and advance personalized learning.

(Source: NAE Grand Challenges for Engineering, www.engineeringchallenges.org, viewed 2/1/2016.) The huge tasks of providing solutions to these problems will challenge the technical community beyond anyone's imagination.

Engineers of today have nearly instantaneous access to a wealth of information from technical, economic, social, and political sources. A key to the success of engineers in the future will be the ability to study and absorb the appropriate information in the time allotted for producing a design or solution to a problem. A degree in engineering is only the beginning of a lifelong period of study in order to remain informed and competent in the field.

Engineers of tomorrow will have even greater access to information and will use increasingly powerful computer systems to digest this information. They will work with colleagues around the world solving problems and creating new products. They will assume greater roles in making decisions that affect the use of energy, water, and other natural resources. Engineering design solution considerations for energy, the environment, infrastructure, and global competitiveness are addressed in the following sections.

3.6.1 Energy

In order to develop technologically, nations of the world require vast amounts of energy. With a finite supply of our greatest energy source, fossil fuels, alternate supplies must be developed and existing sources must be controlled with a worldwide usage plan. A key factor in the design of products must be minimum use of energy.

As demand increases and supplies become scarcer, the cost of obtaining the energy increases and places additional burdens on already financially strapped regions and individuals. Engineers with great vision are needed to develop alternative sources of energy from the sun, radioactive materials, wind, biomaterials, and ocean and to improve the efficiency of existing energy consumption devices (Figure 3.8). Ethanol and biodiesel are two fuels that are produced in the United States from renewable resources that can assist in reducing America's dependence on foreign sources of energy. Waste-to-energy and biomass resources are also recognized by the U.S. Department of Energy as renewable energy source and

Figure 3.8

Windmill farms are an increasingly significant factor in the electrical infrastructure.
© Corbis

are included in the department's tracking of progress toward achieving the federal government's renewable energy goal.

Along with the production and consumption of energy come the secondary problems of pollution and global warming. Such pollutants as smog, acid rain, heavy metals, nutrients, and carbon dioxide must receive attention in order to maintain the balance of nature. Also, increasing concentrations of greenhouse gases are likely to accelerate the rate of climate change, thus causing global warming. According to the National Academy of Sciences, the Earth's surface temperature has risen by about 1 degree Fahrenheit in the past century, with accelerated warming during the past two decades.

3.6.2 Environment

Our insatiable demand for energy, water, and other national resources creates imbalances in nature that only time and serious conservation efforts can keep under control (Figure 3.9). The concern for environmental quality is focused on four areas: cleanup, compliance, conservation, and pollution prevention. Partnerships among industry, government, and consumers are working to establish guidelines and regulations in the gathering of raw materials, the manufacturing of consumer products, and the disposal of material at the end of its designed use.

The American Plastics Council publishes a guide titled *Environmental Initiatives Affecting Product Design* (www.plactics.americanchemistry.com/ Design-Guide-for-Information-and-Technology-Equipment, viewed 2/1/2016), which describes environmental issues and initiatives affecting product design.

Figure 3.9

Hydroelectric generating stations produce electricity important for industry and residence areas.
© Corbis

All engineers need to be aware of these initiatives and how they apply in their particular industries:

Design for the Environment (DFE): Incorporate environmental considerations into product designs to minimize impacts on the environment.

Environmentally Conscious Manufacturing (ECM) or Green Manufacturing: Incorporating pollution prevention and toxics use reduction into product manufacturing.

Extended Product or Producer Responsibility (Manufacturer's Responsibility or Responsible Entity): Product manufacturers are responsible for taking back their products at the product's end of life and managing them according to defined environmental criteria.

Life Cycle Assessment (LCA): Quantified assessment of the environmental impacts associated with all phases of a product's life, often from the extraction of base minerals through the product's end of life.

Pollution Prevention: Prevent pollution by reducing pollution sources (e.g., through design) as opposed to addressing pollution after it is generated.

Product Life Cycle Management (PLCM): Managing the environmental impacts associated with all phases of a product's life, from inception to disposal.

Product Takeback: The collection of products by manufacturer at the product's end of life.

Toxic Use Reduction: Reduce the amount, toxicity, and number of toxic chemicals used in manufacturing.

As you can see from these initiatives, all engineers regardless of discipline must be environmentally conscious in their work. In the next few decades we will face tough decisions regarding our environment. Engineers will play a major role in making the correct decisions for our small, delicate world.

The basic water cycle—from evaporation to cloud formation, then to rain, run-off, and evaporation again—is taken for granted by most people. (See Figure 3.10.) However, if the rain or the runoff is polluted, then the cycle is interrupted and our water supply becomes a crucial problem. In addition, some highly populated areas have a limited water supply and must rely on water distribution systems from other areas of the country. Many formerly undeveloped agricultural regions are now productive because of irrigation systems. However, the irrigation systems deplete the underground streams of water that are needed downstream.

These problems must be solved in order for life to continue to exist as we know it. Because of the regional water distribution patterns, the federal government must be a part of the decision-making process for water distribution. One of the concerns that must be eased is the amount of time required to bring a water distribution plan into effect. Government agencies and the private sector are strapped by regulations that cause delays of several years in planning and construction. Greater cooperation and a better informed public are goals that public works engineers must strive to achieve. Developing nations around the world need additional water supplies because of increasing population growth. Many of these nations do not have the necessary freshwater and must rely on desalination, a costly process. The continued need for water is a concern for leaders of the world, and engineers will be asked to create additional sources of this life-sustaining resource.

Figure 3.10

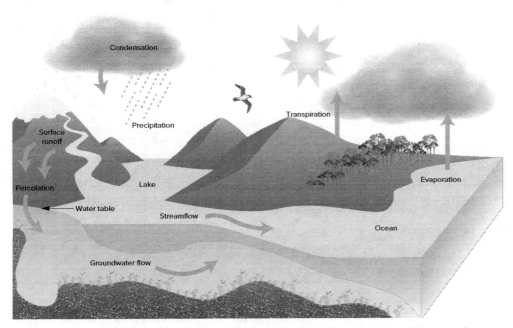

Understanding the water cycle (hydrologic cycle) is necessary in order to be able to engineer systems to control water pollution to our water resources.

3.6.3 Infrastructure

All societies depend on an infrastructure of transportation, waste disposal, and water distribution systems for the benefit of the population (Figure 3.11). In the United States much of the infrastructure is in a state of deterioration without sound plans for upgrading. For example:

1. Commercial jet fleets include aircraft that are 35 to 40 years old. Major programs are now underway to extend safely the service life of these jets. In order to survive economically, airlines must balance new replacement jets with a program to keep older planes flying safely.
2. One-half of the sewage treatment plants cannot satisfactorily handle the demand.
3. The interstate highway system, over 50 years old in many areas, needs major repairs throughout. Over-the-road trucking has increased wear and tear on a system designed primarily for the automobile. Local paved roads are deteriorating because of a lack of infrastructure funds.
4. Many bridges are potentially dangerous to the traffic loads on them.
5. Railroads continue to struggle with maintenance of railbeds and rolling stock in the face of stiff commercial competition from the air freight and truck transportation industries.
6. Municipal water and wastewater systems require billions of dollars in repairs and upgrades to meet public demands and stricter water-quality requirements.

It is estimated that the total value of the public works facilities is over $2 trillion. To protect this investment, innovative thinking and creative funding must be fostered.

Figure 3.11

Development of new and improved infrastructure, such as this new rail system, are important to the economy of our nation.
© Corbis

Some of this is already occurring in road design and repair. For example, a new method of recycling asphalt pavement actually produces a stronger product. Engineering research is producing extended-life pavement with new additives and structural designs. New, relatively inexpensive methods of strengthening old bridges have been used successfully.

3.6.4   A Competitive Edge in the World Marketplace

We have all purchased or used products that were manufactured outside the country. Many of these products incorporate technology that was developed in the United States. In order to maintain our strong industrial base, we must develop practices and processes that enable us to compete not just with other U.S. industries but with international industries (Figure 3.12). Engineers must also be able to design products that will be accepted by other cultures and work in their environments. It is therefore most important that engineers develop their global awareness and cultural adaptability competence.

The goal of any industry is to generate a profit. In today's marketplace this means creating the best product in the shortest time at a lower price than the competition. A modern design process incorporating sophisticated analysis procedures and supported by high-speed computers with graphical displays increases the capability for developing the "best" product. The concept of integrating the design and manufacturing functions

Figure 3.12

A global design team at work on an engineering design problem.
© *Gregory Kramer/Getty Images*

shortens the design-to-market time for new products and for upgraded versions of existing products. The development of the automated factory is an exciting concept that is receiving a great deal of attention from manufacturing engineers today. Remaining competitive by producing at a lesser price requires a national effort involving labor, government, and distribution factors. In any case engineers are going to have a significant role in the future of our industrial sector.

Problems

3.1 Complete the statement "I want to become an engineer to design . . ." in as much detail as you can.

3.2 Choose an engineering company that you would someday consider working for. From the information found on their website, write a one-page paper on the engineering problems that they are solving and how they are addressing their customer's needs.

3.3 Find three textbooks that introduce the engineering design process. Copy the steps in the process from each textbook. Compare with the six steps given in Section 3.1. Note similarities and differences and write a paragraph describing your conclusions.

3.4 Interview an engineer working in your chosen field of study, describe in a one-page paper what steps of the design process he/she is engaged with in their job.

3.5 Select a specific discipline of engineering and list at least 20 different companies and/or government agencies that utilize engineers from this field.

3.6 Choose a product that was most likely designed by an engineer in your chosen field of study. Identify what problem this product solved, what constraints were applied to its design, and what criteria were most likely used to evaluate this design.

3.7 Choose one of the National Academy of Engineering's Grand Challenges found in Section 3.6 and write a one-page paper on how you as an engineer could be involved in helping to solve this challenge.

3.8 Choose one of the products from the list below and note key features and functions for the product as produced today. Then, go back one generation (18–25 years) to family, relatives, or friends and ask them to describe the key features and functions of the same product as produced at that time. Note changes and improvements and prepare a brief report.

   (a) bicycle

   (b) electric coffeemaker

   (c) color television

   (d) landline telephone

   (e) cookware (pots, pans, skillets)

   (f) vacuum cleaner

   (g) microwave oven

3.9 Choose a product that you use every day and evaluate how effective the company that designed it was in meeting your customer needs and the needs of others. What suggestions would you make to help the designers improve the project? How could this product be used for another application?

3.10 Choose a device or product that you believe can be improved upon. Answer the following questions: (1) what do you already know about this device/product; (2) what do you think you know about this device/product; and (3) what do you need to know about this device/product? Based on your responses to these questions, conduct research to confirm or reveal what you know and don't know. Write a short report to summarize your findings. Use proper citation methods to list your research sources.

3.11 Choose one of the following topics (or one suggested by your instructor) and write a paper that discusses technological changes that have occurred in this area in the past 15 years. Include commentary on the social and environmental impact of the changes and on new problems that may have arisen because of the changes.

(*a*) passenger automobiles
(*b*) electric power-generating plants
(*c*) computer graphics
(*d*) heart surgery
(*e*) heating systems (furnaces)
(*f*) microprocessors
(*g*) water treatment
(*h*) road paving (both concrete and asphalt)
(*i*) composite materials
(*j*) robotics
(*k*) air-conditioning

3.12 Investigate current designs for one or more of the items listed below. If you do not have the items in your possession, purchase them or borrow from friends. Conduct the following "reverse engineering" procedures on each of the items:

(*a*) Write down the need that the design satisfies.
(*b*) Disassemble the item and list all the parts by name.
(*c*) Write down the function of each of the parts in the item.
(*d*) Reassemble the item.
(*e*) Write down answers to the following questions:
- Does the item satisfactorily solve the need you stated in part (*a*)?
- What are the strengths of the design?
- What are the weaknesses of the design?
- Can this design be easily modified to solve other needs? If so, what needs and what modifications should be made?
- What other designs can solve the stated need?

The items for your study are the following:
- smartphone
- disposable camera
- flashlight
- calculator
- printer

3.13 The following list of potential design projects can be addressed by following the six-step design process discussed in the chapter. A team approach to a proposed solution, with three or four members on each team, is recommended. Develop a report and oral presentation as directed by your instructor.
- A device to prevent the theft of helmets left on motorcycles
- An improved rack for carrying packages or books on a motorcycle or bicycle
- A solar-powered battery charger
- A device to permit easier draining of the oil pan by weekend mechanics
- A heated steering wheel for cold weather
- A sun shield for an automobile
- An automotic pet feeder for proper metering of food
- A storage system for a cell phone in a car (including charger)
- An improved wall outlet for multiple uses
- A beverage holder for a stand-up work desk

- A key finder for when you loose your keys
- An improved automobile traffic pattern on campus
- An alert for drowsy or sleeping drivers
- Improved bicycle brakes
- A campus transit system
- Improved pedestrian crossings at busy intersections
- Improved parking facilities in and around campus
- A device to attach to a paint can for pouring
- An improved soap dispenser
- A better method of locking weights to a barbell shaft
- A shoestring fastener to replace the knot
- A better jar opener
- A system or device to improve efficiency of limited closet space
- A shoe transporter and storer
- A device to pit fruit without damage
- An automatic device for selectively admitting and releasing pets through an auxiliary door
- A device to permit a person loaded with packages to open a door
- A more efficient toothpaste tube
- A fingernail catcher for fingernail clippings
- A more effective alarm clock for reluctant students
- A device to help a parent monitor small children's presence and activity in and around the house
- A simple pocket alarm that is difficult to shut off, used for discouraging muggers
- An improved storage system for luggage, books, and so on in dormitories
- A lampshade designed to permit one roommate to study while the other is asleep
- A device that would permit blind people to vote in an otherwise conventional voting booth
- A bicycle for a child with disabilities
- A silent wake-up alarm
- Home aids for the blind (or deaf)
- A safer, more efficient, and quieter air mover for room use
- A can crusher
- A rain-sensitive house window that would close automatically when it rains
- A better grass catcher for a riding lawn mower
- A built-in auto refrigerator
- A better camp cooler
- A dormitory cooler
- An impact-hammer adapter for electric drills
- An improved method of detecting and controlling the level position of the bucket on a bucket loader
- An automatic tractor-trailer-hitch aligning device
- A jack designed expressly for motorcycle use (special problems involved)
- Improved road signs for speed limits, curves, deer crossings, and so on
- A device for dealing with oil slicks
- An egg container (light, strong, compact) for camping and canoeing
- Ramps or other facilities for handicapped students

CHAPTER 4

Engineering Solutions

Chapter Objectives

When you complete your study of this chapter, you will be able to:

- Recognize the importance of engineering problem analysis
- Recall and explain the engineering method
- Apply general guidelines for problem-solving presentation and solution documentation
- Develop an ability to solve and present simple or complex problems in an orderly, logical, and systematic way

4.1 Introduction

The practice of engineering involves the application of accumulated knowledge and experience to a wide variety of technical situations. Two areas, in particular, that are fundamental to all of engineering are design and problem solving. The professional engineer is expected to approach, analyze, and solve a range of technical problems intelligently and efficiently. These problems can vary from single-solution, reasonably simple problems to extremely complex, open-ended problems that require a multidisciplinary team of engineers.

Problem solving is a combination of experience, knowledge, process, and art. Most engineers through either training or experience solve many problems by a process. The design process, for example, is a series of logical steps that when followed produce an optimal solution given time and resources as two constraints. The total quality (TQ) method is another example of a process. This concept suggests a series of steps leading to desired results while exceeding customer expectations.

This chapter provides a basic guide to problem analysis, organization, and presentation. Early in your education, you must develop an ability to solve and present simple or complex problems in an orderly, logical, and systematic way.

4.2 Problem Analysis

A distinguishing characteristic of a qualified engineer is the ability to solve technical problems. Mastery of problem solving involves a combination of art and science. By *science* we mean the knowledge of the principles of mathematics, chemistry, physics, mechanics, and other technical subjects that must be learned so that they can be applied correctly. By *art* we mean the proper judgment, experience, common sense, and know-how that must be used to reduce a real-life problem to such a form that science can be applied to its solution. To know when and how rigorously science should be applied and whether the resulting answer reasonably satisfies the original problem is an art.

Much of the science of successful problem solving comes from formal education in school or from continuing education after graduation. But most of the art of problem solving cannot be learned in a formal course; rather, it is a result of experience and common sense. Its application can be more effective, however, if problem solving is approached in a logical and organized method—that is, if it follows a process.

To clarify the distinction, let us suppose that a manufacturing engineer and a logistics specialist working for a large electronics company are given the task of recommending whether the introduction of a new computer that will focus on the computer-aided-design (CAD) market can be profitably produced. At the time this task is assigned, the competitive selling price has already been estimated by the marketing division. Also, the design group has developed working models of the computer with specifications of all components, which means that the approximate cost of these components is known. The question of profit thus rests on the costs of assembly and distribution. The theory of engineering economy (the science portion of problem solving) is well known and applicable to the cost factors and time frame involved. Once the production and distribution methods have been established, these costs can be computed using standard techniques. Selection of production and distribution methods (the art portion of problem solving) depends largely on the experience of the engineer and logistics specialist. Knowing what will or will not work in each part of these processes is a must in the cost estimate; however, these data cannot be found in handbooks, but, rather, they are found in the minds of the logistics specialist and the engineer. It is an art originating from experience, common sense, and good judgment.

Before the solution to any problem is undertaken, whether by a student or a practicing professional engineer, a number of important ideas must be considered. Think about the following questions: How important is the answer to a given problem? Would a rough, preliminary estimate be satisfactory, or is a high degree of accuracy demanded? How much time do you have and what resources are at your disposal? In an actual situation, your answers may depend on the amount of data available or the amount that must be collected, the sophistication of equipment that must be used, the accuracy of the data, the number of people available to assist, and many other factors. Most complex problems require some level of computer support such as a spreadsheet or a math analysis program. What about the theory you intend to use? Is it state of the art? Is it valid for this particular application? Do you currently understand the theory, or must time be allocated for review and learning? Can you make assumptions that simplify without sacrificing needed accuracy? Are other assumptions valid and applicable?

The art of problem solving is a skill developed with practice. It is the ability to arrive at a proper balance between the time and resources expended on a problem and the accuracy and validity obtained in the solution. When you can optimize time and resources versus reliability, problem-solving skills will serve you well.

4.3 The Engineering Method

The *engineering method* is an example of process. It consists of six basic steps:

1. ***Recognize and understand the problem.*** Perhaps the most difficult part of problem solving is developing the ability to recognize and define the problem precisely. This is true at the beginning of the design process and when applying the engineering method to a subpart of the overall problem. Many academic

problems that you will be asked to solve have this step completed by the instructor. For example, if your instructor asks you to solve a quadratic–algebraic equation and provides all the coefficients, the problem has been completely defined before it is given to you, and little doubt remains about what the problem is.

   If the problem is not well defined, considerable effort must be expended at the beginning in studying the problem, eliminating the things that are unimportant, and focusing on the root problem. Effort at this step pays great dividends by eliminating or reducing false trials, thereby shortening the time taken to complete later steps.

2. ***Accumulate data and verify accuracy.***   All pertinent physical facts, such as sizes, temperatures, voltages, currents, costs, concentrations, weights, times, and so on, must be ascertained. Some problems require that Steps 1 and 2 be done simultaneously. In others, Step 1 might automatically produce some of the physical facts. Do not mix or confuse these details with data that are suspect or only assumed to be accurate. Deal only with items that can be verified. Sometimes it will pay to verify data that you believe are factual but actually may be in error.

3. ***Select the appropriate theory or principle.***   Select appropriate theories or scientific principles that apply to the solution of the problem; understand and identify limitations or constraints that apply to the selected theory.

4. ***Make necessary assumptions.***   Perfect solutions to real problems do not exist. Simplifications need to be made if real problems are to be solved. Certain assumptions can be made that do not significantly affect the accuracy of the solution, yet other assumptions may result in a large reduction in accuracy.

   Although the selection of a theory or principle is stated in the engineering method as preceding the introduction of simplifying assumptions, there are cases when the order of these two steps should be reversed. For example, if you are solving a material balance problem, you often need to assume that the process is steady, uniform, and without chemical reactions so that the applicable theory can be simplified. Note that many of the engineering equations used in practice only apply when specific assumptions are made.

5. ***Solve the problem.***   If Steps 3 and 4 have resulted in a mathematical equation (model), it is normally solved by an application of mathematical theory, although a trial-and-error solution that employs the use of a computer or perhaps some form of graphical solution also may be applicable. The results normally will be in numerical form with appropriate units. Make sure to show the resulting answer with appropriate significant digits.

6. ***Verify and check results.***   In engineering practice, the work is not finished merely because a solution has been obtained. It must be checked to ensure that it is mathematically correct and that units have been properly specified. Correctness can be verified by reworking the problem by using a different technique or by performing the calculations in a different order to be certain that the numbers agree in both trials. The units need to be examined to ensure that all equations are dimensionally correct. And finally, the answer must be examined to see if it makes sense. An experienced engineer will generally have a good idea of the order of magnitude to expect.

   If the answer doesn't seem reasonable, there is probably an error in the mathematics, in the assumptions, or perhaps in the theory used. Judgment is critical. For example, suppose that you are asked to compute the monthly payment required to repay a car loan of $5 000 over a three-year period at an annual interest rate of 12 percent. Upon solving this problem, you arrived at an answer of $11 000 per month. Even if you are inexperienced in engineering economy, you know that this answer is not reasonable, so you should reexamine your theory and computations. Examination and evaluation of an answer's reasonableness are habits you should strive to acquire. Your instructor and employer alike will not accept results that you have indicated are correct if the results are obviously incorrect by a significant percentage.

4.4   Problem Presentation

The engineering method of problem solving as presented in the previous section is an adaptation of the well-known *scientific problem-solving method.* It is a time-tested approach to problem solving that should become an everyday part of the engineer's thought process. Engineers should follow this logical approach to the solution of any problem while at the same time learn to translate the information accumulated into a well-documented problem solution.

The following steps parallel the engineering method and provide reasonable documentation of the solution. If these steps are properly executed during the solution of problems in this text and all other courses, it is our belief that you will gradually develop an ability to solve and properly document a wide range of complex problems.

1. *Problem statement.*   State, as concisely as possible, the problem to be solved. The statement should be a summary of the given information, but it must contain all essential material. Clearly state what is to be determined. For example, find the temperature (K) and pressure (Pa) at the nozzle exit.
2. *Diagram.*   Prepare a diagram (sketch or computer output) with all pertinent dimensions, flow rates, currents, voltages, weights, and so on. A diagram is a very efficient method of showing given and needed information. It also is an appropriate way of illustrating the physical setup, which may be difficult to describe adequately in words. Most often a two-dimensional representation is adequate (e.g., a free-body diagram of a beam with associated loads and moments). Data that cannot be placed in a diagram should be listed separately.
3. *Theory.*   The theory used should be presented. In some cases, a properly referenced equation with completely defined variables is sufficient. At other times, an extensive theoretical derivation may be necessary because the appropriate theory has to be derived, developed, or modified.
4. *Assumptions.*   Explicitly list, in complete detail, any and all pertinent assumptions that have been made to realize your solution to the problem. This step is vitally important for the reader's understanding of the solution and its limitations. Steps 3 and 4 might be reversed or integrated in some problems.
5. *Solution steps.*   Show completely all steps taken in obtaining the solution. This is particularly important in an academic situation because your reader, the instructor, must have the means of judging your understanding of the solution technique. Steps completed, but not shown, make it difficult for evaluation of your work and therefore difficult to provide constructive guidance.
6. *Identify results and verify accuracy.*   Clearly identify (double underline or enclose in a box) the final answer. *Assign proper units.* An answer without units (when it should have units) is meaningless. Remember, this final step of the

engineering method requires an examination of the answer to determine if it is realistic, so check solution accuracy and, if possible, verify the results.

7. ***Discussion/Conclusion***   It is important to write a concise summary of your results. What do the results mean? Do you have any observations? This step should include whether the results are reasonable and what would happen if one or more of the dependent variable were changed (e.g., what if the temperature increased by five degrees?).

4.5   Standards of Problem Presentation

Once the problem has been solved and checked, it is necessary to present the solution according to some standard. The standard will vary from school to school and industry to industry.

On most occasions, your solution will be presented to other individuals who are technically trained, but you should remember that many times these individuals do not have an intimate knowledge of the problem. However, on other occasions, you will be presenting technical information to persons with nontechnical backgrounds. This may require methods that are different from those used to communicate with other engineers; thus, it is always important to understand who will be reviewing the material so that the information can be clearly presented.

One characteristic of engineers is their ability to present information with great clarity in a neat, careful manner. In short, the information must be communicated accurately to the reader. (Discussion of drawings or simple sketches will not be included in this chapter, although they are important in many presentations.)

Employers insist on carefully prepared presentations that completely document all work involved in solving the problems. Thorough documentation may be important in the event of legal considerations for which the details of the work might be introduced into court proceedings as evidence. Lack of such documentation may result in the loss of a case that might otherwise have been won. Moreover, internal company use of the work is easier and more efficient if all aspects of the work have been carefully documented and substantiated by data and theory.

Each industrial company, consulting firm, government agency, and university has established standards for presenting technical information. These standards vary slightly, but all fall into a basic pattern, which we will discuss. Each organization expects its employees to follow its standards. Details can be easily modified in a particular situation once you are familiar with the general pattern that exists in all of these standards.

It is not possible to specify a single problem layout or format that will accommodate all types of engineering solutions. Such a wide variety of solutions exists that the technique used must be adapted to fit the information to be communicated. In all cases, however, one must lay out a given problem in such a fashion that it can be easily grasped by the reader. No matter which technique is used, it must be logical and understandable.

We have listed guidelines for problem presentation. Acceptable layouts for problems in engineering also are illustrated. The guidelines are not intended as a precise format that must be followed but, rather, as a suggestion that should be considered and incorporated whenever applicable.

Two methods of problem presentation are typical in academic and industrial environments. Presentation formats can be either freehand or computer generated. As hardware technology and software developments continue to provide better tools, the use of the computer as a method of problem presentation will continue to increase. If you were working on a team, you may need to utilize shared document software in order to collaborate more effectively on a problem presentation (e.g., Google Docs, Dropbox, etc.).

If a formal report, proposal, or presentation is the choice of communication, a computer-generated presentation is the correct approach. The example solutions that are illustrated in Figures 4.1 through 4.4 include both freehand work and computer output. Check with your instructor to determine which method is appropriate for your assignments. Figure 4.1 illustrates the placement of information.

The following nine general guidelines should be helpful as you develop the freehand skills needed to provide clear and complete problem documentation. The first two examples, Figures 4.1, 4.2a, and 4.2b are freehand illustrations. The third example, Figures 4.3a, 4.3b, and 4.4 are computer generated with a word processor, and Figure 4.4 uses a spreadsheet for the computations and graphing.

These guidelines are most applicable to freehand solutions, but many of the ideas and principles apply to computer generation as well.

1. One common type of paper frequently used is called engineering problems paper. It is ruled horizontally and vertically on the *reverse* side, with only heading and margin rulings on the front. The rulings on the reverse side, which are faintly visible through the paper, help one maintain horizontal lines of lettering and provide guides for sketching and simple graph construction. Moreover, the lines on the back of the paper will not be lost as a result of erasures.

2. The completed top heading of the problems paper should include such information as name, date, course number, and sheet number. The upper right-hand block should normally contain a notation such as *a/b,* where *a* is the page number of the sheet and *b* is the total number of sheets in the set.

3. When using freehand presentation, work should ordinarily be done in pencil using an appropriate lead hardness (HB, F, or H) so that the line work is crisp and not smudged. Erasures should always be complete, with all eraser particles removed. Letters and numbers must be dark enough to ensure legibility when photocopies are needed.

4. When using freehand illustration, either vertical or slant letters may be selected as long as they are not mixed. Care should be taken to produce good, legible lettering but without such care that little work is accomplished.

5. Spelling should be checked for correctness. There is no reasonable excuse for incorrect spelling in a properly done problem solution.

6. Work must be easy to follow and not crowded. This practice contributes greatly to readability and ease of interpretation.

7. If several problems are included in a set, they must be distinctly separated, usually by a horizontal line drawn completely across the page between problems. Never begin a second problem on the same page if it cannot be completed there. Beginning each problem on a fresh sheet is usually better, except in cases when two or more problems can be completed on one sheet. It is not necessary to use a horizontal separation line if the next problem in a series begins at the top of a new page.

8. Diagrams that are an essential part of a problem presentation should be clear and understandable. You should strive for neatness, which is a mark of a professional. Often a good sketch is adequate, but using a straight edge or a simple graphic software tool can greatly improve the appearance and accuracy of a diagram. A little effort in preparing a sketch or computer drawing to approximate scale can pay great dividends when it is necessary to judge the reasonableness of an answer, particularly if the answer is a physical dimension that can be seen on the sketch.

Figure 4.1

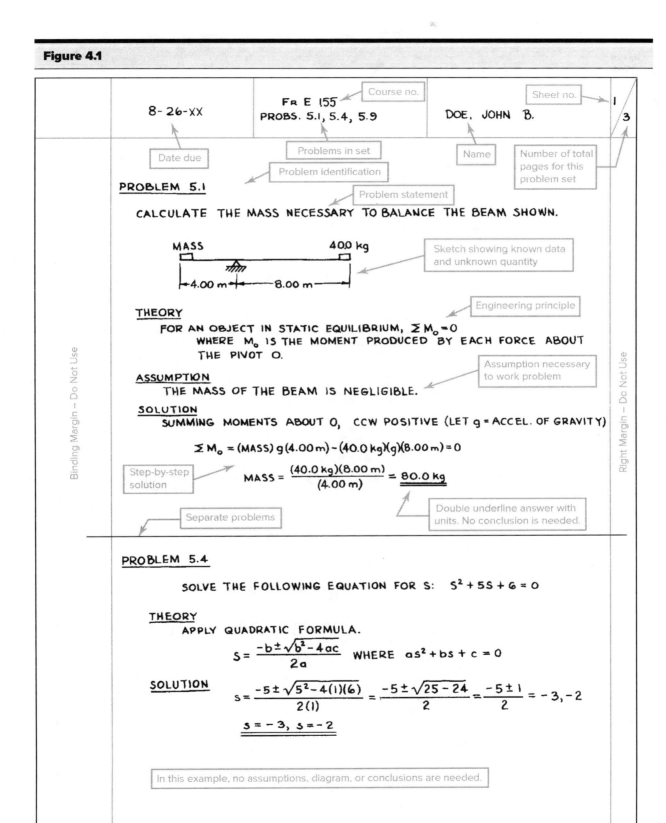

Elements of a problem layout.

Figure 4.2a

		FR E 160		1
	8-22-XX	PROBLEM 13.1	DOE, JANE A.	2

PROBLEM 13.1   SOLVE FOR THE VALUE OF RESISTANCE R IN THE CIRCUIT SHOWN BELOW.

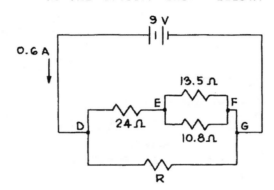

THEORY

- FOR RESISTANCES IN PARALLEL: $\frac{1}{R_{TOTAL}} = \frac{1}{R_1} + \frac{1}{R_2} + \frac{1}{R_3} + \cdots$

   THUS FOR 2 RESISTANCES IN PARALLEL

   $$R_{TOTAL} = \frac{R_1 R_2}{R_1 + R_2}$$

- FOR RESISTANCES IN SERIES: $R_{TOTAL} = R_1 + R_2 + R_3 + \cdots$

- OHM'S LAW: $E = RI$ WHERE E = ELECT. POTENTIAL IN VOLTS
                            I = CURRENT IN AMPERES
                            R = RESISTANCE IN OHMS

SOLUTION

- CALCULATE EQUIVALENT RESISTANCE BETWEEN POINTS E AND F. RESISTORS ARE IN PARALLEL.

   $$\therefore R_{EF} = \frac{R_1 R_2}{R_1 + R_2} = \frac{(13.5)(10.8)}{13.5 + 10.8} = \frac{145.8}{24.3} = 6.00 \ \Omega$$

- CALCULATE EQUIVALENT RESISTANCE OF UPPER LEG BETWEEN D AND G.

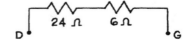

   SERIES CIRCUIT

   $$\therefore R'_{DG} = R_{24} + R_6 = 24 + 6 = 30 \ \Omega$$

In this example, no assumptions were necessary.

Sample problem presentation done freehand.

Figure 4.2b

| | 8-22-XX | FR E 160
PROBLEM 13.1 | DOE, JANE A. | 2 2 |

- CALCULATE EQUIVALENT RESISTANCE BETWEEN D AND G.

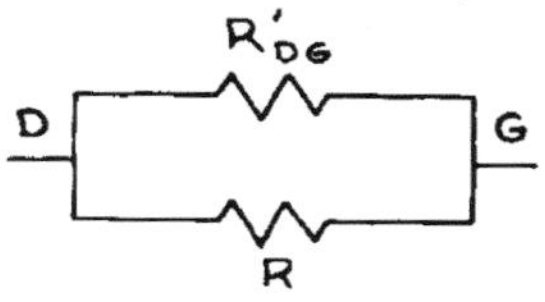

PARALLEL RESISTORS, SO

$$R_{DG} = \frac{(R'_{DG})(R)}{R'_{DG} + R}$$

- CALCULATE TOTAL RESISTANCE OF CIRCUIT USING OHM'S LAW.

$$R_{DG} = \frac{E}{I} = \frac{9V}{0.6A} = 15 \, \Omega$$

- CALCULATE VALUE OF R
  FROM PREVIOUS EQUATIONS.

$$R_{DG} = 15 \, \Omega = \frac{(R'_{DG})(R)}{R'_{DG} + R} = \frac{(30)(R)}{30 + R}$$

SOLVING FOR R:

$$(30 + R)(15) = 30R$$

$$30 + R = 2R$$

$$\underline{R = 30 \, \Omega}$$

Sample problem presentation done freehand.

Figure 4.3a

Date   *Engineering*   *Name:*_____

<u>*Problem*</u>

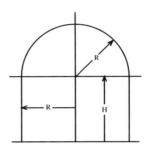

    A tank is to be constructed that will hold 5.00×10^5 L when filled. The shape is to be cylindrical, with a hemispherical top. Costs to construct the cylindrical portion will be \$300/m², while costs for the hemispherical portion are slightly higher at \$400/m².

<u>*Find*</u>

    Calculate the tank dimensions that will result in the lowest dollar cost.

<u>*Theory*</u>

Volume of cylinder is... $V_c = \pi R^2 H$

Volume of hemisphere is... $V_H = \dfrac{2\pi R^3}{3}$

Surface area of cylinder is... $SA_c = 2\pi RH$

Surface area of hemisphere is... $SA_H = 2\pi R^2$

<u>*Assumptions*</u>

    Tank contains no dead air space
    Construction costs are independent of size
    Concrete slab with hermetic seal is provided for the base
    Cost of the base does not change appreciably with tank dimensions

<u>*Solution*</u>

    1. Express total volume in meters as a function of height and radius.

$$V_{Tank} = f(H, R)$$
$$= V_C + V_H$$
$$500 = \pi R^2 H + \frac{2\pi R^3}{3}$$

Note: $1\text{m}^3 = 1\,000$ L

Sample problem presentation done with a word processor.

Figure 4.3b

2. Express cost in dollars as a function of height and radius

$$C = C\,(H,\,R)$$

$$= 300\,(SA_C) + 400\,(SA_H)$$

$$= 300\,(2\pi RH) + 400\,(2\pi R^2)$$

Note: Cost figures are exact numbers

3. From part 1 solve for $H = H\,(R)$

$$H = \frac{500}{\pi R^2} - \frac{2R}{3}$$

4. Solve cost equation, substituting $H = H\,(R)$

$$C = 300\left[2\pi R\left(\frac{500}{\pi R^2} - \frac{2R}{3}\right)\right] + 400\,(2\pi R^2)$$

$$C = \frac{300\,000}{R} + 400\,\pi R^2$$

5. Develop a table of cost versus radius and plot graph.

6. From graph select minimum cost.

$$R = \underline{5.00\text{ m}}$$
$$C = 91\,000$$

7. Calculate H from part 3 above

$$H = \underline{3.033\text{ m}}$$

8. Verification/check of results from the calculus:

$$\frac{dC}{dR} = \frac{d}{dR}\left[\frac{300\,000}{R} + 400\,\pi R^2\right]$$

$$= \frac{-300\,000}{R^2} + 800\,\pi R = 0$$

$$R^3 = \frac{300\,000}{800\,\pi}$$

$$R = \underline{4.92\text{m}}$$

9. Discussion/Conclusion: The minimum cost for the tank is found when the radius is 5.0 m and the height is 3.0 m. The height cost is found between a radius of 1.0 m and 2.0 m.

Cost versus Radius

Radius, R, m	Cost, C, \$
1.0	301 257
2.0	155 027
3.0	111 310
4.0	95 106
5.0	91 416
6.0	95 239
7.0	104 432
8.0	117 925
9.0	135 121
10.0	155 664

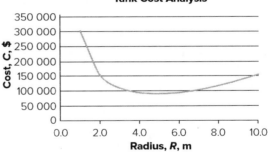

Figure 4.4

Date: 10-14-xx   ENGR 160   John Q. Public

Problem 3-5

Analyze the buckling load for steel columns ranging from 50 to 100 ft long in increments of 5 ft.
The cross-sectional area is 7.33 in², the least radius of gyration is 3.19 in and modulus of elasticity is 30×10^6 lb/in².
Plot the buckling load as a function of column length for hinged ends and fixed ends.

Theory

Euler's equation gives the buckling load for a slender column.

$$F_B = \frac{n\pi^2\, EA}{(L/r)^2}$$

where

F_B = buckling load, lb
E = modulus of elasticity, lb/in²   3.00E+07
A = cross-sectional area, in²   7.33
L = length of column, in
r = least radius of gyration, in   3.19
The factor n depends on the end conditions: If both ends are hinged, $n = 1$;
if both ends are fixed, $n = 4$; if one end is fixed and the other is hinged, $n = 2$

Assumption: The columns being analyzed meet the slenderness criterion for Euler's equation

Solution

Length, ft	Buckling load (fixed), lb	Buckling load (hinged), lb
50	245 394	61 348
55	202 805	50 701
60	170 412	42 603
65	145 204	36 301
70	125 201	31 300
75	109 064	27 266
80	95 857	23 964
85	84 911	21 228
90	75 739	18 935
95	67 976	16 994
100	61 348	15 337

Discussion: The buckling load decreases with length for end conditions. The buckling load for the fixed ends condition is always higher, but becomes closer to the hinged condition with increased length.

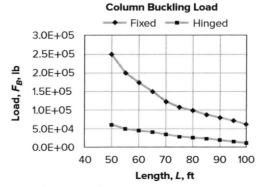

Sample problem presentation done with a spreadsheet.

9. The proper use of symbols is always important, particularly when the International System (SI) of Units is used. It involves a strict set of rules that must be followed so that absolutely no confusion of meaning can result. There also are symbols in common and accepted use for engineering quantities that can be found in most engineering handbooks. These symbols should be used whenever possible. It is important that symbols be consistent throughout a solution and that they are all defined for the benefit of the reader and for your own reference.

The physical layout of a problem solution logically follows steps that are similar to those of the engineering method. You should attempt to present the process by which the problem was solved, in addition to the solution, so that any reader can readily understand all the aspects of the solution. Figure 4.1 illustrates the placement of the information.

Figures 4.2a, 4.2b, 4.3a, 4.3b, and 4.4 are examples of typical engineering problem solutions. You may find these examples to be helpful guides as you prepare your problem presentations.

Problems

4.1 The Cartesian components of a vector $\overline{B}$ are shown in Figure 4.5. If $B_x = 7.2$ m and $\Delta = 35°$, find α B_y, and $\overline{B}$.

4.2 Refer to Figure 4.5. If $\alpha = 51°$ and $B_y = 4.9$ km, what are the values of Δ, B_x, and $\overline{B}$?

4.3 In Figure 4.6, side YZ is 1.0×10^6 m. Determine the length of side XZ.

4.4 Calculate the length of side AB in Figure 4.7 if side $AC = 3.6 \times 10^3$ m.

Figure 4.5

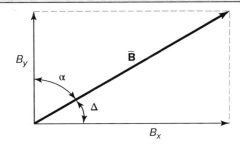

Figure 4.6

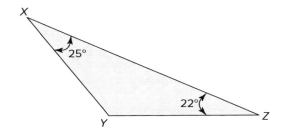

Figure 4.7

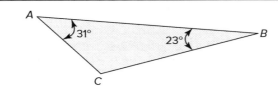

4.5 The vector $\overline{\mathbf{C}}$ in Figure 4.8 is the sum of vectors $\overline{\mathbf{A}}$ and $\overline{\mathbf{B}}$. Assume that vector $\overline{\mathbf{B}}$ is horizontal. Given that $\alpha = 31°$, $\beta = 22°$, and the magnitude of $B = 29$ m, find the magnitudes and directions of vectors $\overline{\mathbf{A}}$ and $\overline{\mathbf{C}}$.

4.6 Vector $\overline{\mathbf{R}}$ in Figure 4.9 is the difference between vectors $\overline{\mathbf{T}}$ and $\overline{\mathbf{S}}$. If $\overline{\mathbf{S}}$ is inclined at $25°$ from the vertical and the angle between $\overline{\mathbf{S}}$ and $\overline{\mathbf{T}}$ is $35°$, calculate the magnitude and direction of vector $\overline{\mathbf{R}}$. The magnitudes of $\overline{\mathbf{S}}$ and $\overline{\mathbf{T}}$ are 21 cm and 38 cm, respectively.

4.7 An aircraft has a glide ratio of 12 to 1. (Glide ratio means that the plane drops 1 m in each 12 m it travels horizontally.) A building 45 m high lies directly in the glide path to the runway. If the aircraft clears the building by 12 m, how far from the building does the aircraft touch down on the runway?

Figure 4.8

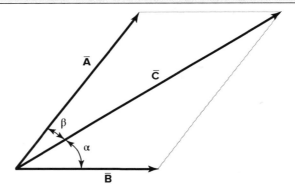

Figure 4.9

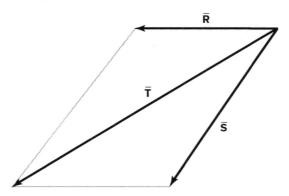

4.8 A pilot of an aircraft knows that the vehicle in landing configuration will glide 2.0×10^1 km from a height of 2.00×10^3 m. A TV transmitting tower is located in a direct line with the local runway. If the pilot glides over the tower with 3.0×10^1 m to spare and touches down on the runway at a point 6.5 km from the base of the tower, how high is the tower?

4.9 A simple roof truss design is shown in Figure 4.10. The lower section, *VWXY*, is made from three equal length segments. *UW* and *XZ* are perpendicular to *VT* and *TY,* respectively. If *VWXY* is 2.0×10^1 m and the height of the truss is 2.5 m, determine the lengths of *XT* and *XZ.*

4.10 An engineer is required to survey a nonrectangular plot of land but is unable to measure side *UT* directly due to a water obstruction (see Figure 4.11). The following data are taken: $RU = 130.0$ m, $RS = 120.0$ m, $ST = 90.0$ m, angle $RST = 115°$, and angle $RUT = 100°$. Calculate the length of side *UT* and the area of the plot.

4.11 A park is being considered in a space between a small river and a highway as a rest stop for travelers (see Figure 4.12). Boundary *BC* is perpendicular to the highway and boundary *AD* makes an angle of 75° with the highway. BC is measured to be 160.0 m, *AD* is 270.0 m, and the boundary along the highway is 190.0 m long. What are the length of side *AB* and the magnitude of angle *ABC*?

Figure 4.10

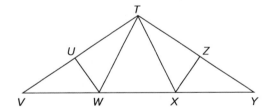

Figure 4.11

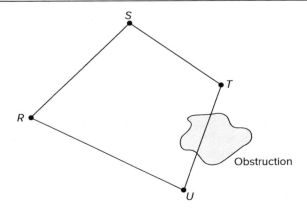

Figure 4.12

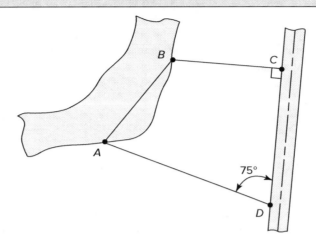

Figure 4.13

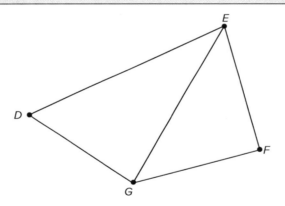

4.12 *D, E, F,* and *G* in Figure 4.13 are surveyed points in a land development on level terrain so that each point is visible from each other. Leg *DG* is physically measured as 500.0 m. The angles at three of the points are found to be: angle $GDE = 55°$, angle $DEF = 92°$, angle $FGD = 134°$. Also, angle DGE is measured at 87°. Compute the lengths of *DE, EF, FG,* and *EG.*

4.13 The height of an inaccessible mountain peak, *C,* in Figure 4.14 must be estimated. Fortunately, two smaller mountains, *A* and *B,* which can be easily scaled, are located near the higher peak. To make matters even simpler, the three peaks lie on a single straight line. From the top of mountain A, altitude 2.000×10^3 m, the elevation angle to *C* is 12.32°. The elevation of *C* from mountain *B* is 22.73°. Mountain *B* is 1.00×10^2 m higher than *A.* The straight line (slant) distance between peaks *A* and *B* is 3.000×10^3 m. Determine the unknown height of mountain *C.*

4.14 A narrow belt is used to drive a 20.00 cm diameter pulley from a 35.00 cm diameter pulley. The centers of the two pulleys are 2.000 m apart. How long must the belt be if the pulleys rotate in the same direction? In opposite directions?

4.15 A motorcycle sprocket on the rear wheel has a diameter of 15 cm, and the driver sprocket has a diameter of 5.0 cm. The driver sprocket shaft and rear axle are 75 cm apart. What is the minimum chain length for this application?

Figure 4.14

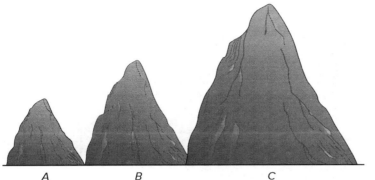

A   B   C

Figure 4.15

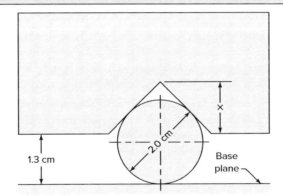

4.16 A block of metal has a 90° notch cut from its lower surface. The notched part rests on a circular cylinder of diameter 2.0 cm, as shown in Figure 4.15. If the lower surface of the part is 1.3 cm above the base plane, how deep is the notch?

4.17 A 1.00 cm diameter circular gauge block is used to measure the depth of a 60° notch in a piece of tool steel. The gauge block extends a distance of 4.7 mm above the surface. How deep is the notch? See Figure 4.16.

4.18 An aircraft moves through the air with a relative velocity of 3.00×10^2 km/h at a heading of N30°E. In a 35 km/h wind from the west,

(*a*) Calculate the *true* ground speed and heading of the aircraft.

(*b*) What heading should the pilot fly so that the *true* heading is N30°E?

4.19 To cross a river that is 1 km wide, with a current of 6 km/h, a novice boat skipper holds the bow of the boat perpendicular to the far riverbank, intending to cross to a point directly across the river from the launch point. At what position will the boat actually contact the far bank? What direction should the boat have been headed to actually reach a point directly across from the launch dock? The boat is capable of making 10 km/h.

Figure 4.16

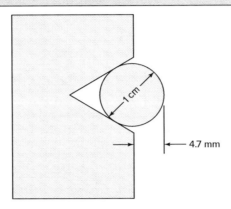

Figure 4.17

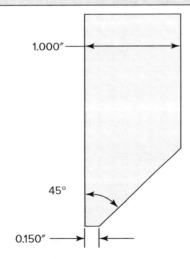

4.20 What heading must a pilot fly to compensate for a 125 km/h west wind to have a ground track that is due south? The aircraft cruise speed is 6.00×10^2 km/h. What is the actual ground speed?

4.21 A tooling designer is designing a jig that will insert pins into the flip-up handles of a coffeemaker. The bin to hold the pins should hold enough pins for 3 h of work before reloading. The engineering estimate for the rate of inserting the pins is 300/h. The pin diameter is 0.125 in. Because of space constraints, the bin must be designed as shown in Figure 4.17. The bin can be only the width of one pin. What is the minimum height that the bin should be if there is 0.250 in. at the top when it has been filled with the required number of pins?

4.22 Two friends are planning to go on RAGBRAI (Register's Annual Great Bike Ride Across Iowa) next year. One is planning to ride a mountain bicycle with 26 in. tires, and the other has a touring bicycle with 27 in. tires. A typical RAGBRAI is about 480 mi long.

(*a*) How many more revolutions will the mountain bike tires make in that distance than the touring bike?

(*b*) Typical gearing for most bicycles ranges from 30 to 50 teeth on the chain wheel (front gears) and 12 to 30 teeth on the rear cog. Find how many more revolutions of the pedals the mountain biker will make during the trip, using an average pedaling time of 85 percent of the trip and a 42-tooth chain wheel and a 21-tooth rear cog for your calculations.

(*c*) If both cyclists have 170 mm cranks on their bikes, what will be the mechanical advantage (considering only the movement of the feet with a constant force for walking and riding), in percent, that each rider will have achieved over walking the same distance? (This can be found by dividing the distance walked by the distance the feet move in riding.)

4.23 An engineer has been given the assignment of finding how much money can be saved over a year's time by redesigning the press plates from the pattern shown in Figure 4.18a to the pattern shown in Figure 4.18b for stamping out 2.400 in. diameter disks. The stamping material is 14-gauge sheet metal and can be purchased in 100 ft rolls in varying widths in 0.5 in. increments. One square foot of metal weighs 3.20 lb. The metal is sold for $0.20/lb. Do not consider the ends of the rolls. The company expects to produce 38 000 parts this year. How much can be saved?

4.24 Sally is making a sine bar, which is used to machine angles on parts (see Figure 4.19). She has a 1.250 in. thick bar that needs 90° grooves machined into it for precision ground 1.0000 in. diameter cylinders. A sine bar is used by placing different thicknesses under one of the cylinders so that the proper angle is attained. Sally wants the distance between the centers of the cylinders to be 5.000 in.

(*a*) How deep should she mill the 90° grooves so that the top of the sine block is 2 in. tall?

(*b*) Once her sine block is finished, she wants to mill a 22.5° angle on a brass block. What thickness of gage blocks will produce this angle for this sine plate?

4.25 Standing at the edge of the roof of a tall building, you throw a ball upward with a velocity of 15 m/s (meters per second). The ball goes straight up and begins its downward descent just missing the edge of the building. The building is 40 m tall.

(*a*) What is the velocity of the ball at its uppermost position?

(*b*) How high above the building does the ball go before beginning its descent?

(*c*) What is the velocity of the ball as it passes the roof of the building?

(*d*) What is the speed of the ball just before it hits the ground?

(*e*) How long does it take for the ball to hit the ground after leaving your hand?

Figure 4.18

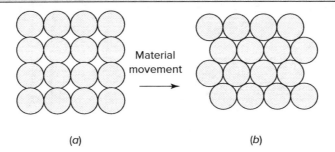

Material movement

(*a*)   (*b*)

Figure 4.19

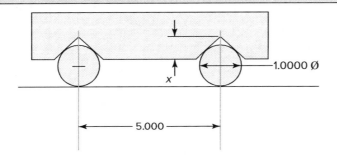

1.0000 Ø

x

5.000

4.26 A stuntwoman is going to attempt a jump across a canyon 74 m wide. The ramp on the far side of the canyon is 25 m lower than the ramp from which she will leave. The takeoff ramp is built with a 15° angle from horizontal.

(*a*) If the stuntwoman leaves the ramp with a velocity of 28 m/s, will she make the jump?

(*b*) How many seconds will she be in the air?

4.27 An engineering student has been given the assignment of designing a hydraulic holding system for a hay-baling system. The system has four cylinders with 120 mm diameter pistons with a stroke of 0.320 m. The lines connecting the system are 1 cm id (inside diameter). There are 15.5 m of lines in the system. For proper design, the reserve tank should hold a minimum of 50 percent more than the amount of hydraulic fluid in the system. If the diameter of the reserve tank is 30.48 cm, what is the shortest height it should be?

4.28 The plant engineer for a large foundry has been asked to calculate the thermal efficiency of the generating plant used by the company to produce electricity for the aluminum melting furnaces. The plant generates 545.6 GJ of electrical energy daily. The plant burns 50 t (tons) of coal a day. The heat of combustion of coal is about 6.2×10^6 J/kg (joules/kilogram). What was the answer? (Efficiency $= W/J_{heat}$)

4.29 Using these three formulas

$$V = IR \qquad R = (\rho L)/A \qquad A = \pi(0.5d)^2$$

find the difference in current (I) that a copper wire ($\rho = 1.72 \times 10^{-8}$ Ω · m) can carry over an aluminum wire ($\rho = 2.75 \times 10^{-8}$ Ω · m) with equal diameters (d) of 0.5 cm and a length (L) of 10 000 m carrying 110 V (volts).

4.30 The light striking a pane of glass is refracted as shown in Figure 4.20. The law of refraction states that $n_a \sin \theta_a = n_b \sin \theta_b$, where n_a and n_b are the refractive indexes of the materials through which the light is passing and the angles are from a line that is normal to the surface. The refractive index of air is 1.00. What is the refractive index of the glass?

Figure 4.20

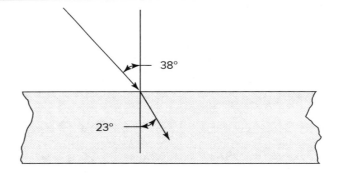

23°   38°

CHAPTER 5

Representation of Technical Information*

Chapter Objectives

When you complete your study of this chapter, you will be able to:

- Recognize the importance of collecting, recording, plotting, and interpreting technical data for engineering analysis and design
- Put into practice methods for graphical presentation of scientific data and graphical analysis of plotted data
- Develop the ability to graph data using uniform and nonuniform scales
- Apply methods of selected points and least squares for determining the equation that gives the best-fit line to the given data
- Determine the most appropriate family of curves (linear, power, or exponential) that gives the best fit to the given data

5.1 Introduction

This chapter begins with an example of an actual freshman engineering student team project. This team consisted of aerospace, electrical, and mechanical engineering students who were assigned to find how temperature and pressure varied with altitude in the atmosphere. The team was not given specific instructions as to how this might be accomplished, but once the information had been collected, they were expected to record, plot, and analyze the data.

After a bit of research, the team decided to request a university-owned plane that was equipped with the latest Rockwell Collins avionics gear, and since it was a class assignment, they asked if the university's Air Flight Service would consider helping them conduct this experiment free of charge. Because the pilots do periodic maintenance flights, they agreed to allow the students to ride along.

Using the plane's sophisticated data-acquisition equipment, the students were able to collect and record the data needed for the assignment (see Table 5.1) along the flight path as the plane ascended to 12 000 feet. They decided that one would record, one would make temperature readings, and the third would make pressure readings.

When the students returned to the hangar, they made a freehand plot (with straight-edge) of the collected information (see Figure 5.1).

---

*Users will find Appendices A, E, and the inside covers useful reference material for this chapter.

Table 5.1

Height, H, ft	Temperature, T,°F	Pressure, P, lbf/in²
0	59	14.7
1 000	55	14.2
2 000	52	13.7
3 000	48	13.2
4 000	44	12.7
5 000	41	12.2
6 000	37	11.8
7 000	34	11.3
8 000	30	10.9
9 000	27	10.5
10 000	23	10.0
11 000	19	9.7
12 000	16	9.3

Since the plot demonstrated linear results, the students returned to campus to prepare the required report, including an analysis of the data collected.

They decided the written report should include a computer-generated table, a computer-generated plot of the data, and a computer-generated least-squares curve fit to determine the mathematical relationship between the variables.

Table 5.2 shows the computer-generated table prepared after the students returned to campus. This could have been done with word processing, spreadsheet, or other commercially available software packages.

Figures 5.2 and 5.3 show how spreadsheet applications can be powerful and convenient for plotting once the fundamentals of good graph construction are understood. Figure 5.2 is an example of a Microsoft Excel spreadsheet using a scatter plot with each data point connected with a straight line. Figure 5.3 is an example of a scatter plot with only the data points plotted. A *trendline* is then applied using the method of least squares with the equation of the line included. Further discussion of the use of the trendline/method of least squares will occur later in this chapter, with more details given in the chapter on statistics.

Table 5.2

Height, *H*, ft	Temperature, *T*, °F	Pressure, *P*, lbf/in²
0	59	14.7
1 000	55	14.2
2 000	52	13.7
3 000	48	13.2
4 000	44	12.7
5 000	41	12.2
6 000	37	11.8
7 000	34	11.3
8 000	30	10.9
9 000	27	10.5
10 000	23	10.0
11 000	19	9.7
12 000	16	9.3

Figure 5.1

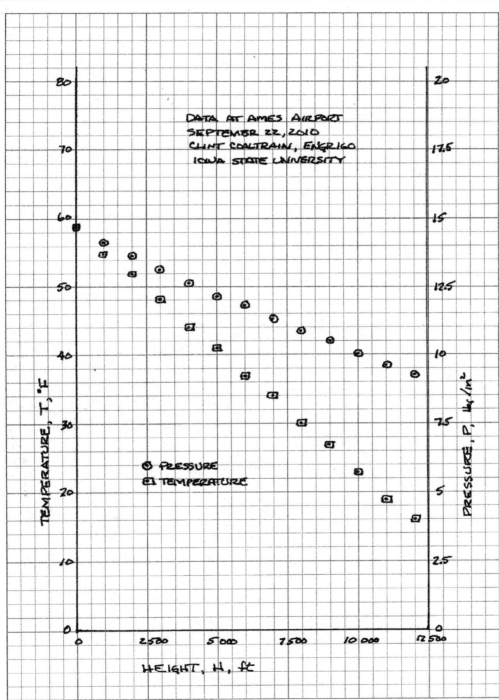

Freehand plot of how temperature and pressure vary with altitude.

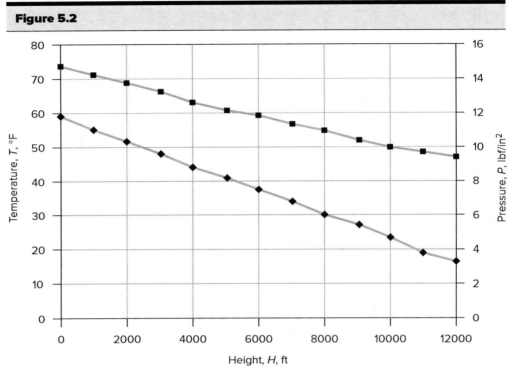

Figure 5.2

Excel spreadsheet hard copy of data displayed in Figure 5.1.

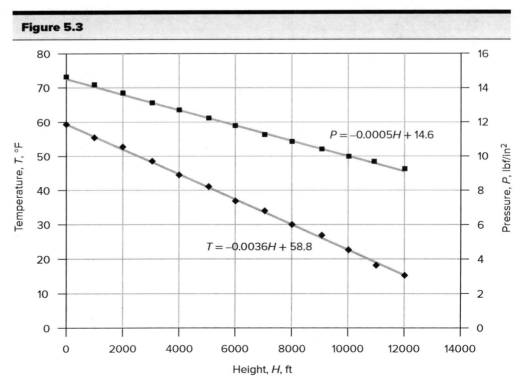

Figure 5.3

$P = -0.0005H + 14.6$

$T = -0.0036H + 58.8$

Excel spreadsheet hard copy of data displayed in Figure 5.1 with trendline.

This chapter contains examples and guidelines as well as helpful information that will be needed when collecting, recording, plotting, and interpreting technical data. Two processes are (1) graphical presentation of scientific data and (2) graphical analysis of plotted data.

Humans find it difficult to observe relationships among data shown in a table. We are much better at understanding relationships when the data are put into a graphical or pictorial format. We can immediately recognize the form of the relationship between two data sets (for example) when they are plotted on a graph. We can see whether the relationship is linear (straight line) or curved in some fashion. Perhaps we can even determine that the relationship appears to be in the form of a sine wave or a parabolic curve. Sometimes, just the impression of how the data relate is enough. More often, though, we need to obtain an equation that relates one variable to the other.

We have at our disposal computers and software that can make the production of a graph easy to accomplish and can help us to determine the relationship between variables in equation form. Much of this chapter is devoted to learning about engineering standards for graph production and methods for producing equations between variables that have been presented on a graph.

5.1.1   Software for Recording and Plotting Data

Data are recorded in the field as shown in Table 5.1. A quick freehand plot of the data is produced to provide a visual impression of the results while still in the field (see Figure 5.1). This allows you to obtain corrected or additional data if the quick plot suggests it. Alternatively, the data could be entered into a laptop computer or a smartphone and processed initially in the field.

Upon returning to the laboratory, however, spreadsheet software, such as Excel, provides enormous recording and plotting capability. The data are entered into the computer, and by manipulation of software options, both the data and a graph of the data can be configured, stored, and printed (Table 5.2 and Figures 5.2 and 5.3).

Programs such as TK Solver, MATLAB, and Mathcad provide a range of powerful tools designed to help analyze numerical and symbolic operations as well as to present a visual image of the results.

Software is also widely available to provide methods of curve fitting once the data have been collected and recorded.

Even though it is important for the engineer to interpret, analyze, and communicate different types of data, it is not practical to include in this chapter all forms of graphs and charts that may be encountered. For that reason, popular-appeal or advertising charts such as bar charts, pie diagrams, and distribution charts, although useful to the engineer, are not discussed here.

Even though commercial software is very helpful during the presentation and analysis process, the results are only as good as the original software design and its use by the operator. Some software provides a wide range of tools but only allows limited data applications and minimal flexibility to modify default outputs. Other software provides a high degree of in-depth analysis for a particular subject area with considerable latitude to adjust and modify parameters.

Inevitably, the computer together with its array of software will continue to provide an invaluable analysis tool. However, it is absolutely essential that you be knowledgeable of the software and demonstrate considerable care when manipulating the data.

You need to understand the software's limitations and accuracies, but above all you must know what plotted results are needed and what the engineering standards are for producing them.

For this reason, the sections that follow are a combination of manual collection, recording, plotting, and analysis and computer-assisted collection, recording, plotting, and analysis.

5.2 Collecting and Recording Data

5.2.1 Manual Entry

Modern science was founded on scientific measurement. Meticulously designed experiments, carefully analyzed, have produced volumes of scientific data that have been collected, recorded, and documented. For such data to be meaningful, however, certain procedures must be followed. Field books, such as those shown in Figure 5.4, or data sheets should be used to record all observations. Information about equipment, such as the instruments and experimental apparatus used, should be recorded. Sketches illustrating the physical arrangement of equipment can be very helpful. Under no circumstances should observations be recorded elsewhere or data points erased. The data sheet or field book is the "notebook of original entry." If there is reason for doubting the value of any entry, it may be canceled (i.e., not considered) by drawing a line through it. The cancellation should be done in such a manner that the original entry is not obscured in case you want to consider it later.

As a general rule it is advantageous to make all measurements as carefully as time and the economics of the situation allow. Errors do enter into all experimental work regardless of the amount of care exercised.

It can be seen from what we have just discussed that the analysis of experimental data involves not only measurements and collection of data but also careful documentation and interpretation of results.

Experimental data once collected are normally organized into some tabular form, which is the next step in the process of analysis. Data, such as that shown in Table 5.1, should be carefully labeled and neatly lettered so that the data are not misunderstood. This particular collection of data represents atmospheric pressure and temperature measurements recorded at various altitudes by students during a flight in a light aircraft.

Although the manual tabulation of data is frequently a necessary step, you will sometimes find it difficult to visualize a relationship between variables when simply viewing a column of numbers. Therefore, a most important step in the sequence from collection to analysis is the construction of appropriate graphs or charts.

5.2.2 Computer-Assisted Techniques

A variety of equipment has been developed that will automatically sample experimental data for analysis. We expect to see expansion of these techniques along with visual displays that will allow us to interactively control the experiments. As an example, the flight data collected onboard the aircraft could be entered directly into a laptop computer through digital interfaces with the flight instruments and then printed as in Table 5.2.

Figure 5.4

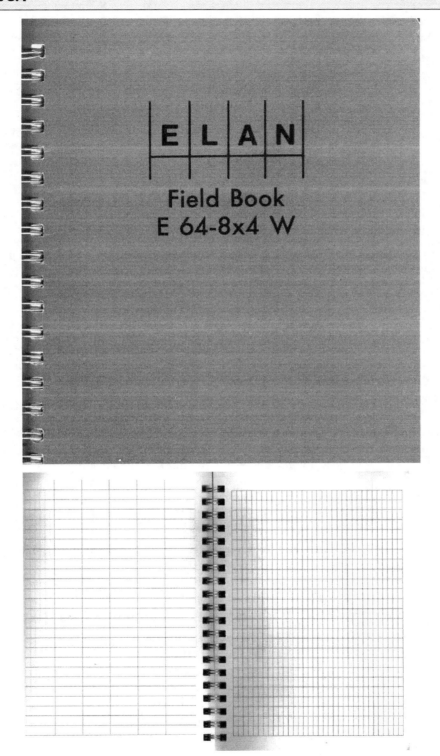

Field book typically used by civil engineers.

5.3   General Graphing Procedures

Many examples appear throughout this chapter to illustrate methods of graphical presentation because their effectiveness depends to a large extent on the details of construction.

The proper manual construction of a graph from tabulated data can be described by a series of steps. Each of these steps will be discussed and illustrated in detail in the following sections. Once you understand the manual process of graph construction, the step to computer-generated graphs will be simple.

1. Select the type of graph paper (rectangular [also known as rectilinear], semilog, log-log) and grid spacing for best representation of the given data.
2. Choose the proper location of the horizontal and vertical axes.
3. Determine the scale units (range) for each axis to display the data appropriately.
4. Graduate and calibrate the axes using the *1, 2, 5 rule.*
5. Identify each axis completely.
6. Plot points and use permissible symbols.
7. Check any point that deviates from the slope or curvature of the line.
8. Draw the curve or curves.
9. Identify each curve, add title, and include other necessary notes.
10. Darken lines for good reproduction.

5.3.1   Graph Paper

Printed coordinate graph paper is commercially available in various sizes with a variety of grid spacing. Rectangular ruling can be purchased in a range of lines per inch or lines per centimeter, with an overall paper size of 8.5 × 11 in. most typical.

Closely spaced coordinate ruling is generally avoided for results that are to be printed or photoreduced. However, for accurate engineering analyses requiring some amount of interpolation, data are normally plotted on closely spaced, printed coordinate paper. Graph paper is available in a variety of colors, weights, and grades. Translucent paper can be used when the reproduction system requires a material that is not opaque.

If the data require the use of log-log or semilog paper, such paper can also be purchased in different formats, styles, weights, and grades. Both log-log and semilog grids are available from 1 to 5 cycles per axis. (A later section will discuss different applications of log-log and semilog paper.) Examples of commercially available log and semilog paper are given in Figures 5.5a and 5.5b.

5.3.2   Axes Location and Breaks

The axes of a graph consist of two intersecting straight lines. The horizontal axis, normally called the *x-axis,* is the *abscissa.* The vertical axis, denoted by the *y-axis,* is the *ordinate.* Common practice is to place the independent variable values along the abscissa and the dependent variable values along the ordinate, as illustrated in Figure 5.6.

It is not always clear which variable is the independent variable and which is the dependent variable. You can think in terms of an experiment where one variable is set (independent variable) and another is determined (dependent variable). For example, in a test of an electrical circuit, if the voltage is set it is the independent variable and if the current is read from an instrument as a result of this voltage setting it is the dependent variable. You can also think in terms of reading from a graph. Normally you would find

Figure 5.5

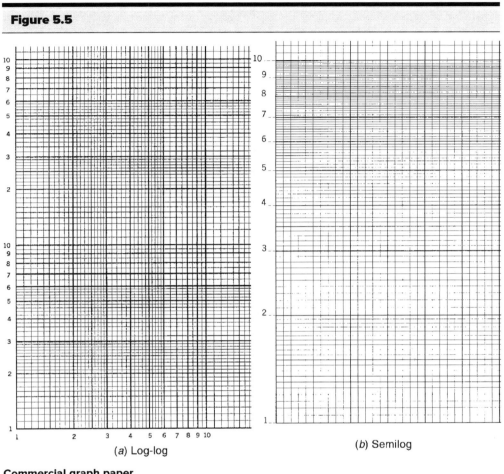

(*a*) Log-log

(*b*) Semilog

Commercial graph paper.

Figure 5.6

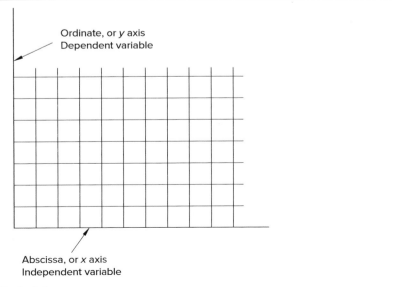

Ordinate, or *y* axis
Dependent variable

Abscissa, or *x* axis
Independent variable

Abscissa (x) and ordinate (y) axes.

Figure 5.7

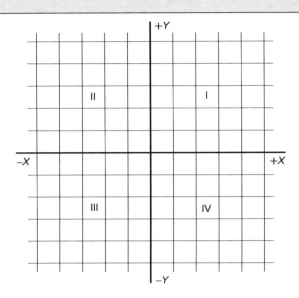

Coordinate axes.

the value of the variable you set along the horizontal axis (independent variable) and read the value of the other (dependent variable) from the curve using the vertical axis.

Sometimes mathematical graphs contain both positive and negative values of the variables. This necessitates the division of the coordinate field into four quadrants, as shown in Figure 5.7. Positive values increase toward the right and upward from the origin.

On any graph, a full range of values is desirable, normally beginning at zero and extending slightly beyond the largest value. To avoid crowding, one should use the entire coordinate area as completely as possible. However, certain circumstances require special consideration to avoid wasted space. For example, if values plotted along the axis do not range near zero, a "break" in the grid or the axis may be used, as shown in Figures 5.8a and 5.8b.

Figure 5.8

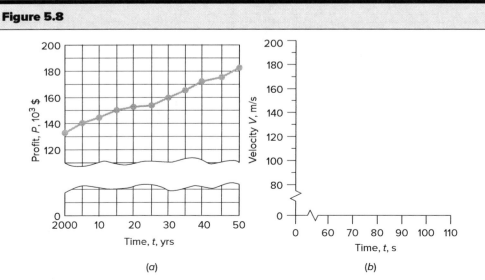

Typical axis breaks.

When judgments concerning relative amounts of change in a variable are required, the axis or grid should not be broken or the zero line omitted, with the exception of time in years, such as 2016, 2017, and so on, because that designation normally has little relation to zero.

Since most commercially prepared grids do not include sufficient border space for proper labeling, the axes should preferably be placed 20 to 25 mm (approximately 1 in.) inside the edge of the printed grid to allow ample room for graduations, calibrations, axes labels, reproduction, and binding. The edge of the grid may need to be used on log scales because it is not always feasible to move the axis inside the grid. However, with careful planning, the vertical and horizontal axes can usually be repositioned.

5.3.3 Scale Graduations, Calibrations, and Designations

The scale is a series of marks, called *graduations,* laid down at predetermined distances along the axis. Numerical values assigned to significant graduations are called *calibrations.*

A scale can be *uniform* or *linear,* with equal spacing along the axis, as found on the metric or engineer's scales. If the scale represents a variable whose exponent is not equal to 1 or a variable that contains trigonometric or logarithmic functions, the scale is called a *nonuniform,* or *functional, scale.* Examples of both these scales together with graduations and calibrations are shown in Figure 5.9. When you plot data, one of the most important considerations is the proper selection of scale graduations. A basic guide to follow is the *1, 2, 5 rule,* which only applies to uniform axes and can be stated as follows:

> Scale graduations are selected so that the smallest division of the axis is a positive or negative integer power of 10 times 1, 2, or 5.

The justification and logic for this rule are clear. Graduation of an axis by this procedure allows better (more accurate) interpolation of data between graduations when plotting or reading a graph. Figure 5.10 illustrates both acceptable and unacceptable examples of scale graduations.

Violations of the *1, 2, 5 rule* that are acceptable even for uniform axes involve certain units of time as a variable. Days, months, and years can be graduated and calibrated as illustrated in Figure 5.11.

Scale graduations follow a definite rule, but the number of calibrations included is a matter of good judgment. Each application requires consideration based on the scale length and range as well as the eventual use. Figure 5.12 demonstrates how calibrations can differ on a scale with the same range. Both examples obey the *1, 2, 5 rule,* but as you can see, too many closely spaced calibrations make the axis difficult to read.

Figure 5.9

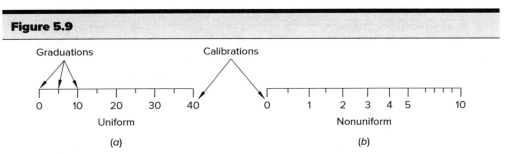

(a)   (b)

Scale graduations and calibrations.

Figure 5.10

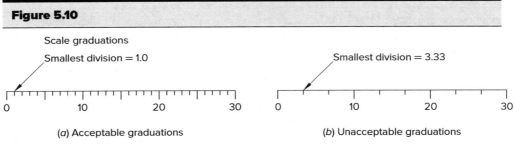

Scale graduations
Smallest division = 1.0

Smallest division = 3.33

(a) Acceptable graduations

(b) Unacceptable graduations

Acceptable and unacceptable scale graduations.

Figure 5.11

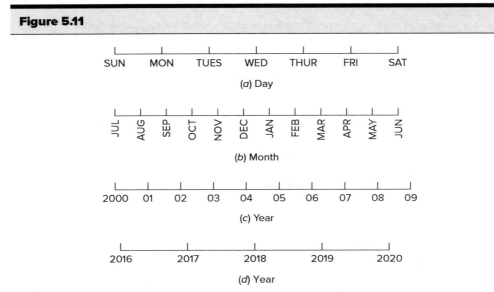

SUN   MON   TUES   WED   THUR   FRI   SAT

(a) Day

JUL   AUG   SEP   OCT   NOV   DEC   JAN   FEB   MAR   APR   MAY   JUN

(b) Month

2000   01   02   03   04   05   06   07   08   09

(c) Year

2016   2017   2018   2019   2020

(d) Year

Time as a variable.

Figure 5.12

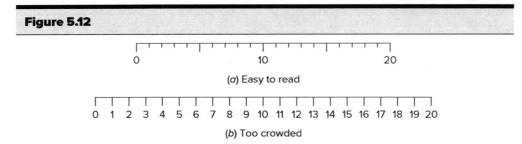

0   10   20

(a) Easy to read

0 1 2 3 4 5 6 7 8 9 10 11 12 13 14 15 16 17 18 19 20

(b) Too crowded

Acceptable and unacceptable scale calibrations.

The selection of a scale deserves attention from another point of view. If the rate of change is to be depicted accurately, the slope of the curve should represent a true picture of the data. By compressing or expanding one of the axes, you could communicate an incorrect impression of the data. Such a procedure should be avoided. Figure 5.13 demonstrates how the equation $Y = X$ can be misleading if not properly plotted. Occasionally, distortion is desirable, but it should always be carefully labeled and explained to avoid misleading conclusions.

If plotted data consist of very large or small numbers, the SI prefix names (milli-, kilo-, mega-, etc.) may be used to simplify calibrations. As a guide, if the numbers to

Figure 5.13

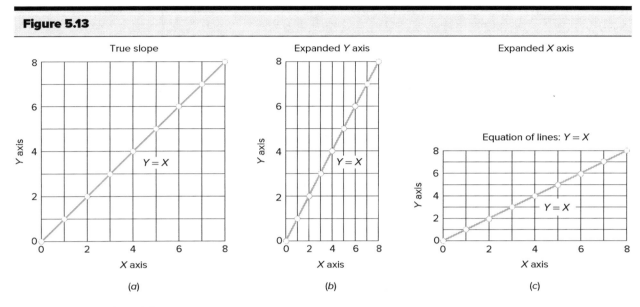

Proper representation of data.

Figure 5.14

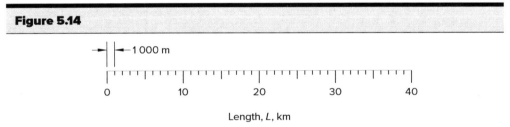

Reading the scale.

be plotted and calibrated consist of more than three digits, it is customary to use the appropriate prefix; an example appears in Figure 5.14.

The length scale calibrations in Figure 5.14 contain only two digits, but the scale can be read by understanding that the distance between the first and second graduation (0 to 1) is a kilometer; therefore, the calibration at 10 represents 10 km.

Certain quantities, such as temperature in degrees Celsius and altitude in meters, have traditionally been tabulated without the use of prefix multipliers. Figure 5.15 depicts a procedure by which these quantities can be conveniently calibrated. Note in particular that the distance between 0 and 1 on the scale represents 1 000°C.

Figure 5.15

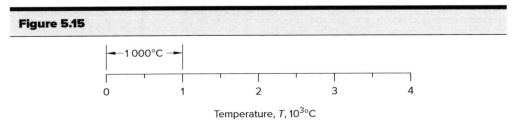

Reading the scale.

Figure 5.16

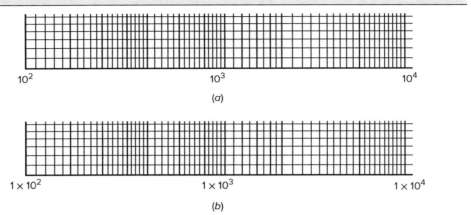

(a)

(b)

Calibration of log scales.

Figure 5.17

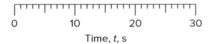

Time, t, s

Axis identification.

The calibration of logarithmic scales is illustrated in Figure 5.16. Since log-cycle designations start and end with powers of 10 (i.e., 10^{-1}, 10^0, 10^1, 10^2, etc.) and since commercially purchased paper is normally available with each cycle printed 1 through 10, do not use the printed values as your calibrations. Instead, provide your own calibrations and use the printed numbers as a reference to be sure you understand what each line of the grid represents. Since the axes are nonuniform, it is sometimes difficult to determine what each grid line represents without those printed numbers. Figures 5.16a and 5.16b demonstrate two preferred methods of calibration.

5.3.4 Axis Labeling

Each axis should be clearly identified. At a minimum, the axis label should contain the name of the variable, its symbol, and its units. Since time is frequently the independent variable and is plotted on the x-axis, it has been selected as an illustration in Figure 5.17. Scale designations should preferably be placed outside the axes, where they can be shown clearly. Labels should be lettered parallel to the axis and positioned so that they can be read from the bottom or right side of the page, as illustrated in Figure 5.22.

5.3.5 Point-Plotting Procedure

Data can be described in one of three ways: as observed, empirical, or theoretical. Observed and empirical data points are usually located by various symbols, such as a small circle or square around each data point, whereas graphs of theoretical relations (equations) are normally constructed smooth, without the use of symbol designation. Figure 5.18 illustrates each type.

5.3.6 Curves and Symbols

On graphs prepared from observed data resulting from laboratory experiments, points are usually designated by various symbols (see Figure 5.19). If more than one curve is plotted on the same grid, several of these symbols may be used (one type for each curve). To avoid confusion, however, it is good practice to label each curve. When several curves are plotted on the same grid, another way they can be distinguished from each other is by using different types of lines, as illustrated in Figure 5.20. Solid lines are normally reserved for single curves, and dashed lines are commonly used for extensions; however, a different line type can be used for each separate curve. The line weight of plotted curves should be heavier than the grid ruling.

A key, or legend, should be placed in an available portion of the grid, preferably enclosed in a border, to define point symbols or line types that are used for curves. Remember that the lines representing each curve *should never be drawn through the symbols,* so that the precise point is always identifiable. Figure 5.21 demonstrates the use of a key and the practice of breaking the line at each symbol.

Figure 5.18

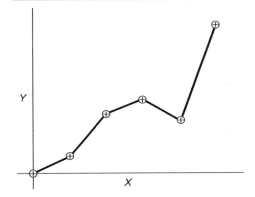

(*a*) Observed: Usually plotted with observed data points connected by straight, irregular line segments. Line does not penetrate the circles.

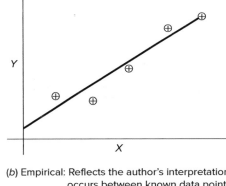

(*b*) Empirical: Reflects the author's interpretation of what occurs between known data points. Normally represented as a smooth curve or straight line fitted to data. Data points may or may not fall on curve.

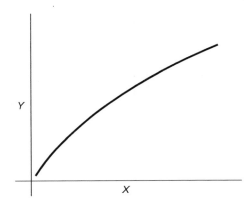

(*c*) Theoretical: Graph of an equation. Curves or lines are smooth and without symbols. Every point on the curve is a data point.

Plotting data points.

Figure 5.19

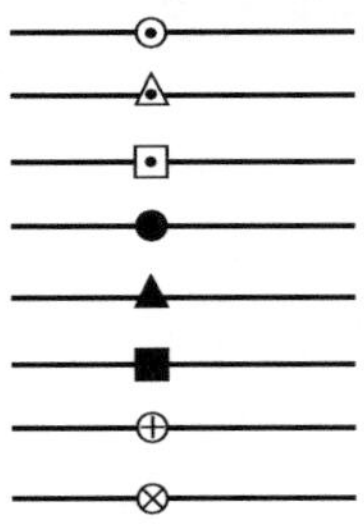

Symbols.

Figure 5.20

Line types.

Figure 5.21

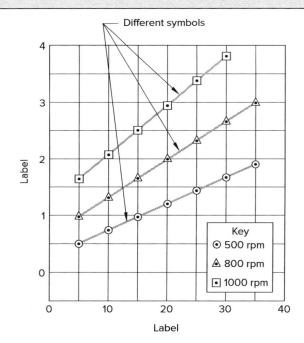

An example of a key.

5.3.7 Titles

Each graph must be identified with a complete title. The title should include a clear, concise statement of the data represented, along with items such as the name of the author, the date of the experiment, and any and all information concerning the plot, including the name of the institution or company. Titles may be enclosed in a border.

All lettering, the axes, and the curves should be sufficiently bold to stand out on the graph paper. Letters should be neat and of standard size. Figure 5.22 is an illustration of plotted experimental data incorporating many of the items discussed in the chapter.

5.3.8 Computer-Assisted Plotting

Several types of software are available to produce graphs (e.g., Mathcad, MATLAB, TK Solver, Excel). The quality and accuracy of these computer-generated graphs vary depending on the sophistication of the software as well as on the plotter or printer employed. Typically, the software will produce an axis scale graduated and calibrated to accommodate the range of data values that will fit the paper. This may or may not produce a readable or interpretable scale. Therefore, it is necessary to apply judgment depending on the results needed. For example, if the default plot does not meet needed scale readability, it may be necessary to specify the scale range to achieve an appropriate scale graduation, since this option allows greater control of the scale drawn.

Figure 5.22

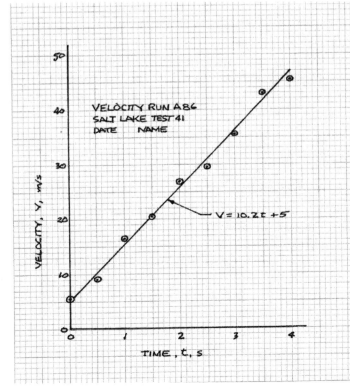

Necessary steps to follow when manually plotting a graph:

1. Select the type of graph paper (rectilinear, semilog, log-log) and grid spacing for best representation of the given data.

2. Choose the proper location of the horizontal and vertical axes.

3. Determine the scale units (range) for each axis to display the data appropriately.

4. Graduate and calibrate the axes using the *1, 2, 5 rule.*

5. Identify each axis completely.

6. Plot points using permissible symbols.

7. Check any point that deviates from the slope or curvature of the line.

8. Draw the curve or curves.

9. Identify each curve, add title, and necessary notes.

10. Darken lines for good reproduction.

Sample plot.

Figure 5.23

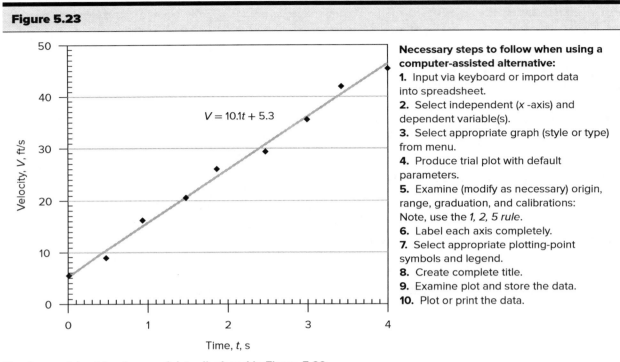

Necessary steps to follow when using a computer-assisted alternative:
1. Input via keyboard or import data into spreadsheet.
2. Select independent (*x*-axis) and dependent variable(s).
3. Select appropriate graph (style or type) from menu.
4. Produce trial plot with default parameters.
5. Examine (modify as necessary) origin, range, graduation, and calibrations: Note, use the *1, 2, 5 rule.*
6. Label each axis completely.
7. Select appropriate plotting-point symbols and legend.
8. Create complete title.
9. Examine plot and store the data.
10. Plot or print the data.

Excel spreadsheet hard copy of data displayed in Figure 5.22.

Computer-produced graphs with uniform scales may not follow the *1, 2, 5 rule,* particularly because the software plots the independent variable based on the data collected. If the software has the option of separately specifying the range—that is, plotting the data as an *X-Y* scatter plot—you will be able to achieve scale graduations and calibrations that do follow the *1, 2, 5 rule,* making it easier to read values from the graph. The hand-plotted graph that was illustrated in Figure 5.22 is plotted using Excel with the results shown in Figure 5.23 using an *X-Y* scatter plot with a linear curve-fit and the equation of the line using the method of least squares (see Section 5.6).

5.4 Empirical Functions

Empirical functions are generally described as those based on values obtained by experimentation. Since they are arrived at experimentally, equations normally available from theoretical derivations are not always available. However, mathematical expressions can be modeled to fit experimental data, and it is possible to classify many empirical results into one of four general categories: (1) linear, (2) exponential, (3) power, or (4) periodic.

A linear function, as the name suggests, will plot as a straight line on uniform rectangular coordinate paper. Likewise, when a curve representing experimental data is a straight line or a close approximation to a straight line, the relationship of the variables can be expressed by a linear equation, such as $y = mx + b$.

Correspondingly, exponential functions, when plotted on semilog paper, will be linear. Why? Because the basic form of the equation is $y = be^{mx}$, all we do is take the log of both sides. If it is written in log (base 10) form, it becomes $\log y = mx \log e + \log b$. Alternatively, using natural logarithms, the equation becomes $\ln y = mx + \ln b$ because

$\ln e = 1$. The independent variable x is plotted on the abscissa, and the dependent variable y is plotted on the functional ln (natural log) scale as ln y.

The power equation has the form of $y = bx^m$. Written in log form, it becomes log $y = m \log x + \log b$. This equation will plot as a straight line on log-log paper because the log of the independent variable x is plotted against the log of the dependent variable y.

The periodic type, often seen in alternating current, for example, is not covered in this text.

When the data represent experimental results and a series of points are plotted to represent the relationship between the variables, it is unlikely that a straight line can be constructed through every point because some error (instruments, readings, recordings) is inevitable. If all points do not lie on a straight line, an approximation technique or averaging method may be used to arrive at the best possible fit. This method of straight-line approximation is called curve fitting.

5.5   Curve Fitting

Different methods or techniques are available to arrive at the best "straight-line" fit. Two methods commonly employed for finding the best fit are

1. Method of selected points
2. Method of least squares

The most accurate method, least squares, is discussed in more detail in the chapter on statistics. However, several examples are presented in this chapter to demonstrate correct methods for plotting technical data using both the method of selected points and the method of least squares.

5.6   Method of Selected Points and Least Squares

The method of selected points is a valid method of determining the equation that best fits data that exhibit a linear relationship. Once the data have been plotted and you have decided that a linear equation would be a good fit, a line is positioned that appears to best fit the data. This is most often accomplished by visually selecting a line that goes through as many data points as possible and has approximately the same number of data points on either side of the line.

Once the line has been drawn, two points, such as *A* and *B*, are selected *on the line* and at a reasonable distance apart (the further apart the better). The coordinates of both points $A(X_1, Y_1)$ and $B(X_2, Y_2)$ must satisfy the equation of the line because both are points on the line.

The method of least squares is a more accurate approach that will be illustrated as computer-assisted examples in most problems that follow. The method of least squares is a most appropriate technique for determination of the best-fit line. You should understand that the method presented represents a technique called *linear regression* and is valid only for *linear* relationships. The technique of least squares can, however, be applied to power ($y = bx^m$) and exponential ($y = be^{mx}$) relationships as well as $y = mx + b$, if done correctly. The power function can be handled by noting that there is a linear relationship between log y and log x (log $y = m \log x + \log b$, which plots as a straight line on log-log paper). Thus, we can apply the method of least squares to the variables log y and log x to obtain parameters m and log b.

The exponential function written in natural logarithm form is $\ln y = mx + \ln b$. Therefore, a linear relationship exists between $\ln y$ and x (this plots as a straight line on semilog paper). The next examples will demonstrate the use of the selected point method for power and experimental curves.

5.7 Empirical Equations: Linear

When experimental data plot as a straight line on rectangular grid paper, the equation of the line belongs to a family of curves whose basic equation is given by

$$y = mx + b \qquad (5.1)$$

where m is the slope of the line, a constant, and b is a constant referred to as the *y intercept* (the value of y when $x = 0$).

To demonstrate how the method of selected points works, consider the following example.

Example problem 5.1   The velocity V of an experimental automobile is measured at specified time t intervals. Determine the equation of a straight line constructed through the points recorded in Table 5.3. Once an equation has been determined, velocities at intermediate values can be computed.

Procedure

1. Plot the data on rectangular paper. If the results form a straight line (see Figure 5.24), the function is linear and the general equation is of the form

    $$V = mt + b$$

    where m and b are constants.

2. Select two points on the line, $A(t_1, V_1)$ and $B(t_2, V_2)$, and record the value of these points. Points A and B should be widely separated to reduce the effect on m and b of errors in reading values from the graph. Points A and B are identified in Figure 5.24 for instructional reasons. They should not be shown on a completed graph that is to be displayed.

    $A(10, 60)$
    $B(35, 165)$

Table 5.3

Time t, s	0	5	10	15	20	25	30	35	40
Velocity V, m/s	24	33	62	77	105	123	151	170	188

3. Substitute the points A and B into $V = mt + b$.

    Eq(1) $60 = m(10) + b$
    Eq(2) $165 = m(35) + b$

4. The equations are solved simultaneously for the two unknowns.

    $m = 4.2$
    $b = 18$

Figure 5.24

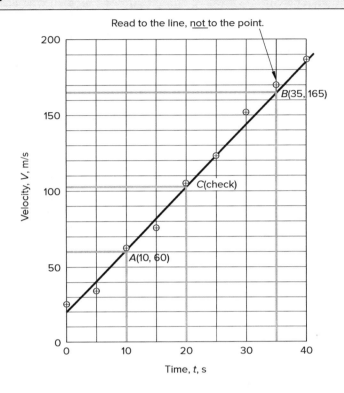

Read to the line, not to the point.

Data plot.

5. The equation of the line for this specific problem can be written as

$$V = 4.2t + 18$$

6. Using another point $C(t_3, V_3)$, check for verification:

$C(20, 102)$
$102 = 4.2(20) + 18$
$102 = 84 + 18 = 102$

7. A computer-assisted alternate:

The data set can be entered into a spreadsheet, and the software will provide a more precise solution. Figure 5.23 illustrates a software solution for data provided in the previous sample plot (Figure 5.22). The computer solution provides a plot of data on rectangular paper with the equation of the line determined by the method of least squares. Once you understand the fundamentals, it can be very time efficient to use computer technology and commercial software.

5.8 Empirical Equations: Power Curves

When experimentally collected data are plotted on rectangular coordinate graph paper and the points do not form a straight line, you must determine which family of curves the line most closely approximates. If you have no idea as to the nature of the data, plot the experimentally collected points on log-log paper and/or semilog paper to determine if the data approximate a straight line. Consider the following familiar example. Suppose a solid object is dropped from a tall building. To anyone who has studied fundamental physics, it is apparent that distance and time should correspond to the general equation for a free-falling body (neglecting air friction): $s = 1/2\ gt^2$.

However, let's assume for a moment that we do not know this relationship and that all we have is a table of values experimentally measured on a free-falling body.

Example problem 5.2   A solid object is dropped from a tall building, and the values time versus distance are as recorded in Table 5.4.

Procedure

1. Make a freehand plot to observe the data visually (see Figure 5.25). From this quick plot, the data points are more easily recognized as belonging to a family of curves whose general equation can be written as

    $$y = bx^m \tag{5.2}$$

Remember that before the method of selected points can be applied to determine the equation of the line, the plotted line must be straight because two points on a curved line do not uniquely identify the line. Mathematically, this general equation can be modified by taking the logarithm of both sides,

$$\log y = m \log x + \log b, \text{ or } \ln y = m \ln x + \ln b$$

This equation suggests that if the logs of all table values of y and x were computed and the results plotted on rectangular paper, the line would likely be straight.

Realizing that the log of zero is undefined and plotting the remaining points that are recorded in Table 5.5 for log s versus log t, the results are shown in Figure 5.26.

Since the graph of log s versus log t does plot as a straight line, it is now possible to use the general form of the equation

$$\log s = m \log t + \log b$$

and apply the method of selected points.

When reading values for points A and B from the graph, we must remember that the logarithm of each variable has already been determined and the values plotted.

$$A(0.2, 1.09)$$
$$B(0.6, 1.89)$$

Table 5.4	
Time t, s	**Distance s, m**
0	0
1	4.9
2	19.6
3	44.1
4	78.4
5	122.5
6	176.4

Figure 5.25

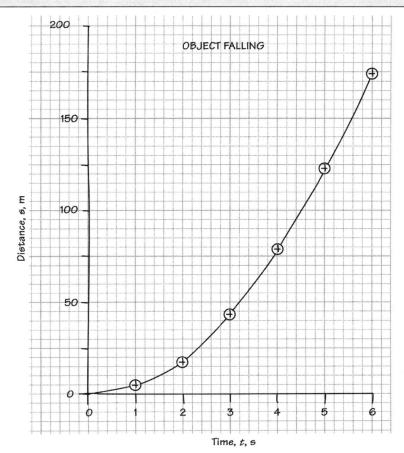

Rectangular graph paper (freehand).

Points *A* and *B* can now be substituted into the general equation log $s = m$ log $t +$ log b and solved simultaneously.

$$1.89 = m(0.6) + \log b$$
$$1.09 = m(0.2) + \log b$$
$$m = 2.0$$
$$\log b = 0.69, \text{ or}$$
$$b = 4.9$$

Table 5.5

Time t, s	Distance s, m	Log t	Log s
0	0		
1	4.9	0.0000	0.6902
2	19.6	0.3010	1.2923
3	44.1	0.4771	1.6444
4	78.4	0.6021	1.8943
5	122.5	0.6990	2.0881
6	176.4	0.7782	2.2465

Figure 5.26

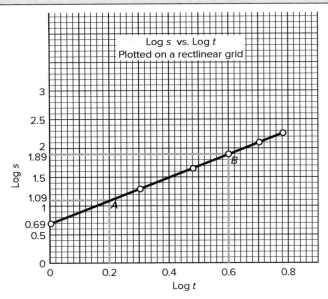

Log-log on rectangular grid paper.

As examination of Figure 5.26 shows, the value of log b (0.69) can be read from the graph where log $t = 0$. This, of course, is where $t = 1$ and is the y intercept for log-log plots.

The general equation can then be written as

$$s = 4.9t^{2.0}$$

or

$$s = 1/2gt^2,$$

where $g = 9.8$ *m/s*^{2}

Note: One obvious inconvenience is the necessity of finding logarithms of each variable and then plotting the logs of these variables. This step is not necessary since functional paper is commercially available with log x and log y scales already constructed. Log-log paper allows the variables themselves to be plotted directly without the need of computing the log of each value.

2. An alternate method for the solution of this problem is as follows:

In the preceding part, once the general form of the equation is determined (Equation 5.2), the data can be plotted directly on log-log paper. Since the resulting curve is a straight line, the method of selected points can be used directly (see Figure 5.27).

The log form of the equation is again used:

$$\log s = m \log t + \log b$$

Select points A and B on the line:

$$A(1.5, 11)$$
$$B(6, 175)$$

Figure 5.27

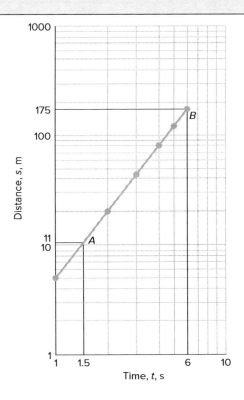

Log-log paper.

Substitute the values into the general equation $\log s = m \log t + \log b,$ taking careful note that the numbers are the variables and *not* the logs of the variables.

$$\log 175 = m \log 6 + \log b$$
$$\log 11 = m \log 1.5 + \log b$$

Again, solving these two equations simultaneously results in the following approximate values for the constants *b* and *m:*

$$b = 4.8978 \cong 4.9$$
$$m = 1.9957 \cong 2.0$$

Identical conclusions can be reached:

$$s = 1/2gt^2$$

This time, however, one can use functional scales rather than calculate the log of each number.

3. A computer-assisted alternate:

The data set can be entered into a spreadsheet, and the software will provide an identical solution. Figure 5.28 illustrates software that provides a plot of data on rectangular paper, including the equation of the line. Figure 5.29 is an example of the data plotted on log-log paper with the software providing the equation.

Figure 5.28

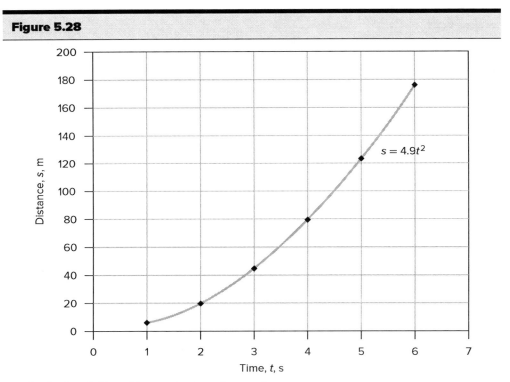

Graph of a free-falling object on rectangular graph paper.

Figure 5.29

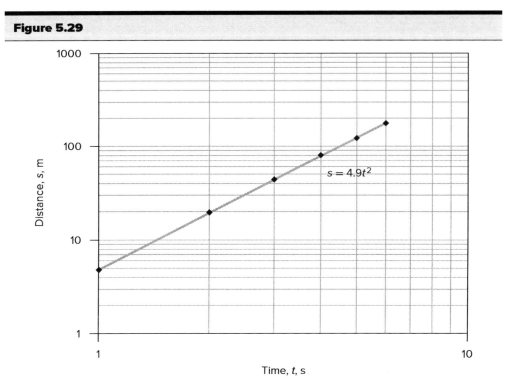

Graph of a free-falling object on log-log paper.

5.9 Empirical Equations: Exponential Curves

Suppose your data do not plot as a straight line on rectangular coordinate paper or the line is not approximately straight on log-log paper. Without experience in analyzing experimental data, you may feel lost about how to proceed. Normally, when experiments are conducted, you have an idea as to how the parameters are related and you are merely trying to quantify that relationship. If you plot your data on semilog graph paper and it produces a reasonably straight line, then it has the general form

$$y = be^{mx} \qquad\qquad (5.3)$$

Example problem 5.3   Vehicle fuel consumption is recorded as shown in Table 5.6. Determine the best-fit equation for the data by the method of selected points and by the method of least squares.

Procedure

1. The data (Table 5.6) when plotted on semilog paper produce the graph shown as Figure 5.30. To determine the constants in the equation $y = be^{mx}$, write it in linear form, either as

    $$\log y = mx \log e + \log b$$

or

$$\ln y = mx + \ln b$$

The method of selected points can now be employed for $\ln FC = mV + \ln b$ (choosing the natural log form). Points $A(15,33)$ and $B(65,470)$ are carefully selected on the line, so they must satisfy the equation. Substituting the values of V and FC at points A and B, we get

$$\ln 470 = 65\, m + \ln b$$

and

$$\ln 33 = 15\, m + \ln b$$

Solving simultaneously for m and b, we have

$$m = 0.0529$$

Table 5.6

Velocity V, m/s	Fuel Consumption (FC), mm³/s
10	25.2
20	44.6
30	71.7
40	115
50	202
60	367
70	608

Figure 5.30

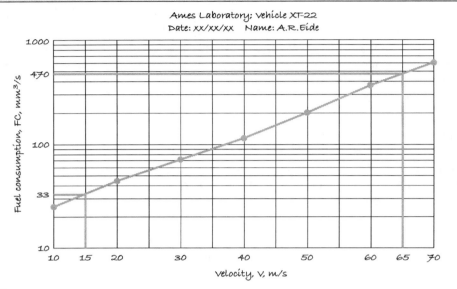

Ames Laboratory; Vehicle XT-22
Date: xx/xx/xx   Name: A.R.Eide

Semilog paper.

and

$$b = 14.8$$

The desired equation then is determined to be $FC = 15e^{(0.05V)}$. This determination can be checked by choosing a third point, substituting the value for V, and solving for FC.

2. A computer-assisted alternate:

The data set can be entered into a spreadsheet, and the software will provide an identical solution. Figure 5.31 illustrates software that provides a plot of data on rectangular paper, including the equation of the line. Figure 5.32 is an example of the data plotted on semilog paper with the software providing the equation.

Problems

5.1 The table shows data from a trial run on the Utah salt flats made by an experimental turbine-powered vehicle.

Time, t, s	Velocity, V, m/s
10.0	15.1
20.0	32.2
30.0	63.4
40.0	84.5
50.0	118.0
60.0	139.0

(*a*) Plot the data on rectangular graph paper.
(*b*) Determine the equation of the line using the method of selected points.
(*c*) Determine the equation of the line using computer-assisted methods.
(*d*) Interpret the slope of the line.

Figure 5.31

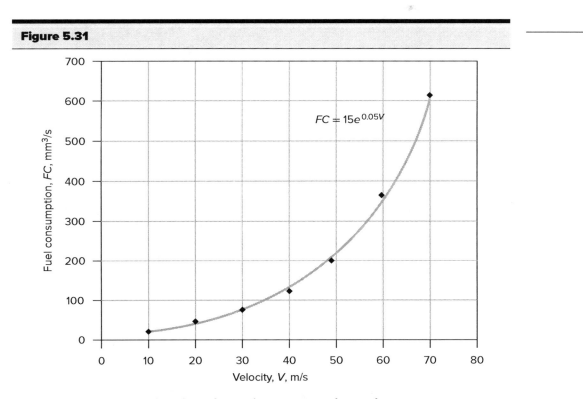

Graph of the fuel consumption of a rocket engine on rectangular graph paper.

Figure 5.32

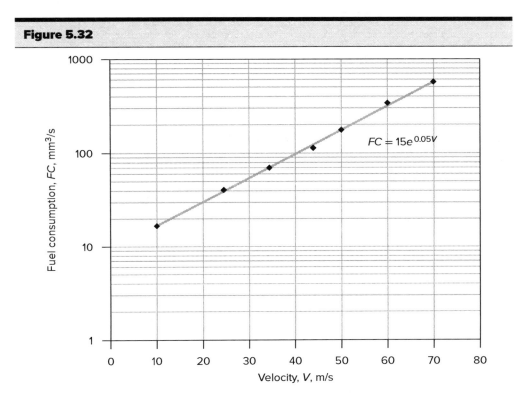

Graph of the fuel consumption of a rocket engine on semilog paper.

5.2   The table lists the values of velocity recorded on a ski jump in Colorado this past winter.

Time, t, s	Velocity, V, m/s
1.0	5.3
4.0	18.1
7.0	26.9
10.0	37.0
14.0	55.2

(a) Plot the data on rectangular graph paper.
(b) Determine the equation of the line using the method of selected points.
(c) Determine the equation of the line using computer-assisted methods.
(d) Give the average acceleration.

5.3   Below is a collection of data for an iron-constantan thermocouple. Temperature is in degrees Celsius, and the electromotive force (*emf*) is in millivolts.

(a) Plot the graph using rectangular graph paper with temperature as the independent variable.
(b) Using the method of selected points, find the equation of the line.
(c) Using computer-assisted methods, find the equation of the line.

Temperature, T, °C	Voltage, *emf*, mV
50.0	2.6
100.0	6.7
150.0	8.8
200.0	11.2
300.0	17.0
400.0	22.5
500.0	26.0
600.0	32.5
700.0	37.7
800.0	41.0
900.0	48.0
1 000.0	55.2

5.4   There are design specifications for the minimum sight distance (distance to see an approaching vehicle measured along the roadway from the intersection of the two roadways) that a driver stopped at a stop sign must have to safely enter a roadway where vehicles do not stop. Values in the table below are for safe entry to *cross* the roadway (not to turn onto the other roadway but to cross) where vehicles do not stop.

Major roadway design speed, DS, mph	Sight distance, SD, ft
25	240
30	290
35	335
40	385
45	430
50	480
60	575
65	625
70	670
75	720

(a) Plot a graph with design speed as the independent variable.
(b) Determine the equation of the relationship using the method of selected points.

(c) Determine the equation of the relationship using computer-assisted methods.

(d) Predict the slight distance required at 55 mph.

5.5 A spring was tested in Chicago last Thursday. The test of the spring, X-19, produced the following data:

Deflection, D, mm	Load, L, kN
2.25	35.0
12.0	80.0
20.0	120.0
28.0	160.0
35.0	200.0
45.0	250.0
55.0	300.0

(a) Plot the data on rectangular graph paper and determine the equation that expresses the deflection to be expected under a given load. Use both the method of selected points and computer-assisted methods.

(b) Predict the load required to produce a deflection of 75 mm.

(c) What load would be expected to produce a deflection of 120 mm?

5.6 An Acme furnace was tested 45 days ago in your hometown to determine the heat generated, expressed in thousands of British thermal units per cubic foot of furnace volume at varying temperatures. The results are shown in the following table:

Heat released, H, 10^3 Btu/ft^3	Temperature, T, °F
0.200	172
0.600	241
2.00	392
4.00	483
8.00	608
20.00	812
40.00	959
80.00	1 305

(a) Plot the data on log-log paper with temperature as the independent variable.

(b) Using the method of selected points, determine the equation that best fits the data.

(c) Using computer-assisted methods, plot the graph and determine the equation of the line.

5.7 The capacity of a 20 cm screw conveyor that is moving dry corn is expressed in liters per second and the conveyor speed in revolutions per minute. A test was conducted in Rock Island, IL, on conveyor model JD172 last week. The results of the test are given below:

Capacity, C, L/s	Angular velocity, V, r/min
3.01	10.0
6.07	21.0
15.0	58.2
30.0	140.6
50.0	245.0
80.0	410.0
110.0	521.0

(a) Plot the data on log-log paper with angular velocity as the independent variable.

(b) Determine the equation that expresses capacity as a function of angular velocity using the method of selected points.

(c) Repeat (a) and (b) using computer-assisted methods.

5.8 Electrical resistance for a given material can be a function of both area/unit thickness and material temperature. Holding temperature constant, a range of areas are tested to determine resistance. The measured resistance recorded in the table is expressed in milliohms per meter of conductor length.

(a) Plot the data on rectangular graph paper with area as the independent variable.
(b) Plot the data on log-log graph paper with area as the independent variable.
(c) Plot the data on semilog graph paper with area as the independent variable.
(d) Compute equations from these three plots using the method of selected points.
(e) Plot and find equations for parts (a), (b), and (c) using computer-assisted methods.
(f) What would be the best curve fit for this application?

Area, A, mm^2	Resistance, R, mV/m
0.05	500
0.1	260
0.2	165
0.5	80
1.0	58
3.0	22
5.0	15
10	9.0

5.9 The area of a circle can be expressed by the formula $A = \pi R^2$. If the radius varies from 0.5 to 5 cm, perform the following:

(a) Construct a table of radius versus area mathematically. Use radius increments of 0.5 cm.
(b) Construct a second table of log R versus log A.
(c) Plot the values from (a) on log-log paper and determine the equation of the line.
(d) Plot the values from (b) on rectangular paper and determine the equation of the line.
(e) Repeat parts (c) and (d) using computer-assisted methods.

5.10 The volume of a sphere is $V = 4/3\pi r^3$.

(a) Prepare a table of volume versus radius allowing the radius to vary from 2.0 to 10.0 cm in 1 cm increments.
(b) Plot a graph on log-log paper showing the relation of volume to radius using the values from the table in part (a) with radius as the independent variable.
(c) Verify the equation given above by the method of selected points.
(d) Repeat parts (b) and (c) using computer-assisted methods.

5.11 A 90° triangular weir is commonly used to measure flow rate in a stream. Data on the discharge through the weir were collected and recorded as shown below:

Height, h, m	Discharge, Q, m^3/s
1	1.5
2	8
3	22
4	45
5	78
6	124
7	182
8	254

(a) Plot the data on log-log paper with height as the independent variable.
(b) Determine the equation of the line using the method of selected points.
(c) Plot and determine the equation using computer-assisted methods.

5.12 According to government statistics, the average selling price of a home in the United States varied as follows:

Year, Y	Price, P, $
1965	21 500
1970	56 600
1975	42 600
1980	76 400
1985	100 800
1990	149 800
1995	158 700
2000	207 000
2005	292 200
2010	265 500

(a) Plot the data on rectangular graph paper and find the best equation using the method of selected points.

(b) Plot the data on semilog paper and find the best equation using the method of selected points.

(c) Prepare linear and semilog plots using a computer-assisted method and determine the best equations for each.

(d) Which curve fit, linear or exponential, best fits these data?

5.13 The density of air is known to change with the temperature of the air. In a lab test, the following data were measured and recorded:

Temperature, T, K	Density, D, kg/m^3
100	3.5
200	1.7
400	0.85
600	0.6
800	0.45
1 000	0.35
1 200	0.3
1 400	0.25
1 600	0.2

(a) Plot these data on linear, semilog, and log-log paper with temperature as the independent variable.

(b) Determine the equation that best fits these data using the method of selected points.

(c) Repeat parts (a) and (b) using a computer-assisted method.

5.14 Voltage across a capacitor during discharge was recorded as a function of time as shown below:

Time, t, s	Voltage, V, V
6	98
10	62
17	23
25	9.5
32	3.5
38	1.9
42	1.3

(*a*) Plot the data on semilog paper with time as the independent variable.

(*b*) Determine the equation of the line best representing the points using the method of selected points.

(*c*) Repeat parts (*a*) and (*b*) using a computer-assisted method.

5.15 When a capacitor is being discharged, the current flows until the voltage across the capacitor is zero. This current flow, when measured as a function of time, resulted in the data given in the following table:

Time, t, s	Current, I, A
0.1	1.81
0.2	1.64
0.3	1.48
0.4	1.34
0.5	1.21
1.0	0.73

(*a*) Plot the data on semilog paper with time as the independent variable.

(*b*) Determine the equation of the line best representing the points using the method of selected points.

(*c*) Repeat parts (*a*) and (*b*) using a computer-assisted method.

5.16 The density of water vapor in air changes rapidly with the change in air temperature. Data were recorded from an experimental test and are shown in the following table:

Air Temperature, T, K	Water Vapor Density, D, kg/m^3
400	0.55
450	0.49
500	0.44
550	0.39
600	0.36
650	0.34
700	0.33
750	0.29
800	0.27

(*a*) Plot the data on linear, semilog, and log-log paper with the air temperature as the independent variable.

(*b*) By the method of selected points, find the best equation relating water vapor density to air temperature.

(*c*) Repeat parts (*a*) and (*b*) using a computer-assisted method.

5.17 All materials are elastic to some extent. It is desirable that a part compresses when a load is applied to assist in making an airtight seal (e.g., a jar lid). The results in the following table are from a test conducted at the Smith Test Labs in Seattle on a material known as Zecon 5.

Pressure, P, MPa	Relative compression, R, %
1.12	27.3
3.08	37.6
5.25	46.0
8.75	50.6
12.3	56.1
16.1	59.2
30.2	65.0

(a) Plot the data on semilog and log-log paper with pressure as the independent variable.

(b) Using the method of selected points, determine the best equation to fit these data.

(c) Using a computer-assisted method, repeat the steps above.

(d) What pressure would cause compression of 10 percent?

5.18 The rate of absorption of radiation by metal plates varies with the plate thickness and the nature of the source of radiation. A test was conducted at Ames Labs on October 11, 2005, using a Geiger counter and a constant source of radiation; the results are shown in the following table:

Plate thickness, W, mm	Counter, C, counts per second
0.20	5 500
5.00	3 720
10.0	2 550
20.0	1 320
27.5	720
32.5	480

(a) Plot the data on semilog graph paper with plate thickness as the independent variable.

(b) Find the equation of the relationship between the parameters using the method of selected points.

(c) Repeat parts (a) and (b) using a computer-assisted method.

(d) What would you expect the counts per second to be for a 2 in. thick plate of the metal used in the test?

5.19 It is expected that power functions represent the surface area and volume of a certain geometric shape. The values of the surface area and volume are given in the table below:

Radius, R, ft	Surface Area, SA, ft²	Volume, V, ft³
1	12.6	4.19
2	50.3	33.5
3	113	113
4	200	268
5	314	524
6	450	905
7	616	1 437
8	800	2 145
9	1 018	3 054
10	1 257	4 189

(a) Using a computer-assisted method, determine the equations of *SA* and *V* as functions of *R*.

(b) What is the geometric shape?

5.20 According to the United States Department of Labor, the Consumer Price Index for several household expense items are shown in the following table. The time period 1982–1984 is established as the basis with an index of 100.

Year	Food	Apparel	Housing	Transportation	Medical Care	Total
1995	148.4	132.0	148.5	139.1	220.5	152.4
1996	153.3	131.7	152.8	143.0	228.2	156.9
1997	157.3	132.9	156.8	144.3	234.6	160.5
1998	160.7	133.0	160.4	141.6	242.1	163.0
1999	164.1	131.3	165.9	144.4	250.6	166.6
2000	167.8	129.6	169.6	153.3	260.8	172.2
2001	173.1	127.3	176.4	154.3	272.8	177.1
2002	176.2	124.0	180.3	152.9	285.6	179.9
2003	180.0	120.9	184.8	157.6	297.1	184.0
2004	186.2	120.4	189.5	163.1	310.1	188.9

(a) Using a computer-assisted method, plot all of these data on the same graph. Be sure to format the graph according to chapter guidelines.

(b) Describe in a couple of paragraphs what the plotted information suggests to you.

5.21 Data from the Federal Reserve, the average prime interest rate, the average home mortgage rate, and the average 6-month CD rate for the years 1972 to 2009 are shown in the table below:

Year	Ave. prime rate, %	Ave. mortgage rate, %	Ave. 6-month CD rate, %
1972	5.25	7.38	5.01
1973	8.03	8.04	9.05
1974	10.81	9.19	10.02
1975	7.86	9.04	6.9
1976	6.84	8.86	5.63
1977	6.83	8.84	5.91
1978	9.06	9.63	8.6
1979	12.67	11.19	11.42
1980	15.26	13.77	12.94
1981	18.87	16.63	15.79
1982	14.85	16.08	12.57
1983	10.79	13.23	9.28
1984	12.04	13.87	10.71
1985	9.93	12.42	8.24
1986	8.33	10.18	6.5
1987	8.21	10.2	7.01
1988	9.32	10.34	7.91
1989	10.87	10.32	9.08
1990	10.01	10.13	8.17
1991	8.46	9.25	5.91
1992	6.25	8.4	3.76
1993	6	7.33	3.28
1994	7.15	8.35	4.96
1995	8.83	7.95	5.98
1996	8.27	7.8	5.47
1997	8.44	7.6	5.73
1998	8.35	6.94	5.44
1999	8	7.43	5.46
2000	9.23	8.06	6.59
2001	6.91	6.97	3.66
2002	4.67	6.54	1.81
2003	4.12	5.82	1.17
2004	4.34	5.84	1.74
2005	6.19	5.86	3.73
2006	7.96	6.41	5.24
2007	8.05	6.34	5.23
2008	5.09	6.04	3.14
2009	3.25	5.04	0.87

(a) Using a computer-assisted method, plot all of these data on the same graph. Be sure to format the graph according to chapter guidelines.

(b) In a short narrative, describe in general terms the relationship among the three interest rates as you see it from your graph.

Source: http://www.federalreserve.gov/releases/h15/data.htm

5.22 Performance data for an experimental truck engine were recorded in a recent laboratory test as shown in the table below:

Engine speed, R, rpm	Rated power output, P, bhp	Full load torque, T, ft-lb	Fuel consumption, F, gal/hr
800	148	959	3.2
900	203	1 155	5.3
1 000	249	1 341	6.3
1 100	330	1 601	8.4
1 200	414	1 762	10.3
1 300	499	2 012	13.5
1 400	545	2 072	16.6
1 500	589	2 049	19.2
1 600	605	2 028	22.9
1 700	644	1 981	27.3
1 800	670	1 919	34.1

As a team

(a) Plot each data set on linear, semilog, and log-log graph paper with engine speed as the independent variable.

(b) Using the method of selected points, compute the best equation fit to these data.

(c) Repeat parts (a) and (b) using computer-assisted methods.

(d) Discuss your results in a form that could be understood by other engineering students who have not solved this problem.

Hint: For data that plot as a convex upward curve, try reversing the independent and dependent variables in a plot before applying a curve fitting method. Once the equation has been found, simply solve for the desired dependent variable as a function of the independent variable.

5.23 As a team, conduct an Internet search for data in a technical field of interest to your team that can be graphed by a computer-assisted method. Find a data set (or sets) of a size that would be difficult to enter by hand, download the data, and directly enter them into your graphing software.

For each set, prepare a graph that follows engineering graphing standards as closely as your software allows. Within the graph, demonstrate the following:

▧ Multiple curves on a graph complete with a legend
▧ Two separate y-axes

Provide documentation to include:

▧ Explanation and interpretation of the data you selected
▧ Source of data
▧ Hard copy from your software with data and graph

CHAPTER **6**

Engineering Measurements and Estimations

Chapter Objectives

When you complete your study of this chapter, you will be able to:

- Determine the number of significant digits in a measurement
- Perform numerical calculations with measured quantities and express the answer with the appropriate number of significant digits
- Define accuracy and precision in measurements
- Define systematic and random errors and explain how they occur in measurements
- Solve problems involving estimations of the required data and assumptions to enable a solution
- Develop and present problem solutions, involving finding or estimating the necessary data, that enable others to understand your method of solution and to determine the validity of the numerical work

6.1 Introduction

The 19th-century physicist Lord Kelvin stated that knowledge and understanding are not of high quality unless the information can be expressed in numbers. Numbers are the operating medium for most engineering functions. In order to perform analysis and design, engineers must be able to measure physical quantities, for example, length, mass, temperature, and express these measurements in numerical form. Furthermore, engineers must have confidence that the measurements and subsequent calculations and decisions made based on the measurements are reasonable.

In this chapter, we will describe how to properly use measurements (numbers) in engineering calculations. In the laboratories that are required in your specific engineering discipline, you will gain experience in selecting and properly using appropriate measuring devices for physical properties.

6.2 Measurements: Accuracy and Precision

In measurements, "accuracy" and "precision" have different meanings and cannot be used interchangeably. *Accuracy* is a measure of the nearness of a value to the correct or true value. *Precision* refers to the repeatability of a measurement, that is, how close successive measurements are to each other. Figure 6.1 illustrates accuracy and precision of the results of four dart throwers. Thrower (a) is both inaccurate and imprecise

Figure 6.1

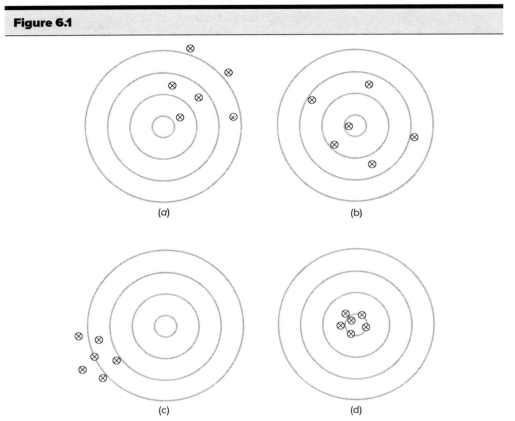

(a)   (b)

(c)   (d)

Illustration of the difference between accuracy and precision in physical measurements.

because the results are away from the bull's-eye (accuracy) and widely scattered (precision). Thrower (b) is accurate because the throws are evenly distributed about the desired result but imprecise because of the wide scatter. Thrower (c) is precise with the tight cluster of throws but inaccurate because the results are away from the desired bull's-eye. Finally, thrower (d) demonstrates accuracy and precision with tight cluster of throws around the center of the target. Throwers (a), (b), and (c) can improve their performance by analyzing the causes for the errors. Body position, arm motion, and release point could cause deviation from the desired result.

Consider for a moment that Figure 6.1 show results of shooters at a rifle range. The results reveal a tendency of results to shift in a particular direction. For example, target (c) results show a tight pattern but a definite shift to the lower left. This shift, called a bias, can be corrected by adjusting the rifle sight so the results appear more like target (d).

As engineers perform computations in analysis and design, the accuracy and precision of data gathered for the computations must be ascertained. For a quantity that is measured by a physical instrument, the exact numerical value of the quantity is likely to remain unknown. Therefore, the measurement must be recorded with the known limitations in accuracy and precision taken into account. To do this engineers apply accepted practices and rules and carefully note the conditions under which the data were obtained. The practices and rules for performing numerical computations are discussed in Section 6.3. A brief discussion of the identification of errors in measurements is found in Section 6.4.

6.3   Measurements: Significant Digits

Numbers used for calculation purposes in engineering design and analysis may be integers (exact) or real (exact or approximate). For example, six one-dozen cartons of eggs include a countable number of eggs, exactly 72. There are 2.54 cm in one inch, an example of an exact real number. Thus if the conversion of inches to centimeters is required in a calculation, 2.54 is not a contributing factor to the precision of the result of the calculation. The ratio of the circumference of a circle to its diameter, π, is an approximate real number that may be written as 3.14, 3.142, 3.14159 . . . , depending on the precision required in a numerical calculation.

Any physical measurement that is not a countable number will be approximate. Errors are likely to be present regardless of the precautions used when making the measurement. Let us look at measuring the length of the metal bar in Figure 6.2 with a scale graduated in tenths of inches. At first glance it is obvious that the bar is between 2 and 3 in. in length. We could write down that the bar is 2.5 ± 0.5 in. long. Upon closer inspection we note the bar is between 2.6 and 2.7 in. in length, or 2.65 ±0.05 in. What value would we use in a computation? 2.64? 2.65? 2.66? We might select 2.64 as the "best" measurement, realizing that the third digit in our answer is doubtful and therefore our measurement must be considered approximate.

It is clear that a method of expressing results and measurements is needed that will convey how "good" these numbers are. The use of significant digits gives us this capability without resorting to the more rigorous approach of computing an estimated percentage error to be specified with each numerical result or measurement. Before we introduce significant digits, it is necessary to discuss the presentation of numerical values in formats that leave no doubts in interpretation.

The following are accepted conventions for the presentation of numbers in engineering work:

1. For numbers less than one, a zero is written in front of the decimal point to omit any possible errors due to copy processes or careless reading. Therefore, we write 0.345 and not .345.
2. A space, not a comma, is used to divide numbers of three orders of magnitude or more. This convention follows the International System of Units (SI) rather than a culturally based system. We write 4 567.8 instead of 4,567.8 and 0.678 91 instead of 0.678,91. The SI notation removes possible confusion in the use of the decimal point and comma. For example, 4 567.8 would be presented as 4,567.8 in the US and UK systems, and as 4.567,8 in Continental Europe.

Figure 6.2

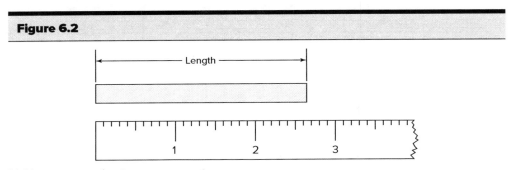

Making an approximate measurement.

3. For very large or very small numbers we use scientific notation to reduce the unwieldy nature of these numbers. For example, supercomputer calculating rates are compared by using the Linpack benchmark performance criteria. One of the criteria used by Linpack is the solving of a very large set of simultaneous linear equations. In the 2014 rankings of supercomputers, the Chinese computer Tianhe-2 (Milky Way-2) was benchmarked at 33 860 000 000 000 000 flops/s. The unit flops/s stands for *fl*oating-point *op*eration*s* per *s*econd, which is computer terminology for calculations using real numbers. In scientific notation this number would be 33.86×10^{15}, an obviously more compact representation. Scientific notation is of great assistance in the determination and representation of significant digits.

Another convenient method of representing measurements is with prefix names that denote multipliers by factors of 10. Table 6.1 illustrates decimal multipliers and their corresponding prefixes and symbols. Thus the Tianhe-2 performance level may also be stated as 33.86 petaflops/s or 33.86 Pflops/s. The highest computational performance in the world in 2009 was established by the Jaguar, a Cray XT5-HE Opteron system, measured at 1 759 Tflops/s or 1.759 Pflops/s. Note that the Tianhe-2 represents an order of magnitude increase in computational performance in a five year period.

The use of prefixes enables us to express any measurement as a number between 0.1 and 1 000 with a corresponding prefix applied to the unit. For example, it is clearer to the reader if the distance between two cities is expressed as 35 kilometers (35 km) rather than 35 000 meters (35 000 m). More on prefixes may be found in the Chapter 7 discussion of the International System of Units (SI).

A *significant digit,* or *significant figure,* is defined as any digit used in writing a number, *except* those zeros that are used only for location of the decimal point or those zeros that do not have any nonzero digit on their left. When you read the number 0.001 5, only the digits 1 and 5 are significant, since the three zeros have no nonzero digit to their left. We would say this number has two significant figures. If the number is written 0.001 50, it contains three significant figures; the rightmost zero is significant.

Table 6.1 Decimal Multiples

Multiplier	Prefix name	Symbol
10^{18}	exa	E
10^{15}	peta	P
10^{12}	tera	T
10^{9}	giga	G
10^{6}	*mega	M
10^{3}	*kilo	k
10^{2}	hecto	h
10^{1}	deka	da
10^{-1}	deci	d
10^{-2}	centi	c
10^{-3}	*milli	m
10^{-6}	*micro	μ
10^{-9}	nano	n
10^{-12}	pico	p
10^{-15}	femto	f
10^{-18}	atto	a

*Most often used.

Figure 6.3

Quantity	Number of Significant Figures
4784	4
36	2
60	1 or 2
600	1, 2, or 3
6.00×10^2	3
31.72	4
30.02	4
46.0	3
0.02	1
0.020	2
600.00	5

Numbers 10 or larger that are not written in scientific notation and that are not counts (exact values) can cause difficulties in interpretation when zeros are present. For example, 2 000 could contain one, two, three, or four significant digits; it is not clear which. If you write the number in scientific notation as 2.000×10^3, then clearly four significant digits are intended. If you want to show only two significant digits, you would write 2.0×10^3. It is our recommendation that if uncertainty results from using standard decimal notation, you switch to scientific notation so your reader can clearly understand your intent. Figure 6.3 shows the number of significant figures for several quantities.

When performing an engineering analysis, physical measurements, exact numbers, real numbers, and unit conversions will be involved. Consider the simple formula for the area of a circle, $A = \pi D^2/4$.

If you measure the diameter, D, with a tape measure, the number of significant figures for the area A is determined from D since π can be expressed to a precision greater than D (3.14159...) and 4 is an exact number. You must establish a reasonable number of significant based on the context of the measurements involved in the analysis and your experience. You should again read the first two paragraphs of this section to reinforce this concept.

When an instrument, such as an engineer's scale, analog thermometer, or fuel gauge, is read, the last digit will normally be an estimate. That is, the instrument is read by estimating between the smallest graduations on the scale to get the final digit. In Figure 6.4a, the reading is between 1.2 and 1.3, or 1.25 ± 0.05. For calculation purposes we might select 1.27 as a best value, with the 7 being a doubtful digit. **It is standard practice to count one doubtful digit as significant, thus the 1.27 reading has three significant figures.** Similarly, the thermometer reading in Figure 6.4b is noted as 52.5° $\pm$ 0.5, and we estimate a best value of 52.8° with the 8 being doubtful. In like fashion, the length of the metal bar in Figure 6.2 was expressed as 2.64 with the 4 being doubtful and the reported answer would have three significant figures.

In Figure 6.4c, the graduations create a more difficult task for reading a fuel level. Each graduation is one-sixth of a full tank. The reading is between 1/6 and 2/6 full, or $3/12 \pm 1/12$. How many significant figures are there? If we convert the reading to 0.25 ± 0.0833, a "best" estimate might be 0.30. In any case you cannot justify more than one significant figure and the answer would be expressed as 0.3. The difficulty in this example is not the significant figures but the scale of the fuel gauge. It is meant to convey

Figure 6.4

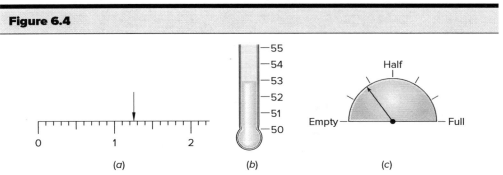

(a)   *(b)*   *(c)*

Reading graduations on instruments will include a doubtful or estimated value.

a general impression of the fuel level and not a numerically significant value. Therefore, the selection of the instrument is an important factor in physical measurements.

Calculators operate with base 10 numbers and maintain integers in exact form up to the capacity of the machine. Fractions may or may not be represented exactly. For example, 1/8 would be represented as 0.125, an exact value. The fraction, 1/3, would be a repeating decimal 0.33333...If you add this repeating decimal several times in a running total, a truncation error will cause the sum to be less than the true value. It needs to be remembered that truncation errors are possible and that some answers may not be accurate to the desired precision.

Computers operate with base 2 (binary) numbers and also maintain integers in exact form up to the capacity of the machine. Fractions in binary form are exact only if the denominator has 2 as the only prime factor. For example, 1/8 in binary is represented exactly as 0.001 $(0 \times 2^{-1} + 0 \times 2^{-2} + 0 \times 2^{-3})$. However 1/3 is represented as a repeating decimal 0.010101...$(0 \times 2^{-1} + 1 \times 2^{-2} + 0 \times 2^{-3} + 1 \times 2^{-4} + 0 \times 2^{-5} + 1 \times 2^{-6}...) = 1/4 + 1/16 + 1/64... = 0.328125 + ...$ Again truncation errors may occur and affect the precision of a computation.

As you perform arithmetic operations using a calculator or computer it is important to not lose the significance of the numerical values you input and assume precision that does not exist. In practice you should set up the problem to be a series of operations (algorithm) leading to a final result. **In engineering problem solving it is standard practice to show appropriate steps leading to the final result. For checking work and assisting those persons reviewing your work, you may output intermediate computations with a reasonable number of significant figures. However, rounded intermediate results are not to be used in subsequent computations.**

When the final result is displayed round it to the predetermined number of significant figures. The rounding rule is: Round a value to the proper number of significant figures, *increase the last digit retained by 1 if the first figure dropped is 5 or greater.* This is the rule normally built into a calculator display control or a control language.

Examples
a.   23.650 rounds to 23.7 for three significant figures.
b.   0.014 3 rounds to 0.014 for two significant figures.
c.   827.48 rounds to 827.5 or 827 for four and three significant digits, respectively.

(*Note:* You must decide the number of significant figures before you round. For example, rounding 827.48 to three significant figures yields 827. However, if you first round to four figures, obtaining 827.5, and then round that number to three figures, the result would be 828—not correct according to the rule.)

It is important to realize that all measurements of physical quantities have a certain amount of uncertainty (error) associated with them. This error must be made as small as possible. Therefore, we must determine, as best we can, what errors are present and account for them in the measurement. Consider the thermometer in Figure 6.4b. After we make the reading of 52.8°, can we say for sure that this is the true temperature with the 8 being a doubtful digit? The answer is no. For example, what if the thermometer has not been calibrated properly and reads high by a degree or two? Maybe the thermometer has been smudged with oil, dirt, or grease and a mistake is made in reading the calibrations. Perhaps the sensor connecting the environment being measured to the thermometer is not connected properly. These and other known error possibilities must be accounted for to obtain an acceptable accuracy in the reading. However, even if you carefully account for possible errors, the measurement will still have some error present. Depending upon the level of accuracy and preciseness required in the measurement, further effort may be needed in error determination. To clarify the presence of error, measurements can be expressed in two parts: (1) a number representing a mean value of the physical quantity measured and (2) an amount of doubt (error) in this mean value. The amount of doubt (error) provides the accuracy of the measurement. For example, our thermometer reading in Figure 6.4b could be expressed as 52.5 ± 0.5, which brackets the upper and lower limits of the measurement based on the calibration of the instrument. To perform computations with measurements we carefully estimate a "best" value of 52.8 with the 8 being in doubt. You should note that error (deviation from the true temperature) is still present and that the true temperature is not known exactly.

A common application of measurement error is in pressure gauges. Suppose a gauge on an air tank is labeled $\pm 2\%$ at 150 lb/in.^{2}. The range of the gauge error would be $(0.02)(150) = 3.0$ lb/in.^{2}. Therefore, a reading of 190 would indicate that the true pressure falls between 187 and 193 lb/in.^{2}.

Errors can be classified into two broad categories for analysis: systematic and random.

6.4.1 Systematic Errors

A systematic error tends to shift a measurement consistently in the same direction from the true value. This indicates a lack of accuracy. The error is defined as

$$\text{Error} = \text{measured value} - \text{true value} \qquad (6.1)$$

Examples of systematic errors include failure to account for some external effect on the measuring instrument (e.g., temperature) and improper use of the instrument (e.g., allowing sag due to gravity in a long measuring tape). Systematic errors must be accounted for as much as possible in any situation. The error can be expressed as a fraction or percent.

$$\text{Fractional error} = \frac{\text{error}}{\text{true value}} = \frac{\text{measured value} - \text{true value}}{\text{true value}} \qquad (6.2)$$

6.4.2 Random Errors

Random errors are those that fluctuate from one measurement to another for the same instrument. One cause is the sensitivity of the instrument. A small change in the quantity measured may not be picked up by the instrument. Such errors are usually distributed equally around the true value. Another random error may occur when an instrument is read by more than one person. Consider a water barometer that measures atmospheric pressure. Close inspection of the water level shows a meniscus which can easily result in different readings from several observers. These readings will very likely divide above and below a mean, or true, value. Statistical analysis is used to provide some insight into random errors. Chapters 10 and 11 provide an introduction to the statistical concepts of central tendency which are a part of the analysis of random errors.

6.5 Estimations

Engineers strive for a high level of precision in their work. However, it is also important to be aware of an acceptable precision and the time and cost of attaining it. There are many instances where an engineer is expected to estimate the result to a problem with reasonable accuracy but under tight time and cost constraints. To do this engineers rely on their basic understanding of the problem under discussion coupled with their previous experience. This knowledge and experience is what distinguishes an "estimation" from a "guess." If greater accuracy is needed, the initial estimation can be refined when time, funds, and the necessary additional data for refining the result are available.

Initial estimates may be in error by perhaps 10 to 20 percent or even more. The accuracy of these estimates depends strongly on what reference materials we have available, how much time is allotted for the estimate, and, of course, how experienced we are with similar problems. The following example problems illustrate a good process to follow when doing an estimate. Begin by stating clearly what the problem is then list the known data, assumptions, and procedure you are going to follow. Then perform the necessary calculations. Complete your work by stating conclusions tempered with limitations on your results.

Example Problem 6.1   Between her freshman and sophomore years of engineering school, Cara obtained a summer job in her home city located in an upper Midwestern state. Her supervisor, the city street maintenance director, asked her to estimate the tons of sand in a pile stored near the city maintenance shed. The director needed the data, along with a justification of the estimate, within the hour in order to complete his winter street maintenance report for the City Council meeting that evening. The sand was needed for the streets during icing conditions.

Discussion   Prior to leaving for the maintenance shed, Cara formulated the problem in her mind. The pile of sand would of course be cone-shaped. She would need to find the volume and that would require knowledge of the base diameter and height of the cone. She could estimate the diameter by walking around the base (circumference) with carefully measured steps. She went to the Internet and found that the cone height could be found by knowing the base diameter and the angle between a diameter and a line drawn from one end of the diameter to the apex of the cone. This angle, called the angle of repose, is a characteristic of cone-shaped piles of loose material. For sand, Cara found the angle of repose to be 32°. When she arrived at the maintenance shed she paced off five careful steps, measured each one, and computed an average of 34 in. per step. Next she walked around the base of the cone, staying as close to the sand as possible and taking a total of 89 steps. Converting steps to feet required multiplying 89 steps by 34 in. per step and dividing by 12 in. per foot and yielded a circumference (C) of 252 feet. From knowledge of the angle of repose (θ) and the cone base diameter (D) the height of the cone (H) can be calculated.

Cara summarized her known data:

Angle of repose, $\theta = 32°$

Circumference, $C = 252$ ft

Density of sand, $\rho = 110$ lbm/ft^3

One ton $= 2\ 000$ lbm

Additional calculations:

Diameter of base, $D = \dfrac{C}{\pi} = 80.2$ ft

Radius of base, $R = \dfrac{D}{2} = 40.1$ ft

$\tan \theta = H/R$

Therefore,

$H = R\tan \theta = (40.1)(\tan 32°) = 22.0$ ft

Volume, $V = \dfrac{\pi}{3} R^2H = \dfrac{\pi}{3} (40.1)^2(22.0) = 37\ 046$ ft^3

Mass, $M = \rho V = (110)(37\ 046) = 4\ 075\ 060$ lbm

Tons $= 4\ 075\ 046/2000 = \underline{2\ 040\ \text{tons}}$

Cara reported her result to the director along with her calculations. Note that the result reported contains three significant figures which is reasonable for the solution procedure she followed. In making an estimation, the time available for obtaining an estimation must be considered along with available funds to carry out the process. Given more time Cara could have asked a colleague to accompany her to the site and the two of them could have used a long steel or cloth tape to measure the circumference more accurately. The keys to good engineering in an estimation process are understanding the problem, establishing a sound solution procedure, and using available tools to reach a solution that can be evaluated and used by the person or organization requesting the estimate.

The following example problems do not require special knowledge in any engineering area. You should focus on the process used to reach a solution and how the students clearly presented and justified their work.

Example Problem 6.2   Suppose your instructor assigns the following problem: Estimate the height of two different flagpoles on your campus. This will be done on a cloudy day so no shadow is present. The poles are in the ground (not on top of a building) and the bases of the poles are accessible. One of the poles is on level ground and you have available a carpenter's level, straight edge, protractor, and masking tape. The other pole is on ground that slopes away from the base and you have available a carpenter's level, straight edge, protractor, and a 12 ft tape. See Figure 6.5 for the response of one student (whom we will call Dave).

Discussion   To estimate the height of the flagpole on level ground, Dave recognizes that he does not have a normal distance measuring device but that he must know

Figure 6.5a

| 9 – 24 – XX | ENGR 160 FLAGPOLE PROBLEM | DAVE DOE | 1/2 |

PROBLEM 5.2

ESTIMATE THE HEIGHT OF 2 FLAGPOLES ON YOUR CAMPUS. ASSUME THE SUN IS NOT SHINING AND THAT THE BASES OF THE POLES ARE AT GROUND LEVEL (NOT ON TOP OF A BUILDING) AND THAT THE BASES ARE ACCESSIBLE.

A. DO THE ESTIMATE FOR POLE 1 WHERE YOU HAVE AVAILABLE A CARPENTER'S LEVEL, STRAIGHT EDGE, PROTRACTOR AND MASKING TAPE. POLE 1 SITS ON LEVEL GROUND.

B. FOR POLE 2, YOU HAVE A CARPENTER'S LEVEL, STRAIGHT EDGE, PROTRACTOR AND A 12' TAPE. THE GROUND AROUND POLE 2 SLOPES AWAY FROM THE BASE.

PART A

ASSUMPTIONS
1. GROUND APPROXIMATELY LEVEL AROUND FLAGPOLE BASE

PROCEDURE
- PLACE A PIECE OF MASKING TAPE AT MY HEIGHT ON THE FLAGPOLE.
- CHOOSE POSITION ABOUT FLAGPOLE HEIGHT AWAY FROM THE BASE AND MEASURE ELEVATION ANGLES TO TOP OF POLE (β) AND TO TAPE (α). SEE FIGURE 1.

DATA

1. MY HEIGHT KNOWN TO BE 6' 1",
2. LEVEL, STRAIGHT EDGE, AND PROTRACTOR CAN SERVE AS A SYSTEM FOR MEASURING ELEVATION ANGLES (FIGURE 2)
3. $\alpha = 7.5°$, $\beta = 48°$

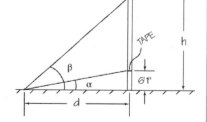

FIGURE 1

SOLUTION

$$\text{TAN } \alpha = \frac{6' 1"}{d} = \text{TAN } 7.5°$$

$$\text{TAN } \beta = \frac{h}{d} = \text{TAN } 48°$$

$$h = d \,(\text{TAN } 48°) = \left(\frac{6' 1"}{\text{TAN } 7.5°} \right) (\text{TAN } 48°) = 51.319 \text{ FT}$$

APPROXIMATE $h = 51'$

FIGURE 2

Student presentation for Example Problem 6.2.

Figure 6.5b

| | 9 – 24 – XX | ENGR 160 FLAGPOLE PROBLEM | DAVE DOE | 2/2 |

PART B

ASSUMPTIONS
1. GROUND HAS CONSTANT SLOPE FROM BASE TO MEASURING POINT.

PROCEDURES
- CHOOSE POINT ABOUT FLAGPOLE HEIGHT AWAY FROM BASE AND MEASURE ELEVATION ANGLES TO TOP(γ) AND TO BASE(Δ)
- MEASURE DISTANCE (d) FROM CHOSEN POINT TO BASE. FIGURE 3.

DATA

1. $\Delta = 3.5°$
2. $\gamma = 44°$
3. $d = 93'4''$

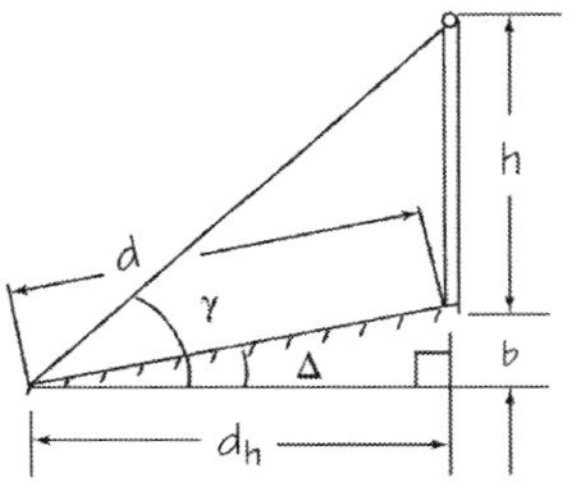

SOLUTION

$$\text{SIN } \Delta = \frac{b}{d}$$

$$b = d \text{ SIN } \Delta = (93'4'') \text{ SIN } 3.5° = 5.6979'$$

$$\text{TAN } \Delta = \frac{b}{d_h}$$

$$d_h = \frac{b}{\text{TAN } \Delta} = \frac{5.6979}{\text{TAN } 3.5°} = 93.1598'$$

$$\text{TAN } \gamma = \frac{h+b}{d_h}$$

$$h = d_h \text{ TAN } \gamma - b = (93.1598) \text{ TAN } 44° - 5.6979$$

$$= 84.265'$$

FIGURE 3

APPROXIMATE $h = 84'$

DISCUSSION/CONCLUSIONS
1. THE ACCURACY OF THE ESTIMATED HEIGHTS COULD BE VERIFIED IF AT LEAST TWO OTHER STUDENTS MADE INDEPENDENT MEASUREMENTS WITH THE SAME INSTRUMENTS
2. TOTAL TIME REQUIRED: 70 MINUTES TO SET UP THE PROCEDURE, TAKE MEASUREMENTS AND DO THE CALCULATIONS; 35 MINUTES FOR WRITEUP.

some distance in order to use trigonometry to solve the problem. He knows that he is 6'1″ tall, and he can mark that height on the pole with masking tape, which he can see from a location several feet from the pole. He can use the level, protractor, and straight edge to estimate angles from the horizontal. The distance away from the pole for measuring the angles is arbitrary, but he chooses a distance that will provide angles that are neither too large nor too small, both of which would be difficult to estimate. Then from this point on the ground he estimates the angles to his 6'1″ masking tape mark and to the top of the pole. Note that Dave has kept all of the significant figures through the calculations and rounded only at the end, reasoning that he does not want intermediate rounding to affect his answer. Based on the method used for estimation, he believes his answer is not closer than the nearest foot so he rounds to that value.

When estimating the height of the pole on sloping ground, Dave had a tape available so it was not necessary to mark his height on the pole. Again, Dave kept all significant figures through the calculation procedure and rounded only the final result.

Example Problem 6.3   A homeowner has asked you to estimate the number of gallons of paint required to prime and finish-coat her new garage. You are told that paint is applied about 0.004 in. thick on smooth surfaces. The siding is to be gray and the roof overhang and trim are to be white. See Figure 6.6 for one approach done by Laura.

Discussion   From experience, Laura knew that one coat of primer would be needed and that two coats of finish paint would be required for a lasting outcome. She also noted that the garage doors were painted by the manufacturer before installation and therefore would not need further paint. She decided to neglect the effect of windows in the garage because of their small size. She observed that the siding was a rough vertical wood type and that the soffit (underside of the roof overhang) was smooth plywood. Since she had limited experience with rough siding, she contacted a local paint retailer and learned that rough siding would take approximately three times as much primer as smooth siding and that because of the siding roughness the finish paint would cover only about 3/4 of the normal area. She carefully documented this fact in her presentation.

Laura took all necessary measurements and computed the areas that must be painted. She determined that the paint film thickness of 0.004 in. corresponds to approximately 400 ft^2/gal coverage. Like Dave in the previous example, Laura retained extra significant figures until finally rounding at the end of the estimate. In this case, except for the primer, she correctly rounded up rather than to the nearest gallon, as the paint would be purchased in whole gallons.

Example Problem 6.4   Estimate the cost of adding a single lane of concrete to Arizona Interstate 19 (I-19) in both directions from Nogales just north of the Mexican border to I-10 in Tucson. I-19 was completed in 1979 and was the first interstate highway with distance signs in metric units (meters, kilometers). Consider only the actual roadbed without a stopping lane or interchanges. Keep an accounting of the time to develop the solution and do the write-up.

Figure 6.6a

| 3 – 16 – XX | ENGR 161
PROBLEM 5.3 | LAURA LYNN | 1/2 |

PROBLEM 5.3

A HOMEOWNER HAS ASKED FOR AN ESTIMATE OF THE NUMBER OF GALLONS OF PAINT REQUIRED TO PRIME AND FINISH COAT HER NEW GARAGE. PAINT SHOULD BE APPLIED ABOUT 0.004 IN. THICK ON SMOOTH SURFACES. THE SIDING IS TO BE GRAY AND THE TRIM WHITE.

ASSUMPTIONS

1. 1 COAT OF PRIMER, 2 FINISH COATS
2. GARAGE DOORS ARE NOT PAINTED.
3. NEGLECT AREA OF SMALL WINDOWS IN GARAGE.

PROCEDURE

MEASURE GARAGE SURFACES TO OBTAIN TOTAL AREA TO BE PAINTED. OBSERVE "SMOOTHNESS" OF SIDING TO ESTIMATE PAINT COVERAGE. COMPUTE AMOUNT OF EACH TYPE OF PAINT.

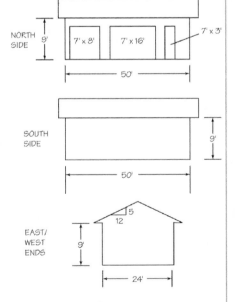

COLLECTED DATA

1. SINCE 1 GAL = 231 IN^3, PAINT THICKNESS OF 0.004 IN RESULTS IN 1 GAL COVERING $\cong$ 400 FT^2 OF SMOOTH SURFACE.
2. OVERHANGS ARE 18 IN.
3. SIDING IS OBSERVED TO BE ROUGH WOOD/VERTICAL. SOFFIT IS SMOOTH PLYWOOD.
4. LOCAL PAINT STORE REPRESENTATIVE SUGGESTED THAT PRIMER ON ROUGH WOOD SIDING COVERS ONLY 1/3 NORMAL AREA AND THAT TOP COAT COVERS ABOUT 3/4 NORMAL AREA.

SOLUTION

NORTH SIDE AREA $= (9)(50) - (7)(8) - (7)(16) - (7)(3) = 261$ FT^2

SOUTH SIDE AREA $= (9)(50) = 450$ FT^2

EAST/WEST END AREA $= 9\,(24) + \frac{1}{2}(24)(5) = 276$ FT^2 /END

OVERHANG AREA $= (53)(1.5)(2) + 2\,(2)(1.5)\left[(13.5)^2 + \left\{\left(\frac{5}{12}\right)(13.5)\right\}^2\right]^{1/2}$

$\qquad\qquad = 159 + 87.75 \cong 247$ FT^2

Student presentation for Example Problem 6.3.

Figure 6.6b

| 3 – 16 – XX | ENGR 161
PROBLEM 5.3 | LAURA LYNN | 2/2 |

TOTAL AREA OF SIDING = 261 + 450 + 2(276) = 1263 FT^2

TOTAL OVERHANG AREA = 247 FT^2

PRIMER NEEDED FOR SIDING = $\left(\frac{1263}{400}\right)$ 3 = 9.47 GAL

PRIMER NEEDED FOR OVERHANG = $\frac{247}{400}$ = 0.62 GAL

TOTAL PRIMER NEEDED = 9.47 + 0.62 = 10.1 GAL

GRAY FINISH COAT FOR SIDING = (2) $\left(\frac{1263}{400}\right)\left(4/3\right)$ = 8.42 GAL

WHITE FINISH COAT FOR OVERHANG/TRIM = (2) $\left(\frac{247}{400}\right)$ = 1.24 GAL

RECOMMENDED PURCHASE :

      PRIMER: 10 GAL

      GRAY TOP COAT: 9 GAL

      WHITE TOP COAT: 2 GAL

DISCUSSION/CONCLUSIONS

1. HOMEOWNER SHOULD BE INFORMED THAT HER PAINTING EXPERIENCE MAY
    AFFECT THE AMOUNT OF PAINT REQUIRED. MAINTAINING A CONSISTENT
    THICKNESS IS DIFFICULT.
2. A FRIEND HELPED ME OBTAIN THE MEASUREMENTS USING A 20 FT STEEL TAPE.
3. TOTAL TIME REQUIRED; 25 MINUTES FOR MEASUREMENTS, A STEP-LADDER
    WAS NEEDED; 40 MINUTES FOR CALCULATIONS AND WRITEUP.

Discussion   Figure 6.7 is a write-up of the solution. The assumptions are listed and simplify the data collection process considerably. Two telephone calls were made to obtain information on interstate highway construction and the cost of concrete. Thus the resulting estimate is based on current design practice and costs. A similar estimation problem relaxing some of the assumptions is provided in Problem 6.29. Note that the computation of the cost was performed in one continuous series of operations on a calculator and then rounded to the appropriate number of significant figures. It may be necessary for a long series of computations to show, for checking purposes, intermediate results. Maintain intermediate results in your computational device while copying down these results if necessary in reporting your work.

Figure 6.7

8-26-XXXX   ENGR 160: Prob 6.4   M. Reagan   Page 1 of 1

Estimate the cost of adding a single lane to Arizona I-19 in both directions from Nogales to I-10 in Tucson. Do not consider stopping lanes or interchanges.

ASSUMPTIONS

    1. Entire roadbed is concrete
    2. Neglect on and off ramps, bridge supports and railings, and emergency stopping lanes

COLLECTED DATA

    1. Concrete costs \$125 per cubic meter delivered to site (estimate from contractor)
    2. Average depth of roadbed is 30.5 cm (Department of Transportation)
    3. Lane width is 3.6576 m (Department of Transportation)
    4. Length of I-19 is 63.4 km

CALCULATIONS

Volume (V) = Length (L) x Width (W) x Depth (D)
Cost (C) = Volume (V) x (cost/cubic meter)

L = (2)(63.4 km)(1000 m/km)

W = 3.6576 m

D = (30.5 cm)(0.01 m/cm)

C = (LWD)(125) = \$17 700 000

Discussion/Conclusions
1.   Cost of concrete may vary considerably in a short time period.
2.   Time estimate: 30 min (obtaining data and calculations) + 30 min (write-up) = <u>60 min</u>

Student presentation, produced on a word processor for Example Problem 6.4.

Problems

6.1   How many significant digits are contained in each of the following quantities?

(*a*) 0.724 70   (*f*) 0.320 00
(*b*) 7 247.0   (*g*) 200.07
(*c*) 0.031   (*h*) 1.3200×10^{-3}
(*d*) 24 000   (*i*) 2 420 000.0
(*e*) 0.10×10^4 (*j*) $3.026\ 7 \times 10^2$

6.2   How many significant digits are contained in each of the following quantities?

(*a*) 14.605   (*f*) 2.54 cm/in.
(*b*) 0.4010   (*g*) 6.000 1
(*c*) 0.002 03   (*h*) $4.065\ 00 \times 10^8$
(*d*) 2.2046 kg/lbm   (*i*) 3 600 s/hr
(*e*) 5 000.01   (*j*) 8.0021×10^{12}

6.3   Perform the computations below and report with the answer rounded to the proper number of significant digits.

(*a*) 74.6/*x*   for $x = 2.377$
(*b*) 74.6 + *y*   for $y = 162.3$
(*c*) 74.6*z*   for $z = 1.66$
(*d*) 74.6 − *x*   for $x = 1.606$
(*e*) $74.6 + 3.2y^2$ for $y = 18.05$
(*f*) $x^2 - 2x + 0.5$ for $x = 0.25$
(*g*) $(1,0 - y)/(1.8 + y^3)$ for $y = 0.36$
(*h*) $z^3 - z^2 - z + 3.00$ for $z = 0.91$
(*i*) $2.33x^{0.5} - 0.050x^3$ for $x = 16.33$
(*j*) $(1.92x - 3.60)(32.35 - 2.66x)$ for $x = 4.592$

6.4   Using the conversion factors given in each problem, perform the calculations below using exact conversions or with enough significant digits that it does not affect the accuracy of the answer.

(*a*) 36.3 miles to feet   1 mi = 5 280 ft
(*b*) 286 degrees to radians   1 radian = 57.296 degrees
(*c*) 92.5 kg to pound mass   1 kg = 2.204 6 lbm
(*d*) 28.75 centimeters to inches   1 in. = 2.54 cm
(*e*) 16.45 cubic meters to cubic feet 1 m = 3.280 8 ft
(*f*) 400 566 seconds to days   1 day = 86 400 s

6.5   Solve the following problems and give the answers rounded to the proper number of significant digits.

(*a*) $v = 0.0214t^2 + 0.363\ 5t + 2.25$ for $t = 32$
(*b*) 24.56 ft × 12 in./ft = ? inches
(*c*) $400 a plate × 24 guests = $?
(*d*) $V = [\pi(4.62\ \text{cm})^2(7.53\ \text{cm})]/3 = ?$ cm³ (volume of a cone)
(*e*) 325.03 + 527.897 − 615.0 =
(*f*) 32¢ per part × 45 250 parts = $?

6.6   A pressure gauge on an air tank reads 210 pounds per square inch (psi). The face of the gauge says ±3% at 180 psi.

(*a*) What is the range of air pressure in the tank when the gauge reads 210 psi?
(*b*) What is the range of air pressure in the tank when the gauge reads 87 psi?

6.7   A vacuum gauge reads 79 kPa. The face of the gauge says ± 3.3 kPa at 85 kPa.

(*a*) What is the actual range of vacuum?
(*b*) What is the range when the gauge reads 135 kPa?

6.8   What is the percent of error if you use a pair of calipers on a 6-in. precision gauge block and get a reading of 6.003?

For problems 6.9 to 6.32, develop and present a solution in a manner demonstrated in Example Problems 6.2, 6.3, or 6.4. Your solution discussion should indicate the amount of time required for developing and preparing the solution. The problems are grouped into four categories: individual in-class, individual homework, team in-class, and team homework. Groups of two or three students are best for the team problems.

Individual in-class problems

6.9 Estimate the amount of time during a typical class day that you spend walking. Also estimate the number of steps you take during this time.

6.10 Estimate the number of hours that you spend watching television in a typical week during the academic semester.

6.11 Estimate the number of tennis balls that will fit in a cubic box 3 ft on a side.

6.12 Estimate the number of quarters that will fit in a box 16 in. by 10 in. by 12 in.

6.13 Estimate the number of basketballs that will fit into your classroom. Assume room is empty of students and furniture.

6.14 Estimate the number of hours you spent on a computer during a typical week this semester. Include "surfing the net" as well as research and class requirements. Carefully document each of the categories of use.

Team in-class problems

6.15 Estimate the amount of paint required to change the color of your classroom walls.

6.16 Estimate the volume required to store 15 000 basketballs.

6.17 Estimate the number of regular M&M's needed to fill a 2 L bottle.

6.18 Estimate the volume of water used to take showers by the members of this class in one academic semester.

6.19 Estimate the volume of snow that must be removed from the street and sidewalk around a square city block after a 14 in. snowfall.

6.20 Estimate the maximum number of cars in a single lane of traffic that would pass a checkpoint in one hour at an average speed of 50 mph. Safe driving practice requires one car length of spacing for each 10 mph of speed.

6.21 Estimate an average weight of backpacks carried regularly by students at your school enrolled in engineering.

Individual homework problems

6.22 Estimate the number of minutes students in your engineering college spend on their cell phones in a typical academic week. A survey of a representative segment of students is necessary. Compare your results with other members of this class.

6.23 Estimate the weight, in pounds, of cars in the parking lot closest to the building where this class is held. Assume all parking spots are occupied.

6.24 Estimate the weight of water in a swimming pool on or near your campus.

6.25 Estimate the area of the running surface of an outdoor track on or near your campus.

6.26 Estimate the maximum volume of a conical pile of road salt that can be stored on an area in the shape of an equilateral triangle 150 ft on a side. You must consider the angle of repose.

6.27 Estimate the weight of concrete in a 4-lane highway segment that begins as a 3 percent grade climb from 1 000 feet of altitude to 4 000 feet and then a 6 percent downgrade to 2 500 feet.

Team homework problems (these problems will involve significant research, a specific plan for activity is strongly recommended)

6.28 Estimate the volume and cost of water used by a family of five living in a detached home during a one-year period.

6.29 Estimate the cost of concrete for a segment of interstate highway designated by your instructor. Include the rural and city components (number of lanes), interchanges, and extended width of lanes for emergency stopping.

6.30 Estimate the number of 25 lb bags of dog food that can be transported in a railroad box car.

6.31 Estimate how much carpet would be needed to carpet the building in which this class is held.

6.32 Your trucking company has been asked to transport a huge pile of sand from a pit to a construction site 35 mi. away. The pit and construction site are both within a mile of the same two-lane paved road. The base of the sand pile covers approximately half an acre. Local laws allow only single-axle dump trucks on the highway. Your company has 14 single-axle trucks and drivers available. Estimate the time, in work days, to move the sand.

CHAPTER 7

Dimensions, Units, and Conversions*

Chapter Objectives

When you complete your study of this chapter, you will be able to:

- Identify physical quantities in terms of dimensions and units
- Differentiate between fundamental and derived dimensions
- Understand the use of non-SI dimensional systems (gravitational and absolute)
- Recognize base, supplementary, and derived SI units
- Apply the appropriate SI symbols and prefixes
- Describe the relationship between U.S. Customary, Engineering System, and SI
- Systematically convert units from one system to another
- Use knowledge of dimensions and units, along with conversion rules, in the solution of engineering problems

7.1 Introduction

Years ago when countries were more isolated from one another, individual governments tended to develop and use their own set of measures. Today, primarily through the development of technology, global communication has brought countries closer together. As countries from one corner of the world to the other interact with each other, the need for a universal system of measurement has become abundantly clear. A standard set of dimensions, units, and measurements is vital if today's wealth of information and knowledge is to be shared and benefit all. The move toward a universal system first requires a thorough understanding of existing systems of measurement. This chapter begins with an explanation of the importance of physical quantities in engineering and explains the difference between dimensions and units. This is followed by the development of procedures for orderly conversion from one system of units to another, ultimately enabling measurements to be expressed in one system—that is, a metric international standard.

---

*Users will find Appendix A useful reference material for this chapter.

7.2   Progress in the United States toward Metrification

The United States Congress considered adoption of the metric system in the 1850s. In fact, the metric system was made legal in the United States in 1866, but its use was not made compulsory. In spite of many attempts in the intervening 150 years, full conversion to the metric system has not yet been realized.

In 1875, the United States together with 16 other nations signed an agreement called the Treaty of the Meter. These signatory nations established a governing body and gave that agency authority and overall responsibility for the metric system. The governing body is called the General Conference of Weights and Measures. That body approved an updated version of the metric system in 1960 called the international metric system, or Système International d'Unités, abbreviated SI. These units are a modification and refinement of earlier versions of the metric system (MKS) that designated the meter, kilogram, and second as fundamental units.

That 1960 standard is currently accepted in all industrial nations but still optional in the United States. In fact, the United States is the only industrialized nation on the globe that does not use the metric system as its predominant system of measurement. Current estimates suggest that the United States is at best 50 percent metric, so engineers must be well versed in the use of a variety of units as well as fluent in SI.

Some corporations within the U.S. economy have become almost 100 percent metric, others are somewhere in the middle, and many have far to go. That is not necessarily the fault of a given company or agency. For example, how many metric highway road signs have you seen lately driving across the United States? It turns out there is only one such location. If you happen to drive from Tucson to Nogales, Arizona on Interstate 19 you would observe the use of metric mileposts. Figure 7.1 is an illustration of such a metric road sign. How many drivers in this country would actually know what 100 km/h really means?

To continue that train of thought, do you as a student give your weight in kilograms and buy gasoline by the liter? If someone tells you it is 30 degrees outside, do you immediately think in Celsius or Fahrenheit? How many of you knew that 30°C is 86°F? It is a difficult two-way street: Manufacturers, wholesalers, and distributors are not going to flood the market with products the consumer does not understand and therefore will not buy. As time marches on, a gradual increase in the use of SI will evolve, but in the meantime, be prepared to handle whatever system of units you encounter.

As a reminder of how important it is to understand the information presented in this chapter, let us review the NASA mission to send the Mars Climate Orbiter to the planet Mars. The $125 million spacecraft had almost completed a ten-month fight plan before it was lost on September 23, 1999, just as the spacecraft reached the planet's atmosphere. NASA convened three panels of experts to investigate what led to the loss of the orbiter. The reason for the loss was simple. One engineering team on a key navigational maneuver of the orbiter used metric units while a different team working on the same project used English units. The result was a major error in the entry trajectory resulting in the destruction of the vehicle.

7.3   Physical Quantities

Engineers are constantly concerned with the measurement of fundamental physical quantities such as length, time, temperature, force, and so on. In order to specify a physical quantity fully, it is not sufficient to indicate merely a numerical value. The

Figure 7.1

© Ilene MacDonald/Alamy Stock Photo

magnitude of physical quantities can be understood only when they are compared with predetermined reference amounts, called *units*. Any measurement is, in effect, a comparison of how many (a number) units are contained within a physical quantity. Given length (*L*) as the physical quantity and 20.0 as the numerical value, with meters (m) as the designated unit, then a general relation can be represented by the expression

$$\text{Length } (L) = 20.0 \text{ m}$$

For this relationship to be valid, the exact reproduction of *a* unit must be theoretically possible at any time. Therefore standards must be established and maintained. These standards are a set of fundamental unit quantities kept under normalized conditions in order to preserve their values as accurately as possible. We shall speak more about standards and their importance later.

7.4 Dimensions

Dimensions are used to describe physical quantities; however, the most important concept to remember is that dimensions are independent of units. As mentioned in Section 7.3, the physical quantity "length" can be represented by the dimension *L,* for which there are a large number of possibilities available when selecting a unit. For example, in ancient Egypt, the cubit was a unit related to the length of the arm from the tip of the middle finger to the elbow. At that time in history measurements were a function of physical stature, with variation from one individual to another. Much later, in Britain, the inch was specified as the distance covered by three barley corns, round and dry, laid end to end.

Today we require considerable more precision. For example, the meter is defined in terms of the distance traveled by light in a vacuum during a specified amount of time. We can draw two important points from this discussion: (1) Physical quantities must be accurately measured and be reproducible, and (2) these units (cubit, inch, and meter), although distinctly different, have in common the quality of being a length and not an area or a volume.

A technique used to distinguish between units and dimensions is to call all physical quantities of length a specific dimension (e.g., L). In this way, each new physical quantity gives rise to a new dimension, such as T for time, F for force, M for mass, and so on. (Note that there is a dimension for each kind of physical quantity.)

However, to simplify the process, dimensions are divided into two areas—fundamental and derived. A fundamental dimension is a dimension that can be conveniently and usefully manipulated when expressing all physical quantities of a particular field of science or engineering. Derived dimensions are a combination of two or more fundamental dimensions. Velocity, for example, could be defined as a fundamental dimension V, but it is more customary as well as more convenient to consider velocity as a combination of fundamental dimensions, so that it becomes a derived dimension, $V = (L)(T)^{-1}$. L and T are fundamental dimensions, and V is a derived dimension because it is made up of two fundamental dimensions (L,T).

For simplicity it is advantageous to use as few fundamental dimensions as possible, but the selection of what is to be fundamental and what is to be derived is not fixed. In actuality, any dimension can be selected as a fundamental dimension in a particular field of engineering or science; for reasons of convenience, it may be a derived dimension in another field.

Once a set of primary dimensions has been adopted, a base unit for each primary dimension must then be specified. So let's look at how this works.

A *dimensional system* can be defined as the smallest number of fundamental dimensions that will form a consistent and complete set for a field of science. For example, three fundamental dimensions are necessary to form a complete mechanical dimensional system. Depending on the discipline, these dimensions may be specified as either length (L), time (T), and mass (M) or length (L), time (T), and force (F). If temperature is important to the application, a fourth fundamental dimension may be added.

The *absolute system* (so called because the dimensions used are not affected by gravity) has as its fundamental dimensions L, T, and M. An advantage of this system is that comparisons of masses at various locations can be made with an ordinary balance, because the local acceleration of gravity has no influence upon the results.

The *gravitational system* has as its fundamental dimensions L, T, and F. It is widely used in many engineering branches because it simplifies computations when weight is a fundamental quantity in the computations. Table 7.1 lists the dimensions used in the absolute and gravitational systems; a number of other dimensional systems are commonly used depending on the specific discipline.

7.5 Units

After a consistent dimensional system has been identified, the next step is to select a specific unit for each fundamental dimension. The problem one encounters when working with units is that there can be a large number of unit systems to choose from for any given dimensional system. It is obviously desirable to limit the number of systems and combinations of systems. The Système International d'Unités (SI) is intended to serve as an international standard that will provide worldwide consistency.

Table 7.1 Two Basic Dimensional Systems

Quantity	Absolute	Gravitational
Length	L	L
Time	T	T
Mass	M	$FL^{-1}T^2$
Force	MLT^{-2}	F
Velocity	LT^{-1}	LT^{-1}
Pressure	$ML^{-1}T^{-2}$	FL^{-2}
Momentum	MLT^{-1}	FT
Energy	ML^2T^{-2}	FL
Power	ML^2T^{-3}	FLT^{-1}
Torque	ML^2T^{-2}	FL

There are three fundamental systems of units commonly used today. The metric system, used in almost every industrial country of the world, is a decimal-absolute system based on the meter, kilogram, and second (MKS) as the units of length, mass, and time, respectively.

In the United States, however, there are two other system of units commonly used. The first, called the U.S. Customary System (formerly known as the British gravitational system), has the fundamental units of foot (ft) for length, pound (lb) for force, and second (s) for time. The second system of units, called the Engineering System, is based on the foot (ft) for length, pound-force (lbf) for force, and second (s) for time. More information regarding the Customary and Engineering Systems will be presented in Section 7.8.

Numerous international conferences on weights and measures over the past 40 years have gradually modified the MKS system to the point that all countries previously using various forms of the metric system are beginning to standardize. SI is now considered the international system of units. Although the United States has officially adopted this system, as indicated earlier, full implementation will be preceded by a long and expensive period of change. During this transition period, engineers will have to be familiar with not only SI but also other systems and the necessary conversion process between or among systems. This chapter will focus on the international standard (SI units and symbols); however, examples and explanations of the Engineering System and the U.S. Customary System will be included.

7.6   SI Units and Symbols

SI, developed and maintained by the General Conference on Weights and Measures (Conférence Générale des Poids et Mesures, CGPM), is intended as a basis for worldwide standardization of measurements. The name and abbreviation were set forth in 1960.

This new international system is divided into three classes of units:

1. Base units
2. Supplementary units
3. Derived units

Table 7.2 Basic Units

Quantity	Name	Symbol
Length	meter	m
Mass	kilogram	kg
Time	second	s
Electric current	ampere	A
Thermodynamic temp.	kelvin	K
Amount of substance	mole	mol
Luminous intensity	candela	cd

There are seven base units in the SI. The units (except the kilogram) are defined in such a way that they can be reproduced anywhere in the world.

Table 7.2 lists each base unit along with its name and proper symbol.

In the following list, each of the base units were defined and adopted at various meetings of the General Conference on Weights and Measures held between 1889 and 1983:

1. **Length.** The meter (m) is a length equal to the distance traveled by light in a vacuum during 1/299 792 458 s.
2. **Time.** The second (s) is the duration of 9 192 631 770 periods of radiation corresponding to the transition between the two hyperfine levels of the ground state of the cesium-133 atom.
3. **Mass.** The standard for the unit of mass, the kilogram (kg), is a cylinder of platinum-iridium alloy kept by the International Bureau of Weights and Measures in France. A duplicate copy is maintained in the United States. It is the only base unit that is nonreproducible in a properly equipped lab.
4. **Electric current.** The ampere (A) is a constant current that, if maintained in two straight parallel conductors of infinite length and of negligible circular cross-sections and placed one meter apart in volume, would produce between these conductors a force equal to 2×10^{-7} newton per meter of length.
5. **Temperature.** The kelvin (K), a unit of thermodynamic temperature, is the fraction 1/273.16 of the thermodynamic temperature of the triple point of water.
6. **Amount of substance.** The mole (mol) is the amount of substance of a system that contains as many elementary entities as there are atoms in 0.012 kg of carbon-12.
7. **Luminous intensity.** The base unit candela (cd) is the luminous intensity in a given direction of a source that emits monochromatic radiation of frequency 540×10^{12} hertz and has a radiant intensity in that direction of 1/683 W per steradian.

The units listed in Table 7.3 are called *supplementary units* and may be regarded either as base units or as derived units.

The unit for a plane angle is the radian (rad), a unit that is used frequently in engineering. The steradian is not as commonly used. These units can be defined in the following way:

Table 7.3 Supplementary Units

Quantity	Name	Symbol
Plane angle	radian	rad
Solid angle	steradian	sr

1. Plane angle: The radian is the plane angle between two radii of a circle that cut off on the circumference of an arc equal in length to the radius.
2. Solid angle: The steradian (sr) is the solid angle which, having its vertex in the center of a sphere, cuts off an area of the sphere equal to that of a square with sides of length equal to the radius of the sphere.

As indicated earlier, derived units are formed by combining base, supplementary, or other derived units. Symbols for them are carefully selected to avoid confusion. Those that have special names and symbols, as interpreted for the United States by the National Bureau of Standards, are listed in Table 7.4 together with their definitions in terms of base units.

Table 7.4 Derived Units

Quantity	SI Unit Symbol	Name	Base Units
Frequency	Hz	hertz	s^{-1}
Force	N	newton	$kg \cdot m \cdot s^{-2}$
Pressure or stress	Pa	pascal	$kg \cdot m^{-1} \cdot s^{-2}$
Energy or work	J	joule	$kg \cdot m^2 \cdot s^{-2}$
Quantity of heat	J	joule	$kg \cdot m^2 \cdot s^{-2}$
Power radiant flux	W	watt	$kg \cdot m^2 \cdot s^{-3}$
Electric charge	C	coulomb	$A \cdot s$
Electric potential	V	volt	$kg \cdot m^2 \cdot s^{-3} \cdot A^{-1}$
Potential difference	V	volt	$kg \cdot m^2 \cdot s^{-3} \cdot A^{-1}$
Electromotive force	V	volt	$kg \cdot m^2 \cdot s^{-3} \cdot A^{-1}$
Capacitance	F	farad	$A^2 \cdot s^4 \cdot kg^{-1} \cdot m^{-2}$
Electric resistance	Ω	ohm	$kg \cdot m^2 \cdot s^{-3} \cdot A^{-2}$
Conductance	S	siemens	$kg^{-1} \cdot m^{-2} \cdot s^3 \cdot A^2$
Magnetic flux	Wb	weber	$m^2 \cdot kg \cdot s^{-2} \cdot A^{-1}$
Magnetic flux density	T	tesla	$kg \cdot s^{-2} \cdot A^{-1}$
Inductance	H	henry	$kg \cdot m^2 \cdot s^{-2} \cdot A^{-2}$
Luminous flux	lm	lumen	cd
Illuminance	lx	lux	$cd \cdot m^{-2}$
Celsius temperature*	°C	degree Celsius	K
Activity (radionuclides)	Bq	becqueret	s^{-1}
Absorbed dose	Gy	gray	$m^2 \cdot s^{-2}$
Dose equivalent	S_v	sievert	$m^2 \cdot s^{-2}$

*The thermodynamic temperature (T_K) expressed in kelvins is related to Celsius temperature (t_C) expressed in degrees Celsius by the equation $t_C = T_K - 273.15$.

Additional derived units, such as those listed in Table 7.5, have no special SI unit names or symbols but are nevertheless combinations of base units and units with special names.

Being a decimal system, the SI is convenient to use because by simply affixing a prefix to the base, a quantity can be increased or decreased by factors of 10 and the numerical quantity can be kept within manageable limits. The proper selection of prefixes will also help eliminate nonsignificant zeros and leading zeros in decimal fractions. One rule to follow is that the numerical value of any measurement should be recorded as a number between 0.1 and 1 000. This rule is suggested because it is easier to make realistic judgments when working with numbers between 0.1 and 1 000. For example, suppose that you are asked the distance to a nearby town. It would be more understandable to respond in kilometers than meters. That is, it is easier to visualize 10 km than 10 000 m.

The use of prefixes representing powers of 1 000, such as kilo, mega, milli, etc., are preferred over multipliers such as deci, deka, etc. However, the three exceptions listed below are still in common use because of convention.

1. When expressing area and volume, the prefixes hecto-, deka-, deci-, and centi- may be used; for example, cubic centimeter.
2. When discussing different values of the same quantity or expressing them in a table, calculations are simpler to perform when you use the same unit multiple throughout.
3. Sometimes a particular multiple is recommended as a consistent unit even though its use violates the 0.1 to 1 000 rule. For example, many companies use the millimeter for linear dimensions even when the values lie far outside this suggested range. The cubic decimeter (commonly called liter) is also used in this manner.

Recalling the importance of significant figures, we see that SI prefix notations can be used to a definite advantage. Consider the previous example of 10 km versus 10 000 m. In an estimate of distance to the nearest town, a round number certainly implies an approximation. Suppose that we were talking about a 10 000 m Olympic

Table 7.5 Additional Derived Units

Quantity	Units	Quantity	Units
Acceleration	$m·s^{-2}$	Molar entropy	$J·mol^{-1}·K^{-1}$
Angular acceleration	$rad·s^{-2}$	Molar heat capacity	$J·mol^{-1}·K^{-1}$
Angular velocity	$rad·s^{-1}$	Moment of force	$N·m$
Area	m^2	Permeability	$H·m^{-1}$
Concentration	$mol·m^{-3}$	Permittivity	$F·m^{-1}$
Current density	$A·m^{-2}$	Radiance	$W·m^{-2}·sr^{-1}$
Density, mass	$kg·m^{-3}$	Radiant intensity	$W·sr^{-1}$
Electric charge density	$C·m^{-3}$	Specific heat capacity	$J·kg^{-1}·K^{-1}$
Electric field strength	$V·m^{-1}$	Specific energy	$J·kg^{-1}$
Electric flux density	$C·m^{-2}$	Specific entropy	$J·kg^{-1}·K^{-1}$
Energy density	$J·m^{-3}$	Specific volume	$m^3·kg^{-1}$
Entropy	$J·K^{-1}$	Surface tension	$N·m^{-1}$
Heat capacity	$J·K^{-1}$	Thermal conductivity	$W·m^{-1}·K^{-1}$
Heat flux density	$W·m^{-2}$	Velocity	$m·s^{-1}$
Irradiance	$W·m^{-2}$	Viscosity, dynamic	$Pa·s$
Luminance	$cd·m^{-2}$	Viscosity, kinematic	$m^2·s^{-1}$
Magnetic field strength	$A·m^{-1}$	Volume	m^3
Molar energy	$J·mol^{-1}$	Wavelength	m

track and field event. The accuracy of such a distance must certainly be greater than something between 5 000 and 15 000 m, which would be the implied accuracy with one significant figure. If, however we use prefix multipliers, such as 10.000 km, then all five numbers are in fact significant, and the race length is accurate to within 1 m (9 999.5 to 10 000.5). If only four numbers are significant (10.00 km), then the race length is accurate to within 10 m (9 995 to 10 005).

There are two logical and acceptable methods available for eliminating confusion concerning zeros or the correct number of significant figures:

1. Use proper prefixes to denote intended significance.

Distance	Precision	Number of significant figures
10.000 km	9 999.5 to 10 000.5 m	5
10.00 km	9 995 to 10 005 m	4
10.0 km	9 950 to 10 050 m	3
10 km	5 000 to 15 000 m	1

How would you express a degree of significance between 10.0 km and 10 km? One viable solution is to use scientific notation.

2. Use scientific notation to indicate significance.

Distance	Precision	Number of significant figures
$1.000\ 0 \times 10^4$ m	9 999.5 to 10 000.5 m	5
1.000×10^4 m	9 995 to 10 005 m	4
1.00×10^4 m	9 950 to 10 050 m	3
1.0×10^4 m	9 500 to 10 500 m	2
1×10^4 m	5 000 to 15 000 m	1

Selection of a proper prefix is customarily the logical way to handle problems of significant figures; however, there are conventions that do not lend themselves to the prefix notation. An example would be temperature in degrees Celsius; that is, $4.00(10^3)°C$ is the conventional way to handle it, not 4.00 k°C.

7.7   Rules for Using SI Units

Along with the adoption of SI comes the responsibility to thoroughly understand and properly apply the new system. Obsolete practices involving both English and metric units are widespread. This section provides rules that should be followed when working with SI units.

7.7.1   Unit Symbols and Names

1. Periods are never used after SI symbols unless the symbol is at the end of a sentence (i.e., SI unit symbols are not abbreviations).
2. Unit symbols are written in lowercase letters unless the symbol derives from a proper name, for example, Ampere (A) or Kelvin (K), in which case the first letter is capitalized.

Lowercase	Uppercase
m, kg, s, mol, cd	A, K, Hz, Pa, C

3. Symbols rather than self-styled abbreviations should always be used to represent units.

Correct	Not correct
A	amp
s	sec

4. An s is never added to the symbol to denote plural.
5. A space is always left between the numerical value and the unit symbol.

Correct	Not correct
43.7 km	43.7 km
0.25 Pa	0.25 Pa

Exception: No space should be left between numerical values and the symbols for degree, minute, and second of angles and for degree Celsius.

6. There should be no space between the prefix and the unit symbols.

Correct	Not correct
mm, MΩ	k m, μ F

7. A unit name is written in lowercase (except at the beginning of a sentence), even if the unit is derived from a proper name.
8. Plurals are used as required when writing unit names. For example, henries is plural for henry. The following exceptions are noted:

Singular	Plural
lux	lux
hertz	hertz
siemens	siemens

With these exceptions, unit names form their plurals in the usual manner.

9. No hyphen or space should be left between a prefix and the unit name. In three cases the final vowel in the prefix is omitted: megohm, kilohm, and hectare.
10. The symbol should be used following a number in preference to the unit name because unit symbols are standardized. An exception to this is made when a number is written in words preceding the unit; for example, we would write *nine meters,* not *nine m.* The same is true the other way, for example, 9 m, not 9 meters.

7.7.2 Multiplication and Division

1. When writing unit names as a product, always use a space (preferred) or a hyphen.

Correct usage

newton meter or newton-meter

2. When expressing a quotient using unit names, always use the word *per* and not a solidus (/). The solidus, or slash mark, is reserved for use with symbols.

Correct usage	Not correct
meter per second	meter/second

3. When writing a unit name that requires a power, use a modifier, such as squared or cubed, after the unit name. For area or volume, the modifier can be placed before the unit name.

Correct usage

millimeter squared or square millimeter

4. When expressing products using unit symbols, the center dot is preferred.

Correct usage

N · m for newton meter

5. When denoting a quotient by unit symbols, any of the following are accepted form:

Correct usage

m/s   or   m · s⁻¹   or $\dfrac{m}{s}$

In more complicated cases, consider using negative powers or parentheses. For acceleration use m/s^2 or $m \cdot s^{-2}$ but not m/s/s. For electrical potential use $kg \cdot m^2/(s^3 \cdot A)$ or $kg \cdot s^{-3} \cdot A^{-1}$ but not $kg \cdot m^1/s^3/A$.

7.7.3 Numbers

1. To denote a decimal point, use a period on the line. When expressing numbers less than 1, a zero should be written before the decimal marker.

Example

15.6
0.93

2. Since a comma is used in many countries to denote a decimal point, its use is to be avoided in grouping data. To avoid confusion, separate the digits into groups of three, counting from the decimal to the left or right, and use a small space to separate the groups.

Correct and recommended procedure

6.513 824	76 851	7 434	0.187 62

7.7.4 Calculating with SI Units

Before we look at some suggested procedures that will simplify calculations in SI, let us review the following positive characteristics of the system.

Only one unit is used to represent each physical quantity, such as the meter for length, the second for time, and so on. The SI metric units are *coherent;* that is, each new derived unit is a product or quotient of the fundamental and supplementary units without any numerical factors. Since coherency is a strength of the SI system, it would be worthwhile to demonstrate this characteristic by the following two examples. The relationship among force, mass and time can be illustrated by Newton's second law, $F \propto ma$. To satisfy coherency the newton (N) becomes a derived unit. Its magnitude is defined as the force required to impart an acceleration of one meter per second squared to a mass of one kilogram. It was not arbitrary determined independent of mass and time. Thus,

$$1.0\ N = (1.0\ kg)(1.0\ m/s^2)$$

Newton's second law can now be written in equation form as follows:

$$F = \frac{ma}{g_C}, \text{ where } g_C = \frac{ma}{F} \text{ or } g_C = \frac{1.0\ kg \cdot 1.0\ m}{N \cdot s^2}$$

This constant of proportionality serves as a reminder that the units are in fact coherent and that the conversion factor is 1.0.

Consider next the joule, the SI equivalent of the British thermal unit, the calorie, foot-pound-force, the electron volt, and the horsepower-hour, intended to represent most forms of energy. The joule is defined as the amount of work done when an applied force of one newton acts through a distance of one meter in the direction of the force. Thus,

$$1.0\ J = (1.0\ N)(1.0\ m)$$

To maintain coherency of units, however, time must be expressed in seconds rather than minutes or hours, since the second is the base unit. Once coherency is violated, then a conversion factor must be included and the advantage of the system is diminished.

But there are certain units *outside* SI that are accepted for use in the United States, even though they diminish the system's coherence. These exceptions are listed in Table 7.6.

Calculations using SI can be simplified if you,

1. Remember that fundamental relationships are simple and easier to use because of coherence.
2. Recognize how to manipulate units and gain a proficiency in doing so. Since watt = J/s = N · m/s, you can algebraically rearrange the units to produce N · m/s = $(N/m^2)(m^3/s)$ = (pressure)(volume flow rate).

Table 7.6 Non-SI Units Accepted for Use in the United States

Quantity	Name	Symbol	SI equivalent
Time	minute	min	60 s
	hour	h	3 600 s
	day	d	86 400 s
Plane angle	degree	°	$\pi/180$ rad
	minute	′	$\pi/10\ 800$ rad
	second	″	$\pi/648\ 000$ rad
Volume	liter	L*	$10^{-3}\ m^3$
Mass	metric ton	t	10^3 kg
	unified atomic mass unit	u	$1.660\ 57 \times 10^{-27}$ kg (approx)
Land area	hectare	ha	$10^4\ m^2$
Energy	electronvolt	eV	1.602×10^{-19} J (approx)

*Both "L" and "l" are acceptable international symbols for liter. The uppercase letter is recommended for use in the United States because the lowercase "l" can be confused with the numeral 1.

3. Understand the advantage of occasionally adjusting all variables to base units; for example, replacing N with kg · m/s^2 and Pa with kg · m^{-1}s^{-2}.

4. Develop a proficiency with exponential notation of numbers to be used in conjunction with unit prefixes.

$$1 \text{ mm}^3 = (10^{-3} \text{ m})^3 = 10^{-9} \text{ m}^3$$

$$1 \text{ ns}^{-1} = (10^{-9} \text{ s})^{-1} = 10^9 \text{ s}^{-1}$$

When calculating with SI the term "weight" can be confusing. Frequently we hear statements such as "The person weighs 100 kg." A correct statement would be "The person has a mass of 100 kg." To clear up any confusion, let's look at some basic definitions.

First, the term *mass* should be used to indicate only a quantity of matter. Mass is measured in kilograms (kg) or pound-mass (lbm) and is always measured against a standard.

Force, as defined by the International Standard of Units, is measured in newtons. By definition the newton was established as the force required to accelerate a mass of one kilogram to one meter per second squared.

The acceleration of gravity varies at different points on the surface of the Earth as well as distance from the Earth's surface. The accepted standard value of gravitational acceleration is 9.806 650 m/s^2 at sea level and 45 degrees latitude.

Gravity is instrumental in measuring mass with a beam balance or scale. If you use a beam balance to compare an unknown quantity against a standard mass, the effect of gravity on the two masses cancels out. If you use a spring scale, mass is measured indirectly, since the instrument responds to the local force of gravity. Such a scale can be calibrated in mass units and be reasonably accurate when used where the variation in the acceleration of gravity is not significant.

The following example problem clarifies the confusion that exists in the use of the term *weight* to mean either force or mass. In everyday use, the term *weight* nearly always means mass; thus, when a person's weight is discussed, the quantity referred to is mass.

Example Problem 7.1   A "weight" of 100.0 kg (the unit itself indicates mass) is suspended by a cable from an I-beam. Calculate the force or tension in the cable in newtons to hold the mass stationary when the local gravitational acceleration is (a) 9.807 m/s^2 and (b) 1.63 m/s^2 (approximate value for the surface of the Moon).

Theory   Tension in the cable or force required to hold the object when the mass is at rest or moving at constant velocity is

$$F = \frac{mg_L}{g_c}$$

where g_L is the local acceleration of gravity and replaces acceleration in Newton's equation $F = ma$, g_c is the proportionality constant, and m is the mass of object. Remember that due to coherence

$$g_c = 1.0 \left[\frac{\text{kg} \cdot \text{m}}{\text{N} \cdot \text{s}^2} \right]$$

Assumption   Neglect the mass of the cable.

Solution

(a) For $g_L = 9.807$ m/s^2

$$F = \frac{mg_L}{g_C}$$

$$F = \frac{(100.0\,\text{kg})(9.807\,\text{m})}{\text{s}^2} \times \frac{\text{N} \cdot \text{s}^2}{1.0\,\text{kg} \cdot \text{m}} = 980.7\ \text{N}$$

$$= 0.980\ 7\ \text{kN}$$

(b) For $g_L = 1.63$ m/s^2

$$F = \frac{(100.0\,\text{kg})(1.63\,\text{m})}{\text{s}^2} \times \frac{\text{N} \cdot \text{s}^2}{1.0\,\text{kg} \cdot \text{m}} = 0.163\ 0\ \text{kN}$$

7.8   U.S. Customary and Engineering Systems

Before you study the material in this section, ask yourself why it is necessary to consider any system of dimensions and units other than SI. Next, think about a few common products that you might purchase for a home remodeling project: threaded fasteners, lumber, nails, paint, and so on. How many of these are available in metric units?

Although SI is ultimately intended to be adopted worldwide, at the present time many segments of the U.S. industrial complex regularly use other systems. For many years to come, engineers in the United States will have to be comfortable and proficient with a variety of unit systems.

As noted earlier in this chapter, there are two systems of units other than SI commonly used in the United States.

7.8.1   U.S. Customary System

The first, the U.S. Customary System has the fundamental units of foot (ft) for length, pound (lb) for force, and second (s) for time (see Table 7.7). However, in this system mass (m) is not a fundamental unit; it is a new derived unit called the slug. Since it is a new derived unit, its magnitude can be established. A slug is defined as a specific amount of mass. In fact, it is the amount of mass that would be accelerated to one foot per second squared given a force of one pound. This system works perfectly well as long as mass is derived totally independent of force. In fact, since we define the derived unit mass as the slug and establish its mass as a quantity of matter that will be accelerated to 1.0 ft/s^2 when a force of 1.0 lb is applied, we have a coherent system of units. We can once again write Newton's second law as an equality,

$$F = \frac{ma}{g_c}, \text{ where } g_c = \frac{ma}{F} \text{ or } g_c = \frac{(1.0)\ \text{slug} \cdot 1.0\ \text{ft}}{\text{lbf} \cdot \text{s}^2}$$

Note that the constant of proportionality, g_c, is included to clarify units, but the conversion factor is (1.0).

Table 7.7   The U.S. Customary System

Quality	Unit	Symbol
Mass	slug	slug
Length	foot	ft
Time	second	s
Force	pound	lb

7.8.2   The Engineering System

The Engineering System, uses length, time, mass, and force as the fundamental dimensions (see Table 7.8). In the Engineering System, the fundamental dimension force was established independently from the other primary dimensions. Recall that in the SI system of units force was determined with relation to Newton's second law. However, in this case, sometime during the fourteenth century, a quantity of matter was selected to be one pound-mass (lbm). At a later time it was decided that one pound-force (lbf) would be the force required to hold a one pound-mass in a gravitational field where the local acceleration of gravity was the standard value of $32.174\,0$ ft/s^2. In fact one pound-force (lbf) is the amount of force that would be required to accelerate a mass of $32.174\,0$ (lbm) to one foot per second squared. Unfortunately, in the Engineering System of units the independent selection of four fundamental dimensions require that we insert a conversion factor in the constant of proportionality (g_c). It is for this reason that we included (g_c) in equations that relate pound-mass and pound-force. It provides us with a visual reminder that

$$g_C = 32.174\,0\,\frac{\text{lbm} \cdot \text{ft}}{\text{lbf} \cdot \text{s}^2}$$

When calculating in the Engineering System, the constant of proportionality g_c and the local gravitational constant g_L can be particularly confusing when using the term "weight." If you were to hold a child in your arms, you might say that this child is heavy, and ask the question, how much does this child weigh? Does the question refer to the amount of force exerted to hold the child (lbf) or the child's mass (lbm)?

Normally the term "weight" refers to pound-mass. In other words the child's mass is 50.0 lbm. Holding the child requires a force of 50.0 lbf where the local acceleration of gravity is exactly $32.174\,0$ ft/s^2.

$$F = \frac{mg_L}{g_C} = \frac{50.0\ \text{lbm}}{1.0} \times \frac{32.174\ \text{ft}}{\text{s}^2} \times \frac{\text{lbf} \cdot \text{s}^2}{32.174\,0\ \text{lbm} \cdot \text{ft}} = 50.0\ \text{lbf}$$

Table 7.8   The Engineering System

Quality	Unit	Symbol
Mass	pound-mass	lbm
Length	foot	ft
Time	second	s
Force	pound-force	lbf

If the local gravitational constant were any value other than 32.174 0, then the force required to hold the child would either be greater than or less than the force required in the example. For instance, on planet x the local acceleration of gravity is 8.72 ft/s^2. In this case the force required to hold the 50.0 lbm child (mass never changes) would be determined as follows:

$$F = \frac{mg_L}{g_C} = \frac{50.0 \text{ lbm}}{1.0} \times \frac{8.72 \text{ ft}}{s^2} \times \frac{\text{lbf} \cdot s^2}{32.174\ 0 \text{ lbm} \cdot \text{ft}} = 13.6 \text{ lbf}$$

So the next time someone asks how much you can bench press, say, "About 600 lbm,"—just don't mention on what planet.

Once again a word of caution when using the Engineering System in expressions such as Newton's second law (F α ma). This particular combination of units—lbf, lbm, ft, and s^2—do not constitute a coherent set. Recall a coherent set of non-SI units involving lbf, slug, and ft/s^2 was the U.S Customary system. So you have a choice. You can either include the conversion factor or always convert mass quantities from lbm to slugs (1.0 slug = 32.174 0 lbm). For example, in the previous problem where the child's weight was 50 lbm it would be necessary to first convert 50.0 lbm to slugs and then simply use the U.S. Customary system.

$$50.0 \text{ lbm} = \frac{50.0 \text{ lbm}}{1.0} \times \frac{\text{slugs}}{32.174 \text{ lbm}} = 1.554 \text{ slugs}$$

$$F = \frac{mg_L}{g_C} = \frac{1.554 \text{ slugs}}{1.0} \times \frac{32.174 \text{ ft}}{s^2} \times \frac{\text{lbf} \cdot s^2}{1.0 \text{ slugs} \cdot \text{ft}} = 50.0 \text{ lbf}$$

7.9   Conversion of Units

The two dimensional systems listed in Table 7.1 can be further divided into the four systems of mechanical units presently encountered in the United States. See Table 7.9. The table does not provide a complete list of all possible quantities; this list is presented to demonstrate the different units that are associated with each unique system. As an example, the physical quantity *L* (length) can be expressed in a variety of units. Fortunately, it is a simple matter to convert the units from any system to the one in which you are working. To do this, the basic conversion for the units involved must be known and a logical series of steps must be followed. This procedure is often referred to as dimensional analysis or the unit-factor method.

First, let's establish a procedure that can be used during the process of converting from one set of units to another. Remember mistakes can be minimized if you realize that a conversion factor relates the same physical quantity in two different unit systems. Next remember that the number 1.0 is a dimensionless number, so always begin the conversion factor as 1.0. For example:

$$1.0 \text{ in.} = 25.4 \text{ mm} \quad \text{or} \quad 1.0 \text{ ft} = 0.304\ 8 \text{ m}$$

Take a moment to review the Table of Conversion Factors given in Appendix A. The column on the left is always preceded with a 1.0 set equal to the conversion factor in the middle column with column three as its corresponding units.

$$1.0 \text{ in.} = 2.54 \text{ cm} \quad \text{or} \quad 1.0 \text{ ft} = 3.048 \times 10^{-1}$$

Next, any number or mathematical expression can be multiplied or divided by (1.0) without changing its value. In this case 1.0 in. and 25.4 mm each describe the exact

Table 7.9   Mechanical Units

Quality	Absolute System		Gravitational System	
	MKS	**CGS**	**Type I**	**Type II**
Length	m	cm	ft	ft
Mass	kg	g	slug	lbm
Time	s	s	s	s
Force	N	dyne	lbf	lbf
Velocity	$m \cdot s^{-1}$	$cm \cdot s^{-1}$	$ft \cdot s^{-1}$	$ft \cdot s^{-1}$
Acceleration	$m \cdot s^{-2}$	$cm \cdot s^{-2}$	$ft \cdot s^{-2}$	$ft \cdot s^{-2}$
Torque	$N \cdot m$	$dyne \cdot cm$	$lbf \cdot ft$	$lbf \cdot ft$
Moment of inertia	$kg \cdot m^2$	$g \cdot cm^2$	$slug \cdot ft^2$	$lbm \cdot ft^2$
Pressure	$N \cdot m^{-2}$	$dyne \cdot cm^{-2}$	$lbf \cdot ft^{-2}$	$lb \cdot ft^{-2}$
Energy	J	erg	$ft \cdot lbf$	$ft \cdot lbf$
Power	W	$erg \cdot s^{-1}$	$ft \cdot lbf \cdot s^{-1}$	$ft \cdot lbf \cdot s^{-1}$
Momentum	$kg \cdot m \cdot s^{-1}$	$g \cdot cm \cdot s^{-1}$	$slug \cdot ft \cdot s^{-1}$	$lbm \cdot ft \cdot s^{-1}$
Impulse	$N \cdot s$	$dyne \cdot s$	$lbf \cdot s$	$lbf \cdot s$

Type I—U.S. Customary
Type II—Engineering

same length quantity, therefore 1.0 in. = 25.4 mm. From this information we can establish what are called unit factors:

$$\frac{1.0 \text{ in.}}{1.0 \text{ in.}} = \frac{25.4 \text{ mm}}{1.0 \text{ in.}} \quad \text{or} \quad \frac{1.0 \text{ in.}}{25.4 \text{ mm}} = \frac{25.4 \text{ mm}}{25.4 \text{ mm}}$$

As an example let's say we wish to convert 65.7 in. to mm. First we ask how many millimeters (x) are there in 65.7 in.?

$$x \text{ mm} = 65.7 \text{ in.} = \frac{65.7 \text{ in.}}{1.0}$$

Next use the correct unit factor given above such that when multiplied the appropriate units cancel.

$$x \text{ mm} = 65.7 \text{ in.} = \frac{65.7 \text{ in.}}{1.0} \times \frac{25.4 \text{ mm}}{1.0 \text{ in.}}$$

Solve this equation for x and determine the proper number of significant figures.

$$x = 1\,668.78 \text{ mm} = 1\,670 \text{ mm}$$

The unit-factor method is actually a sequential application of conversion factors arranged so that similar units appearing in both the numerator and/or denominator of any fractional system can be cancelled leaving the desired set of units.

For example, convert 50 mph to feet per second.

$$x \frac{\text{ft}}{\text{s}} = \frac{50 \text{ miles}}{1.0 \text{ hour}} \times \frac{1.0 \text{ hour}}{60 \text{ min}} \times \frac{1.0 \text{ min}}{60 \text{ s}} \times \frac{5\,280 \text{ ft}}{1.0 \text{ mile}} = 73.33 \frac{\text{ft}}{\text{s}}$$

Remember that each if these unit factors $\dfrac{1.0 \text{ hour}}{60 \text{ min}}, \dfrac{1.0 \text{ min}}{60 \text{ s}}, \dfrac{5\,280 \text{ ft}}{1.0 \text{ mile}}$ are each equal to 1.0.

This unit-factor method for conversion of units can be summarized in the example problem below using a five steps approach.

Problem: Convert 56.7 kg to lbm.

Step 1: Write the following identity starting with the quantity you wish to convert

$$56.7 \text{ kg} = \frac{56.7 \text{ kg}}{1.0}$$

Step 2: Recall or look up the appropriate conversion factor. (See Appendix A.)

$$1.0 \text{ kg} = 2.204\ 6 \text{ lbm}$$

Remember, you can divide both sides by 1.0 kg or you can divide both sides by 2.204 6 lbm.

$$\frac{1.0 \text{ kg}}{1.0 \text{ kg}} = \frac{2.204\ 6 \text{ lbm}}{1.0 \text{ kg}} = 1.0$$

Step 3: Establish an equation with x as the unknown utilizing the appropriate unit factor.

$$x \text{ lbm} = 56.7 \text{ kg} = \frac{56.7 \text{ kg}}{1.0} \times \frac{2.204\ 6 \text{ lbm}}{1.0 \text{ kg}}$$

Step 4: Multiply the two identities to obtain the desired answer

$$x \text{ lbm} = 56.7 \text{ kg} = \frac{56.7 \text{ kg}}{1.0} \times \frac{2.204\ 6 \text{ lbm}}{1.0 \text{ kg}} = 125.0 \text{ lbm}$$

Step 5: Consider significant figures

$$56.7 \text{ kg} = 125 \text{ lbm}$$

Thus, when using the conversion factor 2.204 6 lbm/1.0 kg to convert a quantity in kilograms to lbm, you are multiplying by a factor that is not numerically equal to 1 but is physically identical.

The following five example problems review the procedure outlined above and present a systematic series of steps that can be used when performing a unit conversion. Once you are extremely familiar with the unit conversion process the five steps outlined can be condensed to some smaller number, that is, individual steps can be combined, nevertheless, the construction of a series of individual steps will aid the thought process and help insure a correct unit analysis. Notice the units to be eliminated will cancel algebraically, leaving the desired results. The final answer should be checked to make sure it is reasonable.

Example Problem 7.2 Convert 375 lbm/s to slugs/hr

Step 1: Write the identity you wish to convert

$$375 \text{ lbm/s} = \frac{375 \text{ lbm}}{1.0 \text{ s}}$$

Step 2: List needed conversion factors

$$1.0 \text{ slug} = 32.174\ 0 \text{ lbm} \qquad \text{and} \qquad 1.0 \text{ hr} = 3\ 600 \text{ s}$$

Step 3: Establish the equation and multiply this identity by the appropriate conversion factors

$$x \text{ slugs/hr} = \frac{375 \text{ lbm}}{1.0 \text{ s}} \times \frac{1.0 \text{ slugs}}{32.174 \text{ lbm}} \times \frac{3\ 600 \text{ s}}{1.0 \text{ hr}}$$

Notice that by the correct positioning of conversion factors the desired answer can be realized, that is, lbm and seconds cancel leaving slugs per hour.

Step 4: Multiply the identities to obtain the desired answer

$$x \text{ slugs/hr} = \frac{375 \text{ lbm}}{1.0 \text{ s}} \times \frac{1.0 \text{ slugs}}{32.174 \text{ lbm}} \times \frac{3\ 600 \text{ s}}{1.0 \text{ hr}} = 41\ 959 \text{ slugs/hr}$$

Step 5: Check for both a reasonable answer and significant figures

$$375 \text{ lbm/s} = 4.20 \times (10)^4 \text{ slugs/hr}$$

Example Problem 7.3   Convert 85.0 lbm/ft^3 to kg/m^3.

Solution: Notice in this example steps have been combined

Step 1&2: Write the identity and list conversion factors

$$85.0 \text{ lbm/ft}^3 = \frac{85.0 \text{ lbm}}{1.0 \text{ ft}^3}$$

$$1.0 \text{ ft} = 0.304\ 8 \text{ m} \quad \text{and} \quad 1.0 \text{ lbm} = 0.453\ 6 \text{ kg}$$

Each of which can be written as unit factors:

$$\frac{1.0 \text{ ft}}{0.304\ 8 \text{ m}} \quad \text{and} \quad \frac{1.0 \text{ lbm}}{0.453\ 6 \text{ kg}} \quad \text{or} \quad \frac{0.304\ 8 \text{ m}}{1.0 \text{ ft}} \quad \text{and} \quad \frac{0.453\ 6 \text{ kg}}{1.0 \text{ lbm}}$$

Step 3&4: Establish the equation and multiply this identity by the appropriate conversion factors

Note: Any unit factor can be squared, cubed, etc., as long as the operation is applied to both the nominator and denominator.

$$x \text{ kg/m}^3 = 85.0 \text{ lbm/ft}^3 = \frac{85.0 \text{ lbm}}{1.0 \text{ ft}^3} \times \frac{0.453\ 6 \text{ kg}}{1.0 \text{ lbm}} \times \frac{(1.0 \text{ ft})^3}{(0.304\ 8 \text{ m})^3} = 126.4961 \text{ kg/m}^3$$

Step 5: Check for reasonable answer and significant figures

$$85.0 \text{ lbm/ft}^3 = 1.26 \times 10^2 \text{ kg/m}^3$$

Example Problem 7.4   Determine the gravitation force (in newtons) on an automobile with a mass of 3 645 lbm. The acceleration of gravity is known to be 32.2 ft/s^2.

Solution A: Force, mass, and acceleration of gravity are related by

$$F = \frac{mg_L}{g_C}$$

First, convert lbm to kg

$$x \text{ kg} = \frac{3\,645 \text{ lbm}}{1.0} \times \frac{1 \text{ kg}}{2.204\,6 \text{ lbm}} = 1\,653.36 \text{ kg}$$

Convert g_L in ft/s² to m/s²

$$g_L = \frac{32.2 \text{ ft}}{s^2} \times \frac{0.304\,8 \text{ m}}{1.0 \text{ ft}} = 9.814\,6 \text{ m/s}^2$$

Solve for F

$$F = \frac{mg_L}{g_C} = (1\,653.36 \text{ kg}) \left(\frac{9.814\,6 \text{ m}}{s^2} \right) \left(\frac{1.0 \text{ kg} \cdot \text{m}}{\text{N} \cdot s^2} \right)$$

$$F = 16\,227 \text{ N} = 16.2 \text{ kN}$$

Note: Intermediate values were not rounded to final precision, and we have used either exact or conversion factors with at least one more significant figure than contained in the final answer.

Solution B (combine steps in Solution A into one step)

$$F = \frac{mg_L}{g_C} = \frac{3\,645 \text{ lbm}}{1.0} \times \frac{32.2 \text{ ft}}{1.0 \text{ s}^2} \times \frac{1.0 \text{ kg}}{2.204\,6 \text{ lbm}} \times \frac{0.304\,8 \text{ m}}{1.0 \text{ ft}} \times \frac{\text{N} \cdot s^2}{1.0 \text{ kg} \cdot \text{m}}$$

$$F = 16\,227 \text{ N}$$

If you prefer to express the answer in kN recall that 1.0 kN = 1 000 N so

$$F = \frac{16\,227 \text{ N}}{1.0} \times \frac{1.0 \text{ kN}}{1\,000 \text{ N}} = 16.2 \text{ kN}$$

Note: It is often convenient to include conversions with the appropriate engineering relationship in a single calculation.

Example Problem 7.5 The density of aluminum is 165 lbm/ft³. Convert to SI units. (i.e., kg/m³) As with many unit conversions this problem can be solved a number of different ways. Three solutions are shown below.

Solution 1:

$$x \text{ kg/m}^3 = \frac{165 \text{ lbm}}{1.0 \text{ ft}^3} \times \frac{1.0 \text{ kg}}{2.204\,6 \text{ lbm}} \times \frac{(3.280\,8 \text{ ft})^3}{(1.0 \text{ m})^3}$$

From Appendix A: 1.0 m = 3.280 8 ft   and   1.0 kg = 2.204 6 lbm

Therefore, $x \text{ kg/m}^3 = 2\,642.98 \text{ kg/m}^3 = 2\,640 \text{ kg/m}^3$

Solution 2:

$$x \text{ kg/m}^3 = \frac{165 \text{ lbm}}{1.0 \text{ ft}^3} \times \frac{1.0 \text{ kg}}{2.204\,6 \text{ lbm}} \times \frac{1.0 \text{ ft}^3}{0.028\,317 \text{ m}^3}$$

From Appendix A: 1.0 ft = 0.304 8 m   and   1.0 kg = 2.204 6 lbm

However, when both sides of the unit factor are cubed $(1.0 \text{ ft})^3 = (0.304\ 8\ \text{m})^3$ we see that $1.0\ \text{ft}^3 = 0.028\ 317\ \text{m}^3$

Therefore, $x \text{ kg/m}^3 = 2\ 643.06\ \text{kg/m}^3 = 2\ 640\ \text{kg/m}^3$

Solution 3: Simply look up the direct conversion in Appendix Part 4 Approximate Specific Gravities and Densities.

$$\text{Density of aluminum} = 165\ \text{lbm/ft} = 2\ 640\ \text{kg/m}$$

Example Problem 7.6 Compute the power output of a 225-hp engine in (a) British thermal units per minute and (b) kilowatts.

Solution: Review the five step process.
   Step 1: Write the identity you wish to convert
   Step 2: List needed conversion factors
   Step 3: Establish the equation and multiply this identity by the appropriate
            conversion factors
   Step 4: Multiply the identities to obtain the desired answer
   Step 5: Check for reasonable answer and significant figures

Notice, with sufficient practice all five steps listed can be configured as follows:

$$(a) \quad x \text{ Btu/min} = 225 \text{ hp} = \frac{225 \text{ hp}}{1.0} \times \frac{2.546\ 1 \times 10^3 \text{ Btu}}{1.0 \text{ hp} \cdot \text{h}} \times \frac{1.0 \text{ hr}}{60 \text{ min}}$$

$$= 9.55 \times 10^3 \text{ Btu/min}$$

$$(b) \quad x \text{ kW} = 225 \text{ hp} = \frac{225 \text{ hp}}{1.0} \frac{0.745\ 70 \text{ kW}}{1.0 \text{ hp}} = 168 \text{ kW}$$

7.10 Celsius, Fahrenheit, and Absolute Scales

Temperature scales also appear in two common forms, the Celsius scale (previously called centigrade) and the Fahrenheit scale. The Celsius scale has the same temperature increment as its absolute thermodynamic scale, the Kelvin scale. However, the zero point on the Celsius scale is 273.15 K above absolute zero.

$$t(°C) = T(K) - 273.15 \tag{7.1}$$

Scales more commonly used in the United States are the Fahrenheit scale and its corresponding absolute thermodynamic scale, the Rankine scale. A unit degree on the Fahrenheit scale is precisely the same as a unit degree on the Rankine scale. However, the zero point on the Fahrenheit scale is 459.67°R above absolute zero. (See Table 7.10.)

$$t(°F) = T(°R) - 459.67 \tag{7.2}$$

When these relationships are combined, a convenient equation can be developed for conversion between Celsius and Fahrenheit or vice versa.

$$t(°F) = 9/5 t(°C) + 32°F \tag{7.3}$$

$$t(°C) = 5/9 [t(°F) - 32°F] \tag{7.4}$$

Table 7.10   Temperature scales

	°R	K	°F	°C
Abs Zero	0	0	−459.67	−273.15
°F = °C	419.67	233.15	−40	−40
Zero on °F	459.67	255.37	0	−17.78
Zero on °C	491.67	273.15	32	0
Boiling	671.67	373.15	212	100

If you were to construct the above Rankine and Kelvin scales parallel to each other, they would begin at absolute zero and be graduated and calibrated to the boiling point of water. To simplify the comparison consider only the portion of the scales from freezing to boiling. On the Rankine scale there are 180 degrees (671.67 − 491.67) and on the Kelvin scale only 100 (373.15 − 273.15). When you divide these two quantities by 20 (180/20) and (100/20) it becomes apparent that 9 degrees on the Rankine scale is equivalent to 5 degrees on the Kelvin scale or 9°R = 5 K. So if you are converting from one scale to the other you must use the conversion factor 9°R = 5 K, the factor that makes the scales equivalent.

Example Problem 7.7   Convert 373.15 K to a Rankine temperature.

$$373.15 \text{ K} = \frac{373.15 \text{ K}}{1.0} \times \frac{9°\text{R}}{5 \text{ K}} = 671.67 °\text{R}$$

Example Problem 7.8   The Universal Gas Constant (UGC) in the different unit systems has been determined as follow:

$$\text{UGC} = 1\ 545 \text{ ft} \cdot \text{lbf/lbmol} \cdot °\text{R} = 1.986 \text{ Btu/lbmol} \cdot °\text{R} = 8.314 \text{ kJ/kmol} \cdot \text{K}$$

Show how you would convert from 1 545 · lbf/lbmol · °R to 8.314 kJ/kmol · K

$$1\ 545 \frac{\text{ft} \cdot \text{lbf}}{\text{lbmol} \cdot °\text{R}} = \frac{1\ 545 \text{ ft} \cdot \text{lbf}}{\text{lbmol} \cdot °\text{R}} \times \frac{4.448\ 2 \text{ N}}{\text{lbf}} \times \frac{\text{lbmol}}{0.453\ 59 \text{ kmol}} \times \frac{\text{m}}{3.280\ 8 \text{ ft}}$$

$$\times \frac{9°\text{R}}{5 \text{ K}} \times \frac{\text{J}}{\text{N} \cdot \text{m}} \times \frac{\text{kJ}}{1\ 000 \text{ J}} = 8.313 \text{ kJ/kmol} \cdot \text{K}$$

Example Problem 7.9   Convert 98.6°F to °C.

Solution A

$$t(°\text{C}) = [(t°\text{F}) − 32]5/9 = 333/9 = 37.0°\text{C}$$

Solution B

$$T(°\text{R}) = 98.6 + 459.67 = 558.27°\text{R}$$

$$558.27 °\text{R} = \frac{558.27 °\text{R}}{1.0} \times \frac{5 \text{ K}}{9°\text{R}} = 310.15 \text{ K}$$

$$t(°\text{C}) = 310.15 − 273.15 = 37.0°\text{C}$$

The problem of unit conversion becomes more complex if an equation has a constant with hidden dimensions. It is necessary to work through the equation converting the constant K_1 to a new constant K_2 consistent with the equation units.

Consider the following example problem.

Example Problem 7.10   The velocity of sound in air (c) can be expressed as a function of temperature (T):

$$c = 49.02 \sqrt{T}$$

where c is in feet per second and T is in degrees Rankine.

Find an equivalent relationship when c is in meters per second and T is in kelvins.

Procedure

1. First, the given equation must have consistent units; that is, it must have the same units on both sides. Squaring both sides we see that

$$c^2 \, (\text{ft}^2/\text{s}^2) = 49.02^2 \, T°R$$

From this equation it is apparent that the constant $(49.02)^2$ must have units in order to maintain unit consistency. (The constant must have the same units as c^2/T.)

Solving for the constant,

$$(49.02)^2 = c^2 \, \frac{\text{ft}^2}{\text{s}^2}\left[\frac{1}{T\cdot°R}\right] = \frac{c^2}{T}\left[\frac{\text{ft}^2}{\text{s}^2°R}\right]$$

2. The next step is to convert the constant $49.02^2 \, \text{ft}^2/(\text{s}^2°R)$ to a new constant that will allow us to calculate c in meters per second given T in kelvins. We recognize that the new constant must have units of square meters per second squared per kelvin.

$$\frac{(49.02)^2\text{ft}^2}{\text{s}^2°R} = \frac{(49.02)^2\text{ft}^2}{1.0 \, \text{s}^2°R} \times \frac{(0.304\ 8 \, \text{m})^2}{(1 \, \text{ft})^2} \times \frac{9°R}{5 \, \text{K}} = \frac{401.84 \, \text{m}^2}{1 \, \text{s}^2\text{K}}$$

3. Substitute this new constant 401.84 back into the original equation

$$c^2 = 401.84T$$
$$c = 20.05 \sqrt{T}$$

where c is in meters per second and T is in kelvins. If you wish to verify this new equation, take a temperature in Fahrenheit (80°F) and convert to Rankine (540°R). Take the original equation and compute the value of c (1 139 ft/s).

Next convert 80°F to kelvins (26.67 + 273.15), calculate c (347.17 m/s), and convert back to ft/s.

$$1\ 139 \, \text{ft/s} = \frac{1\ 139 \, \text{ft}}{1.0 \, \text{s}} \times \frac{0.304\ 8 \, \text{m}}{1.0 \, \text{ft}} = 347.17 \, \text{m/s}$$

You will have verified the new constant.

Problems

7.1 Using the correct number of significant figures, convert the following physical quantities into the proper SI units.

(a) 365 hp
(b) 640 acres
(c) 56 000 ft^3
(d) 712 ft/s
(e) 95 mph

(f) 185 slugs
(g) 285 lbm
(h) 3 675 ft
(i) 2 965 gal
(j) 2 345 miles

7.2 Convert the following to SI units, using the correct significant figures.

(a) 815 slugs/min
(b) 22.7 Btu/min
(c) 72°F
(d) 405 oz
(e) 8.75 atm

(f) 182 bushels/acre
(g) 115 hp·hr
(h) 32.6 lbm/ft^3
(i) 0.175×10^4 ft^3/hr
(j) 5 675 lbf

7.3 Convert as indicated giving the answer using proper significant figures.

(a) 19.75 ft to millimeters
(b) 365.5 ft^3 to L
(c) 373 K to degrees Rankine
(d) 5 595 bushels to cubic meters
(e) 455 250 Btu/h to kilowatts

7.4 Convert as indicated giving the answer using proper significant figures.

(a) 7 255 ft·lbf to joules
(b) 14.7 lbf/in^2 to pascals
(c) 29 035 ft to m
(d) 185.7 slugs/ft^3 to grams per cubic centimeter
(e) 32°F to Kelvin

7.5 Using the rules for expressing SI units, correct each of the following if given incorrectly.

(a) 12 amps
(b) 12.5 cm's
(c) 250 degrees Kelvin
(d) 125.0 m m
(e) 152 KW/hours

(f) 6.7 m/s/s
(g) 86.3 j
(h) 3 500 K
(i) 375 n
(j) 4 225 pa

7.6 Using the rules for expressing SI units, correct each of the following if given incorrectly.

(a) 5.50 N
(b) 63.5 C
(c) 108 farads
(d) 65 nM
(e) 17 m per s

(f) 725 N/m/m
(g) 72.0 Kg
(h) 750 J/sec
(i) 95 A's
(j) 1.5 m · m

7.7 If a force of 2.45×10^3 N is required to lift an object with a uniform velocity and an acceleration of gravity shown as follows, determine the mass, in kg, of the object:

(a) 23.7 ft/s^2
(b) 9.43 m/s^2

7.8 If you were on another planet, say, Mars, which of the following, g_C or g_L, would change and which would stay constant? Explain the difference.

7.9 Determine the acceleration of gravity required (meters per second squared) to lift a 1 500 kg object at a uniform velocity when the force exerted is

(a) 2.695×10^3 lbf
(b) 14.6×10^3 N

7.10 The average density of Styrofoam is 1.00 kg/m^3. If a Styrofoam cooler is made with outside dimensions of $50.0 \times 35.0 \times 30.0$ cm and the uniform thickness of the Styrofoam is 3.00 cm (including the lid), what is the volume of the Styrofoam used in cubic inches? What is the mass in lbm? How many gallons of liquid could be stored in the cooler?

7.11 A small town purchased a 35 ft diameter cylindrical tank for potable water in the event of an emergency. The town consists of 4 300 family units. If each family were to collect 35 gallons of water, what would be the minimum height of the tank?

7.12 The *Eurostar* provides international high speed train service between Paris, London, and Brussels through the English Channel Tunnel. *Eurostar* trainsets can operate at maximum speeds of 3.00×10^2 km/h. Assume that the resistance between the train and the track is 115×10^3 newtons. If air resistance adds an additional 25.5×10^3 newtons, determine the horsepower needed to power the engine at maximum speed.
[Note: Power = (force) × (velocity)]

7.13 *Eurostar's* nose is computer-optimized for running in the Channel Tunnel where pressure waves can affect passenger comfort. The tunnel itself is passed at a reduced speed of 1.6×10^2 km/h. Determine the length of time it takes to complete the 23 mile underwater portion of the trip from London to Paris.

7.14 You have recently graduated from college and decided to build a new home. The basement floor and foundation walls will be constructed from poured concrete. The outside dimensions of the foundation walls are 7.0×10^1 ft in length × 5.0×10^1 ft wide × 10 ft high with 8 in. thick walls. The basement floor is poured to the inside of the foundation walls and is 6 in. thick.
(a) How many yards of concrete will need to be ordered rounding up to the nearest cubic yard?
(b) What will be the mass of both the foundation walls and floor in lbm?

7.15 The Hubert H. Humphrey Metrodome in Minneapolis, Minnesota opened in 1982 at a cost of $55 million. To prepare for the footings, etc., 300 000 cubic yards of dirt were removed. Its inflatable roof covers 10.0 acres and its interior volume is 60.0×10^6 cubic feet. During construction, 40.0×10^3 cubic yards of concrete, 11.9×10^3 tons of reinforcing steel, and 5.00×10^2 tons of structural steel were utilized. The roof material includes an outer layer of Teflon-coated fiberglass and an inner layer of woven fiberglass. Given this information, answer the following:
(a) If removed evenly over the 10 acres, how deep of a hole would be formed as a result of the excavation?
(b) What is the total mass of concrete and steel in lbm?
(c) If the two-layer fiberglass roofing material has a mass of 0.6667 lbm/ft², what is the total mass of the roof?
(d) If 10.0 in. of wet snow collected on the roof (this happened in 1982), what is the added mass to the roof? (Assume 1 in. of water equals 10 in. of snow.)

7.16 The U.S. currently imports 9.5×10^6 barrels of oil each day. If a cylindrical storage tank were to be constructed with a base of 50.0 ft.
(a) What would be the height of the container to store this daily consumption?
(b) Recall that Mt. Everest is 29 028 ft. What would the diameter of the cylinder have to be to match the height of Mt. Everest?

7.17 Construction sand is piled in a right cone that has a height of 35.0 feet and a diameter of 95.0 feet. If this sand has a density of 97.0 lbm/ft³,
(a) determine the volume of the cone
(b) determine the mass of the sand in the cone
(c) during the winter months the sand will be spread on county roads. Using a spreadsheet, determine the volume and mass of the sand remaining if the height decreases from 35.0 to 5.00 ft in increments of 1.0 ft. Assume that the base remains constant.

7.18 A cylindrical underground storage tank with a diameter of 18.0 ft and a height of 25.0 ft is filled with gasoline. Given a density of 675 kg/m³, determine the mass of the gas in the tank in both lbm and kg. If the average automobile gas tank holds 25.0 gal, calculate the number of autos that may be filled from this underground facility.

7.19 A cylindrical tank is 25.0 ft long and 10.0 ft in diameter is oriented such that its longitudinal axis is horizontal. Develop a table that will
  (a) Show how many gallons of diesel fuel are in the tank if the fluid level is measured in 1.00 ft increments from the bottom of the tank.
  (b) Show the corresponding mass at each increment, in kg, if the specific gravity is 0.73.

7.20 A southwest rancher constructs a spherical water tank that is 10 ft in diameter. Develop a table that will
  (a) Show how many gallons of water are contained in the tank if the volume is measured in 1.00 ft increments from the bottom to the top of the container.
  (b) Determine the mass of water at each increment in lbm.

7.21 The ideal gas law shows the relationship among some common properties of ideal gases.

$$pV = nRT$$

where

p = pressure

V = volume

n = number of moles of the ideal gas

R = universal gas constant = 8.314 kJ/(kmol K)

T = absolute temperature

If you have 8 moles of an ideal gas at 35 degrees Celsius and it is stored in a cubic container with inside dimensions of 0.750 meters on each side, calculate the pressure in Pa.

7.22 Approximately 50 000 years ago a meteorite hit the earth near Winslow, Arizona. The impact crater is 1 200 m in diameter and 170 m deep. Determine the volume of earth in ft³ removed assuming the crater to be a spherical segment. Verify that the radius of the sphere is approximately 1 150 m.

7.23 Conservation of energy suggests that potential energy is converted to kinetic energy when an object falls in a vacuum. $KE = \dfrac{mV^2}{2g_C}$ and $PE = \dfrac{mg_L h}{g_C}$ Velocity at impact can be determined as follows:

$$V = Constant \sqrt{h}$$

  (a) Determine the constant so that the equation is valid for h in ft and V in feet per second (ft/s).
  (b) Determine the constant so that the equation is valid for h in ft but V in mph.
  (c) If you drop an object from 455 ft, what is the velocity on impact with the ground in mph and ft/s?

7.24 A small portable cylindrical pressure tank has inside dimensions of 14.0 in. (dia) and 36.0 in. end to end. The maximum recommended safety pressure at 70°F is 200 psi. The device has a safety release value set at 250 psi.
  (a) Determine the inside volume of the pressure tank in ft³.
  (b) Calculate the specific volume of the tank at 70°F and 200 psi. (See below)
  (c) Find the mass of air in the tank from part b.
  (d) If the homeowner inserts 3.5 lbm of air into the tank at 70°F, what would be the reading on the tank pressure gauge.
  (e) With the aid of a spreadsheet determine the temperature from part d at which the safety gauge would release starting at 70°F and increasing in 10 degree increments.

$$P_v = RT$$

Pressure, P, lbf/ft²

Sp. Vol., v − ft³/lbm

Gas constant for air, (R_{air} = 53.33 ft · lbf/lbm°R)

Temperature, T − °R

7.25 A Midwest Cooperative needs to store 15 750 gallons of a liquid chemical. They are considering two possible containers, a hollow cylinder or a hollow sphere. The wall of the sphere will need to be 6 in. thick and the wall, top and bottom of the cylinder are each 6 in. thick. Due to space limitations the height of the cylinder must be 26.0 ft.

(a) What will be the outside diameter of the cylinder required to hold the liquid chemical?

(b) What will be the outside diameter of the sphere?

(c) Assume the containers are made of aluminum, which container uses the most material?

CHAPTER **15**

Energy Sources and Alternatives

Chapter Objectives

When you complete your study of this chapter, you will able to:

- Understand the impact that new technology will have on global energy supply and demand.
- Understand the source and use of fossil fuels in the United States, the world, and especially in developing countries
- Distinguish among the positive and negative facets of various alternative energy sources
- Use information gathered on the Internet to summarize the world dependence on petroleum, coal, and natural gas today and 20 years into the future
- Evaluate alternatives to the dependence on fossil fuels in the transportation, home heating, and electricity generation sectors
- Use information from this chapter as a basis for expansion of your knowledge and ability to think, design, and live "GREEN"

15.1   Introduction

Energy is one of the world's most important commodities. If we were to look for one event that characterized the transformation of society during the past 200 years it would be the Industrial Revolution, which provided a direct substitution of machine power for muscle power. This transformation, however, has been sustained by the depletion of natural resources, namely, fossil fuels—primarily oil, coal, and natural gas. Energy from these fossil fuels is converted into forms that can be stored, transported, and used at the appropriate time and place. To some extent the development of any society can be determined by the amount of energy usage. There is a strong correlation between productivity of a nation and its capability to generate energy. Figure 15.1 graphically illustrates the dramatic increase in the consumption of fossil fuels by the United States over the past 150 years. Notice in particular the demand for petroleum, coal, and natural gas.

Unfortunately, the heavy reliance that world economies and in particular the United States have placed on the use of fossil fuels presents a most unique challenge for science and engineering in the near future. As supplies dwindle, either additional fossil fuels must be located or they must be replaced by alternate sources such as nuclear, hydro, geothermal, solar, and wind as well as increased conservation measures.

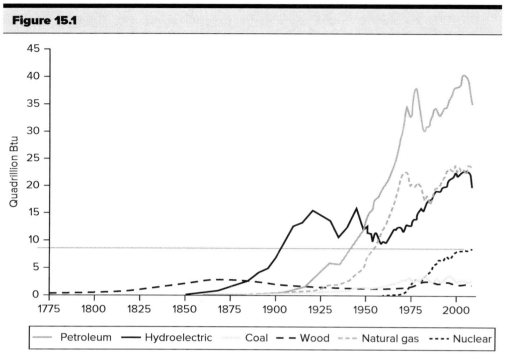

Figure 15.1

History of Energy Consumption in the United States, 1775–2009
Source: **Energy Information Administration, U.S. Department of Energy**

We will begin this chapter with a short history of fossilized fuel formation and recovery. Then we will discuss the major areas of energy consumption in the United States and review some alternative sources of power and energy that will most certainly be a part of your lives and careers.

15.2   Fossil Fuels

Over the past several hundreds of millions of years, energy-rich substances were formed from buried plants and microorganisms. Eventually, when conditions were favorable—if there was sufficient temperature and pressure—this organic material chemically transformed into hydrocarbons. Depending on the time period, the underground formations, and the type of organic materials, these formations ultimately resulted in deposits of petroleum, coal, or natural gas.

15.2.1   Petroleum Formation and Recovery

Petroleum is formed from microscopic plants and bacteria that lived in the ancient oceans and saltwater seas. When these microorganisms died and settled to the seafloor, an organic-rich mud was formed. This mud was covered with heavy layers of sediment; over time, the resulting heat and compression chemically transformed the organic matter into petroleum and natural gas.

In the quest to find oil, geologists search for regions with three primary conditions necessary for petroleum formation: organic-rich source rock, relatively high temperatures that would generate petroleum from organic matter, and petroleum-trapping rock formations such as salt domes.

15.2.2   Coal Formation and Recovery

Coal is a solid fossil fuel formed from trees, ferns, and mosses that grew in ancient swamps, in bogs, and along coastal shorelines. The high pressure and temperature associated with the burial of these plants under heavy layers of sediment caused the original organic matter to become increasingly carbon-rich. The successive stages of coal formation range from peat, which is partially carbonized matter, to anthracite, which is hard coal with the highest carbon content and the lowest moisture content.

The majority of the world's coal beds have been located and are included in the world demonstrated reserve base (DRB). Not all coal in the DRB is recoverable, but the efforts of scientists and engineers in the last century have improved coal-mining methods and increased the recoverable percentage.

15.2.3   Natural Gas Formation and Recovery

Natural gas is formed from plankton (mainly algae and protozoans) that died and settled to the floor of the ancient oceans. Again, the organic matter was buried and compressed under layers of sediment for millions of years. Natural gas is primarily composed of methane and other light hydrocarbons.

Natural gas is much lighter (less dense) and forms a layer over the petroleum or coal deposits with which it is often found. Natural gas deposits are removed by wells drilled deep into the ground. Historically, natural gas was considered a waste byproduct of petroleum and coal mining, but demand has grown for this product because it can be piped directly to commercial plants and residences and because it is a cleaner-burning fuel than either petroleum or coal.

15.3   Finite Supply of Fossil Fuels

Since fossil fuels such as coal, oil, and natural gas took millions of years to form, energy derived from fossil fuels is a truly finite resource. Once fossilized fuels are consumed, they are gone forever and alternative energy sources must be identified and employed to supply our growing demand.

15.3.1   U.S. Oil Reserves, Consumption, and Production

We use the term "oil production" in this text as it refers to petroleum, but that is something of a misnomer. Whereas the objective of oil "producers" is to locate deposits, drill wells, refine, and distribute oil and its byproducts, the producers do not and cannot create or manufacture oil. Oil production by Exxon, British Petroleum, and others simply denotes the ability to make available a resource that is becoming more difficult to provide.

The world's first oil well was drilled in 1859 in Titusville, Pennsylvania. The main byproduct at that time was kerosene, which began to replace whale oil for use in lamps. Shortly thereafter, in 1861, a German entrepreneur invented the first gasoline-burning engine, and the demand for oil as a substitute for coal began to grow (see Figure 15.1). In the mid-1950s petroleum was in high supply, and gasoline cost about $0.25 per gallon. Everyone thought that petroleum was available in limitless quantities and the supply would last for centuries.

One individual, however, did not agree. A geophysicist by the name of M. King Hubbert, working for the Shell Oil Company in the 1950s, predicted that at the rate oil was being extracted from wells in the United States, production would peak in the early 1970s and thereafter forever decline. Hubbert was reasonably correct—U.S. oil production peaked in 1970 at approximately 11 million barrels per day and has in general declined to a 2008 level of about 5 million barrels per day. Hubbert's prediction, which came to be known as Hubbert's peak, proved to be accurate until technology introduced the ability for deep water drilling and hydraulic fracturing. See Section 15.3.8. Figure 15.2 illustrates the peak of oil production in the United States, the rapid increase in consumption, and, most striking, the dramatic increase in net imports needed to offset lower production and increased consumption. As you review Figure 15.2 realize that the production line on the graph includes both crude oil and natural gas plant liquids, and the net import line is imports minus exports.

Until the 1950s the United States produced all the petroleum it needed. Beginning in 1997, the United States imported more petroleum than it produced. In 2008 we consumed 19.5 million barrels of oil per day, of which over 11 million (57 percent) was from net imports. By 2010 consumption was down to 19.1 million barrels per day, with net imports down to 9.4 million (50 percent). Although the United States is starting to move in the right direction, it continues to rely heavily on foreign sources. Worldwide consumption in 2012 was 89.7 million barrels per day, so the United States, which makes up 5 percent of the world population, consumes 20.6 percent of the world's total oil and natural gas production.

Since we are listing production and consumption in both barrels per day and quadrillion (10^{15}) Btu, let's define a barrel. A barrel of oil contains 42 U.S. gallons of crude oil, equivalent to 5 800 000 Btu. Due to a reduction in the density during

Figure 15.2

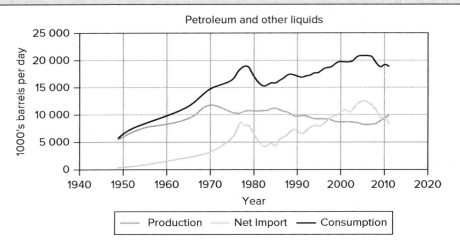

Consumption, Production and Import Trends (1949–2011)
Source: **Energy Information Administration, U.S. Department of Energy**

Table 15.1 Consumption of Petroleum Products

	2008 Barrels of Oil	Percentage	2013 Barrels of Oil	Percentage
Motor Gasoline	8 989	46.1	8 843	46.89
Diesel Fuel and Heating Oil	3 945	20.23	3 827	20.29
Liquefied Petroleum Gases (LPG)	1 954	10.02	2 440	12.94
Kero-Type Jet Fuel	1 539	7.89	1 398	7.41
Still Gas	670	3.44	702	3.72
Residual Fuel Oil	622	3.19	319	1.69
Petroluem Coke	464	2.38	354	1.88
Asphalt and Road Oil	417	2.14	323	1.71
Feedstock Oils	304	1.56	105	0.56
Naptha for Feedstocks	248	1.27	270	1.43
Lubricants	131	0.67	121	0.64
Misc. Products	67	0.34	81	0.43
Special Napthas	44	0.23	52	0.28
Aviation Gas	15	0.08	12	0.06
Kerosene	14	0.07	5	0.03
Waxes	9	0.05	8	0.04
			18 860	
Total	19 498*	100	18 860*	100

*Consumption in 1 000 barrels of oil per day
Source: Energy Information Administration, U.S. Department of Energy

the refining process, a barrel of 42 U.S. gallons of crude oil yields nearly 45 gallons of petroleum products.

Table 15.1 illustrates the actual deposition of petroleum products used each day in the United States during the years 2008 and 2013. Motor gasoline accounts for 46 percent of the total which is used primarily for cars and light trucks.

15.3.2   World Oil Reserves, Consumption, and Production

Scientists and geologists began to extend Hubbert's principles to predict when world petroleum production would peak and then forever decline. Most scientists agree that the world oil peak will occur within the next 10 to 20 years. Remember, the peak of oil production ("peak oil") occurs when approximately half of the oil has been extracted. After the peak has been reached it will take some number of years to extract the remaining oil. The exact time period from peak oil until the last drop depends primarily on rate of extraction.

Within a few years, half of the world's oil reserves will have been depleted. The remaining reserves, estimated at one trillion barrels are being consumed at a rate of 30 billion barrels annually. That suggests it will be 30 to 35 years until the complete depletion of petroleum occurs, assuming that usage stays constant. A more likely scenario is that world demand will increase with a decrease in supply. Additional pressure on oil supply will come not only from the United States, where demand is projected to grow by 2 percent annually, but even more so from the rapidly expanding economies in countries like China and India, where demand is currently expanding between 5 and 10 percent annually.

Figure 15.3

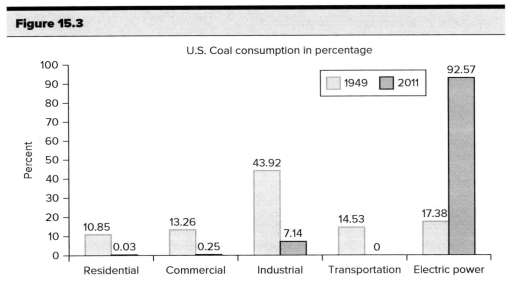

Source: Energy Information Administration, U.S. Department of Energy

15.3.3   U.S. Coal Reserves, Consumption, and Production

The United States has vast reserves of coal. The demonstrated reserve base (DRB) was estimated in 2013 to be 481 billion short tons. However, due to property rights, land use constraints, and environmental restrictions, only about half of the DRB is considered recoverable, in other words 200–250 billion short tons. In recent years approximately 80 to 100 million short tons of coal are consumed annually in the United States. Figure 15.3 illustrates changes in the percentage of coal used by major consumers over a nearly 60 plus year period. Currently, the majority of the coal consumed in the United States (93 percent), is for the generation of electricity.

15.3.4   World Coal Reserves and Consumption

Worldwide, coal is the most abundant of the fossil fuels and its reserves are the most widely distributed. The world's total recoverable reserves are approximately one trillion short tons. The United States has 28 percent of the global coal reserves, Russia 19 percent, China 14 percent, and India 7 percent. At current rates of consumption (five billion metric tons per year) worldwide reserves could, in theory, last for another 200 years.

15.3.5   U.S. Natural Gas Reserves and Consumption

The vast majority of natural gas reserves exist outside the United States (see Figure 15.4). Note that only 4.5 percent or 308 trillion cubic feet of the world natural gas reserves are located the United States. However, the United States accounts for 24 percent of the world annual consumption.

Figure 15.4

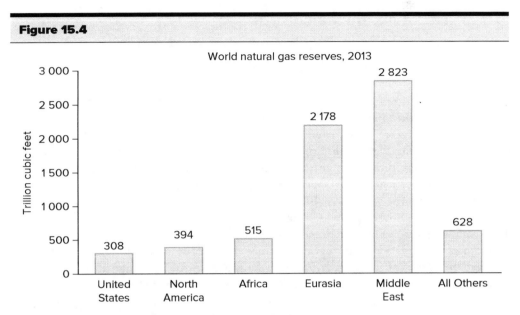

Source: **Energy Information Administration, U.S. Department of Energy**

15.3.6 World Natural Gas Reserves and Consumption

The world reserve of natural gas is estimated to be 6 846 trillion cubic feet with an annual worldwide use of approximately 96 trillion cubic feet, suggesting depletion in about 70 years. But depletion is likely to come sooner than that. In 20 years the world annual consumption is expected to reach 150 trillion cubic feet, a projected increase of nearly 60%, primarily due to increased demand from developing countries.

15.3.7 U.S. Oil and Natural Gas Production in the 21st Century

The total World and U.S. oil and natural gas reserves will not suddenly be multiplied or magically increased because it does in fact require millions of years for those deposits to form. In recent years the United States as well as other countries have developed the ability to locate and extract both oil and natural gas from deep within the earth by methods that were previously not economically feasible. There are two fundamental reasons for this change, an added emphasis on deepwater drilling and even more recently an improvement in a methodology called hydraulic fracturing.

Deepwater drilling, as for example in the Gulf of Mexico, has enhanced our ability to locate and extract additional oil and natural gas. However, as the water becomes deeper drilling becomes more difficult. An example of the danger can be illustrated by the BP oil spill in 2010.

The major reason for the recent increase in oil and natural gas location and extraction, however, is the result of hydraulic fracturing, commonly called fracking.

15.3.8 Hydraulic Fracturing

Hydraulic fracturing differs from conventional drilling methods in the following way.

A conventional well establishes a drilling platform then drills a vertical shaft to the location of the resource. A typical well may be from 6 000 to 10 000 feet. Once it reaches its target, perhaps a layer of shale, the extraction process begins. Recently technology has introduced the ability to start with the same vertical well but once the target or "payzone" is reached it is now possible to modify the drill angle from vertical to horizontal. A single horizontal line can extend up to two miles from the drilling pad. In addition, as many as 20–50 different horizontal lines can be drilled from the same vertical well. Once these shafts have been drilled and secured, the next step in the process is possible. That step is called hydraulic fracturing and it is the process of breaking apart rocks that are rich in oil and natural gas so that these valuable resources can flow back into the well. To accomplish this requires as much as perhaps a million gallon mixture of water, sand, and chemicals that are injected into the well at a very high pressure. Pressures can range from 10 000 to 15 000 psi. This pressurized mixture causes the rock to crack. The mixture consists of approximately 90 percent water, 9.5 percent sand, and the remaining 0.5 percent is a mix of many different chemicals. Once the rock is fractured the sand acts as an agent to keep the rock open thus allowing more oil and gas to be recovered.

Hydraulic fracturing actually began experimentally in 1947. In the beginning it was used to enhance vertically drilled wells, but the process only marginally increased the amount of oil and natural gas. However, with the increased application of horizontal drilling or what is called "smart drilling," the United States has increased its domestic natural gas supply by 34 percent since 2005. The United States is currently the world's leading producer of natural gas. To further emphasize this point, since the fracking boom begin in 2008 the United States has increased its oil production from 7 million barrels per day to 10 million barrels per day in 2014.

Figures 15.5 and 15.6 illustrate the effects that deep water drilling and fracking have had on natural gas and oil production in the United States starting around 2008.

Figure 15.5

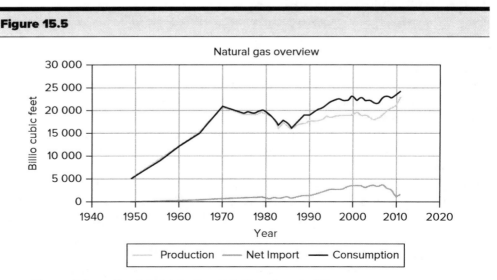

Source: **Energy Information Administration, U.S. Department of Energy**

Figure 15.6

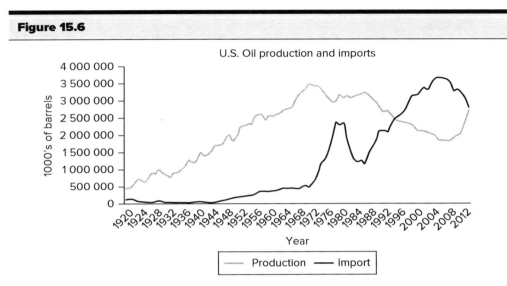

U.S. Oil production and imports

Year

Production — Import

Source: **Energy Information Administration, U.S. Department of Energy**

15.3.9   Conclusion

As authors of this text we have no way of predicting the actual undiscovered reserves, changes in technology, or the future demand for petroleum, coal and natural gas, but we do know that it took millions of years to create these fossil fuels and that they are rapidly being depleted. What we can do is make it perfectly clear that if the United States continues to use large amounts of energy, then a need for the immediate development of alternative forms most certainly exists.

15.4   Major Areas of Energy Consumption in the United States

The four primary areas of energy consumption in the United States are transportation, industrial, residential/commercial, and electric power. Figure 15.7 provides an overview of the quantities of energy from supply sources and the amounts consumed by each sector. Notice in particular the percentage of renewable energy. We see that 82 percent of the nearly 95 quadrillion Btu of energy consumed by the United States in 2012 was provided by fossil fuels.

15.4.1   Transportation

As mentioned earlier, the United States consumes 18.9 million barrels (795 million gallons) of petroleum products each day, almost half of it in the form of gasoline. Consumption of gasoline in 2013 was 135 billion gallons, which is an average of 371 million gallons per day. There are approximately 250 million vehicles in the U.S. that consume gasoline and they each travel over 12 000 miles per year. The majority of gasoline is used in cars and light trucks.

While getting the oil out of the ground and refining it is complicated, moving it from the point of production to the refinery and on to the final consumer is just as complex. The refining process usually involves (1) distillation, or separation of the hydrocarbons

Figure 15.7

Primary energy consumption by source and sector, 2012
(Quadrillion Btu)

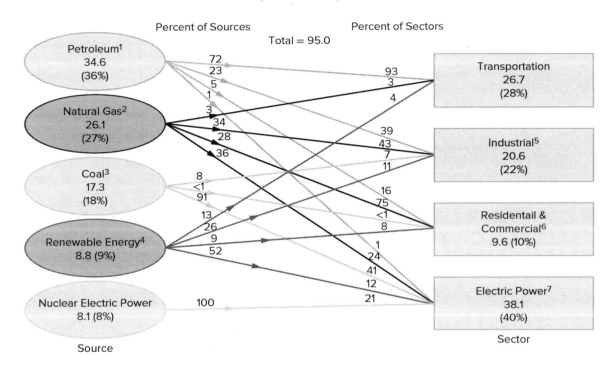

Source: **Energy Information Administration, U.S. Department of Energy**

that make up crude oil so that the heavier products such as asphalt are separated from the lighter products like kerosene; (2) conversion, or cracking of the molecules to allow the refiner to squeeze a higher percentage of light products such as gasoline from each barrel of oil; and (3) treatment or enhancement of the quality of the product, which could entail removing sulfur from such fuels as kerosene, gasoline, and heating oil. The addition of blending components to gasoline is also a part of this process.

After crude oil is refined into gasoline and other petroleum products, the products must be distributed to consumers. The majority of gasoline is delivered first by pipeline—today, there are more than 160 000 miles of pipeline in the United States—to storage terminals near consuming areas, and then loaded into trucks for delivery to individual gas stations.

In 2011 the transportation sector (automobile, truck, train, aircraft, and military) demands were 96 percent dependent on crude oil derivatives. Price levels and economic growth trends both influence the demand for petroleum products (see Figure 15.8). High prices tend to provide incentives for individuals and industry to adopt short-term conservation measures such as reducing discretionary driving as well as long-term measures like design changes that increase fuel efficiency.

Technology is beginning to develop alternatives to the gasoline and diesel vehicles that are the primary sources of transportation in the U.S. today. Research on a wide variety of alternative fuel vehicles includes hybrid, biodiesel, flex-fuel, ethanol, nature gas, propane, hydrogen, electric, and fuel cell.

Figure 15.8

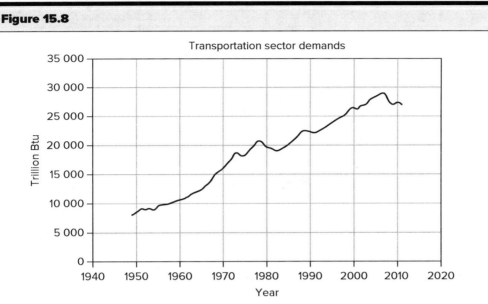

Transportation sector demands

Source: **Energy Information Administration, U.S. Department of Energy**

For example, the hybrid-electric vehicles were some of the first alternatives to the standard gasoline engines, by coupling an electric motor with a gasoline engine to improve fuel economy.

Unlike the all-electric vehicles the hybrid does not need to be plugged into an external source of electricity to be charged.

15.4.2   Generation of Electricity

Approximately 40 quadrillion (40×10^{15}) Btu of energy are consumed annually in the United States to generate electricity. Roughly one-third of that amount is converted into usable electricity provided by utilities to the end user. The other two-thirds is lost as waste heat and other inefficiencies.

American consumers expect electricity to be available whenever they plug in an appliance or flip a switch. Satisfying these instantaneous demands requires an uninterrupted flow of electricity. In order to meet this requirement, utilities operate several types of electric generating facilities, powered by a wide range of fuel sources. In 2014 as illustrated in Figure 15.9 approximately 67 percent of U.S. electrical power generation totaling 4 058 billon kilowatt-hours results from burning fossil fuels.

Dependence on fossil fuels can be replaced with increased use of alternatives like nuclear and renewable resources. It is much more reasonable to envision a changeover in the source fuel for electrical generation sector than it is for changeover in source fuel in the transportation sector.

This use of energy to produce electricity can be achieved by a variety of fuels and generating techniques, including

- *Steam power plants.* In a boiler, water is heated to a high temperature forming high-pressure steam. The steam is sent through a turbine that turns an electric generator.

Figure 15.9

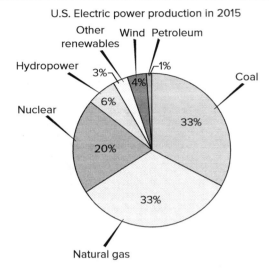

U.S. Electric power production in 2015

Source: **Energy Information Administration, U.S. Department of Energy**

- *Gas turbine power plant.* The fossil fuel is burned to create a hot gas, which goes through the turbine.
- *Internal-combustion equipment.* This method uses petroleum products to drive the internal-combustion equipment that turns the generator.
- *Nuclear reactors.* A nuclear reactor is a controlled fission process that provides energy (heat) to water, which in turn delivers high-temperature, high-pressure steam to the turbine, which drives the electric generator.

Wind turbines, hydroelectric turbines, and geothermal power plants can produce electricity as well. These together with municipal waste heat combustion, solar energy, and wood provide the renewable sources of electrical generation.

15.4.3   Home Heating

The most popular home heating fuel is gas. Fifty-seven percent of U.S. households are heated with natural gas or liquefied petroleum gas (LPG). The second most frequently used energy source is electricity (31.3 percent); the remaining homes use heating oil, kerosene, or wood.

The United States has two sources of heating oil: domestic refineries and imports from foreign countries. Refineries produce heating oil as a part of the "distillate fuel oil" product family, which includes heating oils and diesel fuel. Distillate products are shipped throughout the United States by pipelines, barges, tankers, trucks, and rail cars. Most imports of distillate come from Canada, the Virgin Islands, and Venezuela.

Recall that natural gas is withdrawn from the Earth's interior. It is primarily methane (90 percent) with propane, butane, and ethane. LPG is also a member of the family of light hydrocarbons. It consists of a mixture of propane and butane and it can be obtained from either natural gas or petroleum refinement.

Heat pumps can be used in southern climates for both heating and cooling. In the more northern areas geothermal heat pumps are becoming increasingly popular. Instead of using air as the heat transfer medium, they use water piped underground.

Conservation methods may include adjusting thermostats and improved insulation in newly constructed and existing homes. Again, it is reasonable to consider alternative sources for the U.S. dependence on natural gas as worldwide supplies dwindle.

15.4.4 Energy Projections over the Next 25 Years

The Energy Information Administration (EIA), while preparing projections for its annual energy review, evaluated a number of trends and issues that could affect tomorrow's energy demands. Future trends in energy supply and demand are influenced by factors that make predictions difficult. Factors include public policy decisions, energy prices, economic growth, and technology advances.

The information presented in this section is an abbreviated review of EIA projections to the year 2040. For the complete text of the overview, visit www.eia.doe.gov. Total primary energy consumption as illustrated in Figure 15.10 currently project a slight increase per year. The United States consumed 96.8 quadrillion Btu of energy in 2011, that number is expected to increase slightly to 106 quadrillion Btu annually by 2040.

The EIA projects that electricity generation will increase from 3 826 billion kilowatt-hours in 2012 to 4 954 billion kilowatt-hours in 2040. To meet this projection, a slight increase in the consumption of coal and a much larger increase in the consumption of natural gas is expected.

Figure 15.10

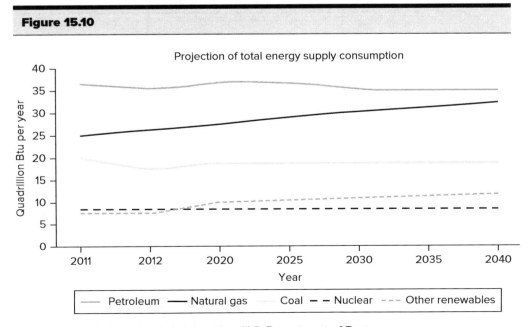

Source: **Energy Information Administration, U.S. Department of Energy**

15.5   Alternate Energy Sources

This section of the text is intended to suggest energy sources other than petroleum, coal, and natural gas. As outlined before, either life as we know it will have to change or alternative fossil fuel sources must be developed. Most certainly energy sources of the future will include nuclear, but they will also include an emerging group of renewable energy sources such as biomass, hydropower, wind, geothermal, and solar. Figure 15.11 illustrates the percentage of each renewable energy source that contributes to the approximately 100 Quadrillion Btu's consumed each year in the U.S. Recall that Figure 15.7 illustrates the demand sectors for this energy.

The engineer must continue to design mechanisms that will perform work by conversion of energy. However, the source of energy used to produce work and its corresponding conversion efficiency of energy into work will play a much greater role in the design procedure.

More is being written today regarding the depletion of fossil fuels and the immediate need to develop alternative energy sources to solve the problem. Many opinions are given with regard to how we should proceed to seek new energy sources and how

Figure 15.11

Renewable energy as share of total primary energy consumption, 2011

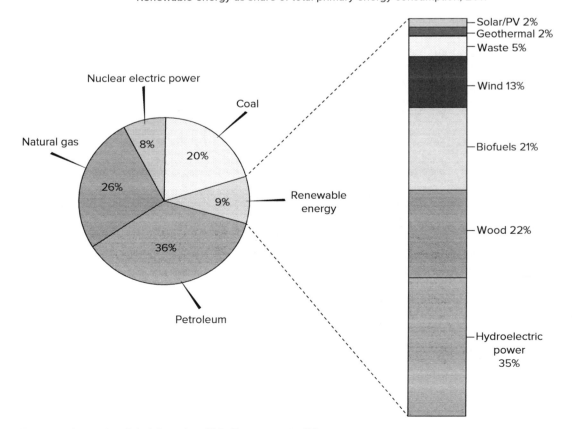

Source: **Energy Information Administration, U.S. Department of Energy**

we should use existing sources. Environmental concerns about energy acquisition and consumption become stronger by the day. The engineer must be able to discriminate between facts and opinions. The following discussion provides an insight into some energy sources that will be utilized in the future.

15.5.1   Nuclear Power

As we reach the end of the age of fossil fuels, the world will have to reconsider increasing the use of nuclear power. Nuclear fission is a well-established technology and it may well be the only proven technology capable of providing an adequate amount of electric power as fossil fuels become either extremely expensive or nonexistent. Issues of safety and disposal of nuclear waste will continue to demand the talents and resources of many engineers.

Nuclear fission is the splitting of an atom of nuclear fuel, usually uranium 235 or plutonium 239, by bombarding it with neutrons. The splitting process releases a great quantity of energy. As the atom splits, it divides approximately in half, releasing two or three free neutrons. The mass of the product after the split is always less than the mass of the reactants. This mass deficiency represents the released energy determined by Einstein's equation $E = mc^2$.

The liberated neutrons are capable of successive fission, which is called a chain reaction. The minimum quantity of fissionable material needed to sustain a chain reaction is called its critical mass. Chain reactions can be controlled or uncontrolled. The atomic bomb is an example of a uncontrolled reaction. To make fission a useful source of energy, a nuclear reactor utilizes a controlled reaction.

As of 2012 there were 100 commercial nuclear reactors at 65 nuclear power plants across our country. They produce approximately 8 percent of the total electrical energy generated in the United States. Palo Verde in Arizona is the largest nuclear plant in the United States (see Figure 15.12). Its three-unit system provides 3 733 megawatts annually, enough power to meet the needs of four million customers. The reactors are used to heat water for use in steam turbines that drive the generators.

Nuclear reactions take place in the reactor's core. A moderator, normally graphite or heavy water, is used to slow the neutrons that were released from the initial fission process to a speed and temperature that will cause succeeding reactions. Steel rods containing boron or cadmium are inserted into the reactor to control the number of free neutrons. The reactor is also shielded with lead and concrete to prevent the escape of dangerous radiation.

Nearly all reactors in use today producing electric energy are fission reactors using U-235. However, U-235 constitutes only 0.7 percent of the natural uranium supply and thus it would quickly become a scarce resource if we were totally dependent on it as a source of energy. Other isotopes, such as U-238 and thorium-232, are relatively abundant in nature. A new series of reactors that can produce new fissionable material and energy at the same time are called breeder reactor. They have been designed to use isotopes that are generally a waste product in current reactors.

The radioactive waste material from nuclear power generation has created disposal problems. The half-life of radioactive materials can be 1 000 years or more, thus creating a perpetual need for secure disposal of the waste materials from a nuclear power–generation facility. Radiation leaks and other environmental concerns have led to the shutdown of some facilities. This has made nuclear power generation a politically sensitive issue. Nuclear engineers and scientists continue to work on the complex

Figure 15.12

A nuclear power plant facility in Arizona.
© *Larry Lee Photography/Corbis/Getty Images*

problems associated with this source of energy. As these problems are solved and the general public becomes aware of the potential afforded by nuclear energy, increased use of nuclear power is likely.

Nuclear fusion—the energy gained from fusing light nuclei into heavier ones—has produced both the hope that it will be the ultimate energy source of the future and frustration. The Sun is the best example of nuclear fusion as it converts hydrogen into helium. The only problem is that the reaction occurs at a temperature of millions of degrees.

Nuclear fusion would use a fuel supply that is nearly inexhaustible, and we know of no scientific principle that forbids it from working. However, it has proved to be remarkably elusive, presenting a multitude of technical problems that have yet to be solved. It has been said that nuclear fusion is the energy source of the future—but it may not be advisable to rely on this technology to solve our immediate energy situation.

15.5.2 Renewable Energy Sources

Biomass (Ethanol and Biodiesel)

Biomass is a term that includes all energy materials that come from biological sources and are available on a renewable or recurring basis. Biomass includes agricultural crops and trees, wood and wood wastes, plants, grasses, fibers, as well as animal and municipal wastes.

Figure 15.13 illustrates each renewable energy source.

However, for this discussion, we will focus on biofuels, specifically ethanol and biodiesel. At its most basic ethanol is grain alcohol produced from a variety of crops, but mostly corn. Pure ethanol is not generally used as a motor fuel; rather it is combined with unleaded gasoline in two primary blends:

E10, 10 percent ethanol and 90 percent gasoline
E85, 85 percent ethanol and 15 percent gasoline used in flexible fuel vehicles (FFV's)

Ethanol production controversy arises as the primary input—corn is a very popular crop. It has many uses besides making ethanol. One third of the crop becomes feed for livestock, 13 percent of the annual U.S. production is exported and it is used to directly feed people.

In response, much research has centered on the use of corn stover—the stocks, leaves and cobs left in a field after harvest. In 2015, DuPont opened the world's largest cellulosic ethanol plant. It is located in Central Iowa and has the capacity to produce 30 million gallons of ethanol each year from the inedible parts of the corn plant a non-food agricultural byproduct. This cellulosic ethanol offers a positive energy balance as well as a way out of the "food or fuel" dilemma plaguing the industry.

Biodiesel is a clean-burning alternative fuel, produced from renewable resources— primarily soybean oil. One bushel of soybeans produces about 1.5 gallons of biodiesel. Biodiesel can be used in its pure form, called "neat biodiesel" B100, or it can be blended at any level with petroleum diesel. The most common mix is B20 (20% biodiesel and 80% petrodiesel). Biodiesel fuels can be used in regular diesel vehicles without any modification to the engine. Biodiesel has exceptional lubricating qualities that contribute to longevity and cleanliness of diesel engines, and in its pure form is biodegradable and nontoxic.

Figure 15.13

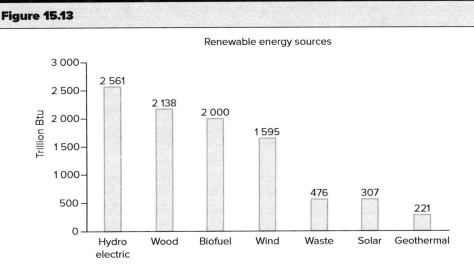

Renewable energy sources

Source: **Energy Information Administration, U.S. Department of Energy**

Biomass (Waste-to-Energy and Wood)

Waste-to-energy facilities produce clean, renewable energy through the combustion of municipal solid waste in specially designed power plants equipped with modern pollution control equipment. Today there are 75 waste-to-energy facilities located in 20 states that handle about 13 percent of U.S. trash, or about 95 000 tons per day. These facilities generate about 2 300 megawatts of electricity to meet the power needs of nearly two million homes. Turning garbage into energy makes sense, as there is a constant need for trash disposal as well as an equally constant demand for reliable electricity generation.

On an annual basis, waste-to-energy facilities remove and recycle more than 700 000 tons of ferrous metals and more than three million tons of glass, metal, plastics, batteries, ash, and yard waste. In addition, communities served by these facilities tend to be more conscious of recycling and therefore sort, reuse, and recycle at a higher rate than the national average rate of 30 percent.

Wood energy is primarily derived from the following sources. Roundwood is a term used by the industrial and electric utilities for timber poles, decking, floors, etc. Wood byproducts are also used in the residential sector for fuel, and wood waste is used in the industrial sector. (See Figure 15.13.)

Hydroelectric

Currently, about 6 percent of U.S. electric power is generated from hydroelectric dams on rivers. The largest hydroelectric facility in the United States is the Grand Coulee Dam, located in the state of Washington, with a generating capacity of 7 100 megawatts. We are, however, near the end of our ability to increase electrical generation by hydropower as dams have already been built nearly everywhere in the world where they are viable. In addition, environmental concerns for the protection of scenic rivers and wildlife will limit the construction of new hydroelectric facilities. (See Figure 15.13 Hydro Electric.)

Tides

The difference between the elevation of the ocean at high tide and at low tide varies from 1 to 2 m in most places but can range from 15 to 20 m in some locations. The idea of using this energy source is not new. This concept is technically feasible—plants are located in France, Canada, and Russia but the economic feasibility is still in serious doubt. The toughest problems seem to be that vast storage volumes are required and suitable basins are rare.

Ocean Currents and Waves

We are also aware of the warming effect that the Gulf Stream provides for the British Isles and Western Europe. This and other ocean currents possess massive amounts of kinetic energy even though they move at very slow velocities. It has been proposed that a series of large (170 m in diameter) turbines be placed in the Gulf Stream off Florida. Ten such turbines could produce power equivalent to that produced by one typical coal-fired power plant. Detractors warn that such installations may reduce the stream velocity to the point that the Gulf Stream's warming of Western Europe would be lost.

No doubt you have watched the surf smash into the beach and have been in awe of the obvious power being displayed. Machines have been made that produce power from the wave action. But to be successful, the installations must be located where the magnitude of the wave action is high and somewhat uniform, and it is difficult and expensive to design such installations against major storms. The best sites in the United States are on the coasts of Washington and Oregon.

Wind Power

Heated equatorial air rises and drifts toward the poles. This phenomenon coupled with the Earth's rotation results in a patterned air flow. In the United States, we see this pattern as weather systems moving from west to east across the country. These weather systems possess enormous energy, but the energy is diffused, variable, and difficult to capture.

Most are familiar with the historical use of the wind to pump water and to grind grain. These methods are still viable, and today a great deal of research is underway in an attempt to capture energy from the wind in an economically feasible manner. Engineers have learned that the power output from a windmill is approximately proportional to the square of the blade diameter and to the cube of the wind velocity. This suggests that to generate high power output, the windmills must be large and must be located in areas where the average wind velocity is high. Thus, coastal regions and the Great Plains are promising locations. In fact, Iowa has set a national record by generating 25 percent of all electricity from wind turbines. However, many people find wind farms unsightly and undesirable near their property.

Figure 15.9 indicates that about 4 percent of U.S. electric power is now generated by the wind. That amount will likely increase as efforts continue toward reducing the costs of wind-power installations and as tax breaks for power producers have made wind power more economically competitive. The supply/demand problem related to wind may be solved by, for example, using excess power generated when the wind is blowing to pump water to an elevated storage area and use the resulting potential energy to drive a water turbine for power generation when the wind is not blowing. (See Figure 15.13; Wind.)

Geothermal Power

It is commonly accepted that the Earth's core is molten rock with a temperature of 10 000 to 12 000°F. This source has the potential to provide a large portion of our energy needs. The Earth's crust varies in thickness from a few hundred feet to perhaps 20 mi. It is composed mostly of layers of rock—some solid, some porous, and some fractured. Engineers are now exploring the use of the Earth's heat (geothermal energy) to produce power from hot water, steam, and heated rock.

There are many areas throughout the world where large amounts of hot water are available from the Earth. The hot water varies in many ways—in quantity, temperature, salinity, and mineral content.

At only a few locations in the world is steam available in sufficient quantities to be used to produce electricity. The only area in the United States producing large quantities of steam is in northern California. Low-cost electricity has been produced there for nearly 50 years. This steam is captured by drilling from 500 to 10 000 ft deep, and it has a temperature of about 350°F but at low pressure. Besides the corrosive nature of the steam, it contains several gases, including ammonia and hydrogen sulfide, that have objectionable odors and are poisonous.

It is clear that using geothermal energy has potential, but many problems need to be solved and solutions will probably come only after large-scale pilot plants have been in operation long enough to obtain reliable efficiency data and operating costs. (See Figure 15.13; Geothermal.)

Solar Power

The sun is an obvious source of energy that we have employed in different ways since the beginning of time. It supplies us with many, many times as much energy as we need. Our problems lie with collecting, converting, and storing the inexhaustible supply. Efforts are being directed primarily toward direct heating, charging batteries, and heat engines—such as turbines that can generate electricity. Others are experimenting with crop drying and metallurgical furnaces. You are no doubt aware of the increasing use of solar energy in building heating and in domestic hot-water supplies. This use will surely continue to increase, particularly in new installations (see Figure 15.14). But we will have to improve on current technology and/or have tax relief and low-interest loans or other incentives to make solar installations economically feasible.

There are two general methods by which energy from the sun is used as a renewable source.

Solar thermal devices use heat directly from the sun, concentrate that heat in some fashion, then use it for numerous applications.

Photovoltaic (PV cells) is a method of converting sunlight directly into electricity using various semiconducting materials. However, sunlight loses much of its intensity as it travels through our atmosphere. Solar cells have been shown to work well on space vehicles but at the present time they are extremely costly. We must increase the efficiency of PV cells and work to reduce their costs in order for this application to come into general use. (See Figure 15.13; Solar.)

Figure 15.14

Solar panels being used in new construction.
© Henglein and Steets/Getty Images

Problems

15.1 Conduct a study detailing current production and consumption of fossil fuels. Determine the estimated annual usage of the fuels on a national and international basis, the geographical locations of the sources, and estimated time until the sources are exhausted at current usage rates. Compare fossil fuel usage rates in the United States with those in Japan, England, Germany, China, India, Russia, and South Africa. Working in teams, develop written reports or oral presentations according to your instructor's direction.

    (*a*) coal

    (*b*) petroleum

    (*c*) natural gas

15.2 Prepare a report or oral presentation on the status of nuclear power in the United States. Include usage data, public opinion on the use of nuclear power, regulations on the industry, and current information on the storage/disposal of spent fuel. Work in teams.

15.3 Prepare a report and give an oral presentation on the status of one of the following renewable sources of power in the United States. Include usage data, geographic locations of these sources, and the ultimate form of energy that is consumed from these sources. Work in teams.

    (*a*) Biomass to include: (*i*) Ethanol and biodiesel (*ii*) Waste-to-energy and wood

    (*b*) Hydropower

    (*c*) Wind power

    (*d*) Geothermal

    (*e*) Solar power

15.4 The transportation sector in the United States presently runs almost exclusively on petroleum-based derivatives (gasoline, diesel, jet fuel). Research the following alternatives.

Hybrid	*Propane*
Diesel & biodiesel	*Hydrogen*
Flex-fuel	*Electric*
Ethanol	*Fuel cell*
Natural gas	

Prepare a one-page paper outlining what you believe may be viable alternatives to the use of fossil fuels. May be assigned as a team or an individual assignment.

15.5 Conservation is another logical method by which the U.S. can reduce its demand for foreign-based petroleum and domestic supplies of coal and natural gas. Prepare a report that will include at least five practical steps that you as an individual could take to reduce energy usage. As an example, consider the house where you grew up, the automobile you drive, the electricity that you consume, etc.

15.6 Explore the possibility of large solar farms in the southwest. Prepare a paper that examines both Thermal and Photovoltaic. How many acres are available? What would be the cost versus conventional electric power delivery? How does it compare with nuclear power generation?

15.7 A wind farm is a cluster of at least three turbines with generating capacities in the order of hundreds of megawatts. Investigate the capabilities of the wind farm nearest your college and determine how much of your school's electrical demand could be met by this resource. Write a paper that considers technical issues like the appropriate spacing of multiple turbines as well as control, stability, and power balance in relation to the power grid.

15.8 Considering the five major sources of renewable energy—biomass, hydropower, wind, geothermal, and solar—prepare a paper outlining what you believe will be the major source of renewable energy in 2015.

15.9 As a college student, you have the opportunity to experiment with various "Green" initiatives. Look into ways to reduce, reuse, and conserve energy in your place of residence, your college classrooms, your recyclables, and your transportation choices. Consider how individual changes that you and other classmates might consider could impact energy consumption.

15.10 As a class, develop a "Green" initiative, design and engineer its impact, market the initiative to the college, university, or city, then implement. Remember, a very small adjustment to the rudder of a large ship can turn the vessel 360 degrees. It only takes time.

CHAPTER 16

Fundamental Energy Principles

Chapter Objectives

When you complete your study of this chapter, you will able to:

- Identify and define the different forms in which energy can be found: potential, kinetic, internal, chemical, and nuclear
- Demonstrate an understanding based on the Conservation of Energy principles as they relate to energy transfer and conversion
- Discuss the limitations of energy conversion into useful work
- Compare actual cyclic efficiencies to Carnot efficiency
- Distinguish between available and unavailable forms of energy
- Conceptualize the fact that a refrigeration cycle is a reversed heat engine

16.1   Introduction to Thermodynamics

Energy is a fundamental concept of thermodynamics and plays a significant role in engineering analysis. If engineers are to provide solutions to energy-related problems, we must understand energy's fundamental principles.

What is energy? It cannot be seen; it has no mass or defining characteristics; it is distinguished only by what it can produce. Energy can be stored within a system in various forms. Energy can also be transformed from one form to another and transferred between systems. In a broad sense, energy may be defined as an ability to produce an effect or change on matter.

Thermodynamics is one of the major areas of engineering science. It is usually introduced to engineering students in a one-semester course, with students in energy-related disciplines continuing with one or more advanced courses. This text will outline some concepts that will help solve basic problems involving the transformation of energy. Our discussion is limited to the first law for closed systems and a brief introduction to the second law, which governs efficiency and power. These terms are explained in the following sections.

16.2   Stored Energy

Let's consider some of the different forms in which energy can be found. Stored energy exists in distinct forms: potential, kinetic, internal, chemical, and nuclear. The ultimate usefulness of stored energy depends on how efficiently the energy can be converted into a form that produces a desirable result.

When an object or mass m is elevated to a height h in a gravitational field (see Figure 16.1) a certain amount of work must be done to overcome the gravitational attraction. Energy is the capacity to do work. (Work is considered further in Section 16.3.) The object may be said to possess the additional energy that was required to elevate it to the new position. In other words, its potential energy has been increased. The quantity of work done to increase its energy is the amount of force multiplied by the distance the object moved in the direction in which the force acts. It is a result of a given mass going from one condition to another. *Gravitational potential energy* is thus stored-up energy due to a change in elevation. It is derived from force and height above a datum plane, not from the means by which the height was attained. Mass m stores up energy as it is elevated to height h and loses this advantage when it comes back to its starting point. When an object is raised, a force is needed to overcome the effect of gravity. The object's increase in potential energy depends upon the distance or change in elevation experienced by the object. Thus,

$$PE = \frac{mg_L h}{g_C} \qquad (16.1)$$

The units for mass m can be kilograms or lbm, those for the local acceleration of gravity g_L can be either meters per second squared or feet per second squared, and those for height h can be either meters or feet with g_c being the appropriate constant of proportionality. The units for potential energy, PE, are newton-meters (joules) or ft · lbf.

It is unnecessary in most cases to evaluate the total energy of an object; however, it is customary to evaluate its energy changes. In the case of potential energy, this is accomplished by establishing a datum plane (see Figure 16.1) and evaluating the energy possessed by objects in excess of that possessed at the datum plane. Any convenient location, such as sea level, may be chosen as the datum plane. The potential energy at any other elevation is then equal to the work required to elevate the object from the datum plane.

A second form of stored energy can be realized by virtue of an object's velocity (V). The energy possessed by the object at a given velocity is called *kinetic energy.*

Figure 16.1

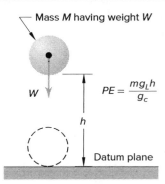

Mass *M* having weight *W*

$$PE = \frac{mg_L h}{g_c}$$

W

h

Datum plane

Potential energy.

Figure 16.2

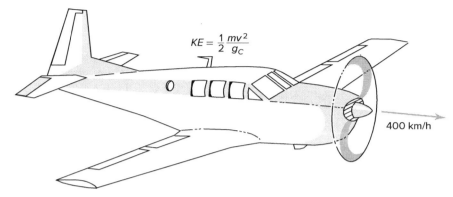

$$KE = \frac{1}{2}\frac{mv^2}{g_C}$$

400 km/h

Kinetic energy.

It is equal to the energy required to accelerate the object from rest to its given velocity (considering the Earth's velocity to be the datum plane). In equation form,

$$KE = \frac{mV^2}{2g_c} \qquad (16.2)$$

where

m = mass, kg

V = velocity, *m/s*

$$g_c = \frac{1.0\,\text{kg} \cdot m}{N \cdot s^2}$$

KE = kinetic energy, in newton-meters or joules. See Figure 16.2.

In many situations in nature, an exchange in the form of energy is common. Consider a ball thrown vertically into the air. It is given kinetic energy when thrown upward. When the ball reaches its maximum altitude, its velocity is zero, but it now possesses a higher potential energy because of the increase in altitude (height). When it begins to fall, the potential energy decreases and the kinetic energy increases until the ball is caught. If other effects such as air friction are neglected and the ball is caught at the same altitude from which it was thrown, there is no change in the total energy although the energy of the ball was transformed from kinetic to potential and then back to kinetic. This phenomenon is called *conservation of energy,* which is discussed in Section 16.4.

All matter is composed of molecules that, at finite temperatures, are in continuous motion. In addition, there are intermolecular attractions which vary as the distance between molecules changes. The energy possessed by the molecules as a composite whole is called *internal energy,* designated by the symbol *U,* which is largely dependent on temperature.

When a fuel is burned, energy is released. When food is consumed, it is converted into energy that sustains human efforts. The energy that is stored in a lump of coal or a loaf of bread is called *chemical energy.* Sunlight is transformed by a natural process called photosynthesis, that is, a process that forms chemical compounds with the aid of light. The stored energy in combustible fuels is generally measured in terms of heat of combustion, or heating value. For example, gasoline has a heating value of $47.7(10^6)$ J/kg, or $20.5(10^3)$ Btu/lbm.

Certain events change the atomic structure of matter. During the processes of *nuclear fission* (breaking the nucleus into two parts, which releases high amounts of energy) and *fusion* (combining lightweight nuclei into heavier ones, which also releases energy), mass is transformed into energy. The stored energy in atoms is called *nuclear energy,* which may need to play an increasing role in meeting energy needs of the future.

16.3   Energy in Transit

Energy is transferred from one form to another during many processes, such as the burning of fossil fuels to generate electricity or the converting of electric energy to heat by passing a current through a resistance. Like all transfer processes, there must be a driving force or potential difference in order to effect the transfer. In the absence of the driving force or potential difference, a state of equilibrium exists and no process can take place. The character of the driving force enables us to recognize the forms of energy in transit, that is, work or heat.

Energy is required for the movement of an object against some resistance. When there is an imbalance of forces and movement against some resistance, mechanical work is performed according to the relationship

$$W = \text{(force)}\text{(distance)}$$

$$= Fd \tag{16.3}$$

where the force is in the direction of movement. See Figure 16.3. If force has units of newtons and distance is expressed in meters, then work has units of joules.

Let's review the relationship between work and kinetic energy. When a body is accelerated by a resultant force, the work done on the body can be considered a transfer of energy, where it is stored as kinetic energy. For example, imagine a body with a given mass (m) moving with a velocity (V_1) and a resultant force (F) with no other external effects is applied to the body. This action alone results in the body moving with a velocity V_2. The work done on the body can be considered a transfer of energy in the form of kinetic energy.

Figure 16.3

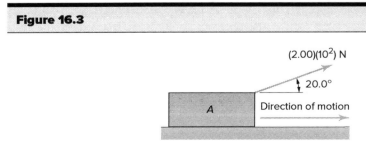

An applied force doing work.

Electric energy is another form of work. This form of energy is transferred through a conducting medium when a difference in electric potential exists in the medium.

Other examples of energy transfer that are classified as work include magnetic, fluid compression, extension of a solid, and chemical reactions. In each case a driving function exists that causes energy to be transferred during a process.

Heat is energy that is transferred from one region to another by virtue of temperature difference. The unit of heat is the joule. The large numerical values occurring in energy-transfer computations has led to the frequent use of the megajoule (10^6 J), or MJ. The symbol used for heat is Q.

The relationship between the energy forms of heat and work during a process is given by the first law of thermodynamics, which is discussed in Section 16.4. In addition, every form of work carries with it a corresponding form of friction that may change some of the work into heat. When this happens, the process is irreversible, meaning that the energy put into the process cannot be totally recovered by reversing the process. Another way of stating this is that heat is a low-grade form of energy and cannot be converted completely to another form such as work. This concept is basic to the second law of thermodynamics (discussed in Section 16.5). The first and second laws of thermodynamics are fundamental to the study of processes involving energy transfer.

Several examples are provided below that illustrate both stored forms of energy and energy in transition. Particular attention should be given to the units and unit conversions in the examples.

Example Problem 16.1   A boulder with mass of 1.000 (10^3) kg rests on a ledge 200.0 m above sea level ($g_L = 9.807$ m/s^2). What type of energy does the object possess and what is its magnitude?

Solution   The object possesses potential energy, so from Equation 16.1,

$$PE = \frac{m g_L h}{g_C}$$

$$= \frac{1\ 000 \ \text{kg} \, (9.807 \ \text{m})(200.0 \ \text{m}) \, \text{N} \cdot \text{s}^2}{1.0 \, \text{kg} \cdot \text{m} \cdot \text{s}^2}$$

$$= 1.961(10^6) \ \text{N} \cdot \text{m}$$

$$= 1.961(10^6) \ \text{J}$$

$$= 1.961 \ \text{MJ}$$

Example Problem 16.2   A 2.00 (10^4) lbm semitrailer is traveling at sea level at a speed of 50.0 mph. Determine the energy form and magnitude possessed by the truck. Express the magnitude in Engineering System units.

Solution   Convert mph to ft/s:

$$50.0 \text{ mi/h} = \frac{50.0\,\text{mi}}{\text{h}} \times \frac{5\,280\,\text{ft}}{\text{mi}} \times \frac{\text{h}}{3\,600\,\text{s}} = 73.33\,\text{ft/s}$$

The truck possesses kinetic energy; therefore, from Equation 16.2,

$$KE = \frac{mV^2}{2g_c}$$

$$= \frac{20\,000\,\text{lbm}}{2} \times \frac{(73.33)^2\text{ft}^2}{\text{s}^2} \times \frac{\text{lbf} \cdot \text{s}^2}{32.174\,0\,\text{lbm} \cdot \text{ft}} = 1\,671\,315\,\text{ft} \cdot \text{lbf}$$

$$= 1.67 \times 10^6 \text{ ft} \cdot \text{lbf}$$

If metric units are desired, this can be converted to SI as follows:

$$1.0 \text{ ft} \cdot \text{lbf} = 1.355\,8 \text{ joules, so}$$

$$KE = 2.27(10^6) \text{ N} \cdot \text{m}$$

$$= 2.27 \text{ MJ}$$

Thus 2.27 MJ is the amount of energy that must be absorbed by the truck brakes in order to bring the vehicle to zero velocity in an emergency stop. If the stop is gradual, some of the energy can be absorbed by the engine and by road friction; in an emergency nearly all of the energy will be absorbed by the brakes and road friction.

Example Problem 16.3   A mass of water is heated from 10.0 to 20.0°C by the addition of $5.00(10^3)$ Btu of energy. What is the final form of the energy? Express the final form of the energy in megajoules.

Solution   The final form of the heat energy added appears as increased internal energy (U) of the water. If state 1 of the water is prior to heating and state 2 is after heat has been added, then $U_2 - U_1 = 5\,000$ Btu.

Converting to SI, we get

$$U_2 - U_1 = 5.00\,(10^3) \text{ Btu} = (5.00 \times 10^3 \text{ Btu})(1\,055.1 \text{ J/Btu})$$

$$= 5.28\,(10^6) \text{ J}$$

$$= 5.28 \text{ MJ}$$

Example Problem 16.4   A force of 2.00×10^2 N acting at an angle of 20.0° with the horizontal is required to move block A along the horizontal surface (see Figure 16.3). How much work is done if the block is moved 1.00×10^2 m?

Solution Work is computed as the product of the force in the direction of motion and the distance moved, as in Equation 16.3:

$$W = Fd$$

$$= (2.00 \times 10^2 \text{ N})(\cos 20.0°)(1.00 \times 10^2 \text{ m})$$

$$= 18\ 800 \text{ N} \cdot \text{m}$$

$$= 18\ 800 \text{ J}$$

$$= 18.8 \text{ kJ}$$

What happened to the energy released by the work done on Block A? There is no increase in potential energy, since height was not changed. There is no velocity change, so the change in kinetic-energy is zero. The energy of the work in this example is dissipated as heat in the form of friction between the block and surface; therefore, the temperature of the block and the surface in the immediate vicinity of the block increased.

Would you believe that the reverse process is possible? That is, could the molecules in the block and surface that are moving faster than the surrounding molecules due to an increased temperature randomly move the object back to its original position as they return to their initial temperature? The first law of thermodynamics does not place any restrictions on the reverse process, other than conservation of energy. That is why there is a second law of thermodynamics, which does not allow certain processes.

16.4 First Law of Thermodynamics: The Conservation of Energy

Conservation of energy in nonnuclear processes means simply that energy can never be created or destroyed, only transformed. In effect, energy is converted from one form to another without loss. Careful measurements have shown that during energy transformations there is a definite relationship in the quantitative amounts of energy transformed. This relationship—the first law of thermodynamics—is a restatement of the principle of the conservation of energy.

When applying the first law to substances undergoing energy changes, it is necessary to define a system and write a mathematical expression for the law. In (Figure 16.4(a)), a generalized closed system is illustrated. In a *closed system,* no material (mass) may cross the boundaries, but the boundaries may change shape. Energy, however, may cross the boundaries and/or the entire system may be moved intact to another position.

Some applications involve analysis of an *open system,* in which mass crosses the defined boundaries and a portion of the energy transformation is carried in or out of the system with the mass (Figure 16.4(b)) An example is an air compressor, which takes atmospheric air, compresses it, and delivers it to a storage tank. (Because of the complexity of analysis and explanation, problems involving open systems will not be considered in this chapter.)

For the generalized closed system, the first law is written as

> Energy in + Energy stored at condition 1 = Energy out +
> Energy stored at condition 2

where conditions 1 and 2 refer to initial and final states of the system.

In thermodynamics all changes in the total energy of a closed system are considered to be made up of three contributions. Two of these changes are kinetic energy and gravitational potential energy. Both of these changes are associated with the motion and position of the system as a whole. All other energy changes are combined together into internal energy of the system.

Energy in any of its forms may cross the boundaries of the system. If the assumption is made that no nuclear, chemical, or electrical energy is involved, then the change in total energy can be written as

$$\Delta E = \Delta KE + \Delta PE + \Delta U$$

If the closed system as a whole is stationary, that is, not changing velocity or changing its elevation, then ΔKE and ΔPE are zero, and the first law can be stated as:

> Heat in + Work done on system + Internal energy at condition
> 1 = Heat out + Work done by the system + Internal energy at
> condition 2

or, combining heat, work, and internal energy quantities at conditions 1 and 2:

$$_1Q_2 = U_2 - U_1 + {_1}W_2 \tag{16.4}$$

where

$$_1Q_2 = \text{heat } \textit{added} \text{ to system}$$

$$_1W_2 = \text{net mechanical work } \textit{done by} \text{ system}$$

$$U_2 - U_1 = \text{change in internal energy from state 1 to state 2 with } \Delta PE \text{ and } \Delta KE \text{ zero}$$

Equation 16.4 is the first law for a closed system when the potential and kinetic energy terms for the system are zero.

Example Problem 16.5   The internal energy of a system decreases by 108 J while 175 J of work is done by the system on the surroundings. Determine if heat is added to or removed from the system.

Solution

$$_1Q_2 = U_2 - U_1 + {_1}W_2$$

$$= -108 + 175$$

$$= +67 \text{ J (heat is added to system)}$$

Example Problem 16.6   Analyze the energy transformations that can take place when the piston in Figure 16.5 moves in either direction (work) and/or heat is transferred.

Figure 16.4

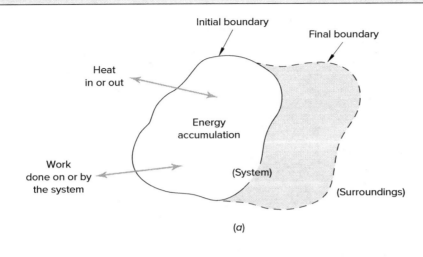

(a)

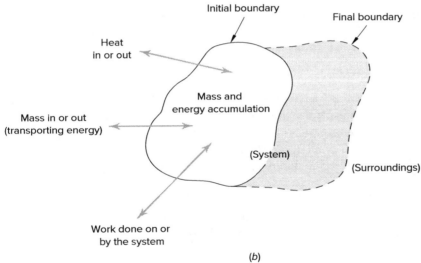

(b)

(a) Closed and (b) open thermodynamic systems.

Solution The air within the piston is considered to be the system. If the position shown is condition 1, there must be a force applied to the piston toward the left to hold its position. The magnitude of the force is

$$F = \text{(pressure of air)(area of piston)}$$

$$= PA \text{ (in newtons)}$$

At this position, with no change in volume of the air, heat could be added or removed, which would increase or decrease, respectively, the internal energy of the system. In terms of the first law:

$$_1Q_2 = U_2 - U_1$$

Figure 16.5

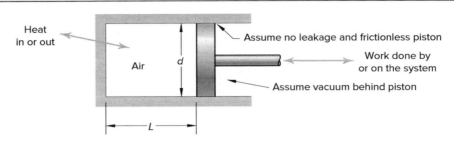

Piston–cylinder combination.

Note the absence of the work term. Work cannot take place without action of a force through a distance. The force (*PA*) is present, but no movement takes place; thus no work is transferred.

It is a different situation if the force to the left is increased slightly, moving the piston left. Work is done because movement occurs as a result of a force. The air temperature may change depending on how much heat is added or removed from the air. The first law for this situation can be written as

$$_1Q_2 = U_2 - U_1 + {_1W_2}$$

The work term, $_1W_2$, as the system moves from state 1 to state 2 will be equal to (*PA*)*L* (at constant pressure) as the piston moves a distance *L* to the left. Since external work is required to move the piston, the work term is negative. In other words, it was work done by the surroundings on the system.

For the case of the piston moving to the right, the first law is still

$$_1Q_2 = U_2 - U_1 + {_1W_2}$$

but $_1W_2$ is positive, because work is done by the system on the surroundings.

If no heat is allowed to transfer across the boundaries, then the first law becomes

$$_1W_2 + U_2 - U_1 = 0$$

This process, where no heat crosses the boundary, is called an *adiabatic process.*

Many engineering applications assume that air and other gases behave ideally, that is, the pressure, volume, and temperature obey an equation of state derived from the laws of Boyle and Charles. One characteristic of a perfect gas is that internal energy is a function of temperature only. If the ideal-gas assumption is made, then a constant-temperature (*isothermal*) process implies that there is no change in internal energy, and therefore the first law for an isothermal process involving an ideal-gas becomes

$$_1Q_2 = {_1W_2}$$

Example Problem 16.7   Let the piston in Figure 16.5 be moved so that the volume of air is reduced to one-half its original value. During this process, 116 MJ of heat is removed from the system. If the process is isothermal and we assume an ideal gas, how much work is done on the system?

Solution

$$_1Q_2 = {}_1W_2$$

$$-116 \text{ MJ} = {}_1W_2$$

The negative sign indicates that work has been done on the air by the surroundings.

Example Problem 16.8   Determine the pressure of the air within the cylinder (Figure 16.5) if the force (F) on the piston is 1.00×10^2 N and its diameter (d) is 0.100 m.

Solution

$$P = F/A$$

$$= 12\ 732.4 \text{ N/m}^2$$

$$= 1.27\ (10^4)\ \text{N/m}^2$$

$$= 1.27\ (10^4)\ \text{Pa}$$

$$= 12.7 \text{ kPa}$$

16.5   Second Law of Thermodynamics

The second law is not an actual proven law; rather, it is an axiom whose verification is in the fact that all experimental evidence about it is always true. Let's begin by considering the similarities between the energy contained in a river and the energy contained in high-temperature, high-pressure steam. Both contain a certain quantity of energy but both have limits on how much useful work can be obtained from them.

The water in the river contains energy in the form of flow rate and elevation. The Sun heats the Earth's surface, causing evaporation that deposits water in the form of rain and snow at high elevations. The water migrates from mountaintop to sea level. In the process, its energy is transformed from potential to kinetic to internal, and eventually the water arrives at the sea with exactly the same amount of energy with which it started. Energy was transformed but conserved.

The questions to be explored: Did the water do any useful work along its path to the sea? What is the maximum amount of work that it could possibly do? If the water is stationary when it starts at the mountaintop and stationary when it arrives at the sea, then its maximum work output is a function of the change in elevation; the constraints on work availability are the height of the mountain and the level of the sea. Did the water do any useful work along the way—for example, generate electricity? That would depend on the construction of mechanical devices to convert water energy into electric energy. If potential and/or kinetic energy is converted into useful work during the process, it is still only possible to capture the portion called available energy. If we assume no mechanical devices to convert water energy to electric energy, then the total energy was conserved and remains in the mass of water at sea level. However, it is now unavailable energy.

High-temperature, high-pressure steam has a parallel limitation. Work available from this fluid is limited by the maximum temperature and pressure that we can safely produce as a starting point and the temperature of the atmosphere into which it is released. These limitations are analogous to the water on the mountaintop and at sea level.

Heat cannot be completely converted to work, but work can be completely converted to heat. Heat can perform work only when it passes from a higher to a lower temperature. In other words, heat will not flow spontaneously from a colder to a hotter substance. This limitation on heat conversion forms the basis of the second law of thermodynamics.

Heat energy at a high temperature is capable of doing work, but the same amount of energy at low temperature is not capable of doing useful work. The total amount of energy is still the same, but its *entropy* has changed. If we think of entropy as a property, then high temperature has low entropy and low temperature has high entropy.

There are numerous statements of the second law. Rudolf Clausius, a German mathematical physicist, in 1865 was the first person to combine the fact that heat will always flow from high temperature to low temperature together with the law of conservation of energy. Clausius stated: "It is impossible for any device to operate in such a way that the sole effect would be an energy transfer of heat from a cooler to a hotter body." Another statement of the second law would read: "No device can completely and continuously transform all of the heat supplied to it into work." The heat that can be transformed into work is called *available energy;* the remaining portion is termed *unavailable energy.*

As indicated earlier, whenever work is performed, friction downgrades some available energy to unavailable energy and some available energy is released into the atmosphere, becoming unavailable energy. This energy released into the atmosphere is heat that is at too low a temperature to perform work under the conditions specified by the system and its surroundings.

For a given system and surroundings, the available and unavailable energies can be computed. The procedures for this computation are beyond the scope of this text.

16.6 Efficiency

It is important to understand what is meant by a cycle. When a system at a given initial state goes through a sequence of processes and then returns to its initial state, the system has executed a thermodynamic cycle.

$$\Delta E_{\text{cycle}} = Q_{\text{cycle}} - W_{\text{cycle}} \qquad (16.5)$$

During a cycle the system is returned to its initial state at the completion of the cycle, so there is no net change in energy; that is, $\Delta E = 0$. This expression can then be written as

$$W_{\text{cycle}} = Q_{\text{cycle}} \qquad (16.6)$$

or

$$\dot{W}_{cycle} = \dot{Q}_{cycle} \qquad (16.7)$$

In Equation 16.7, the overdot represents an expression for time rate of change or power.

Systems undergoing power cycles deliver or transfer a net amount of energy to their surroundings. The net work output of the system equals the net heat transfer to the cycle.

$$W_{cycle} = Q_{in} - Q_{out} \qquad (16.8)$$

where Q_{in} or (Q_H) represents the heat transfer of energy into the system from a hot body and Q_{out} or (Q_L) represents heat transfer out of the system to a cold body.

The high side or energy supplied by heat transfer to a system undergoing a power cycle is normally obtained from the combustion of fossil fuels. The energy Q_{out} is generally discharged to the surrounding atmosphere or a local body of water. The extent of the energy conversion from heat to work is commonly called thermal efficiency:

$$\eta = \frac{W_{cycle}}{Q_{in}} = \frac{Q_{in} - Q_{out}}{Q_{in}} = 1 - \frac{Q_{out}}{Q_{in}} \qquad (16.9)$$

This relationship provides a measure of efficiency for any heat engine.

Another application of the second law is the determination of the maximum efficiency of any device that converts heat into work. These heat engines cannot attain 100% efficiency because of the second law.

A French engineer named Nicolas Leonard Sadi Carnot proposed in 1824 an ideal engine cycle that had the highest attainable efficiency within thermodynamic laws. In reality, any engine following his proposed cycle, called the Carnot cycle, could not be constructed, but the theory provides a basis of comparison for practical engines. The Carnot efficiency can be shown to be

$$\text{Carnot efficiency} = 1 - \frac{T_L}{T_H} \qquad (16.10)$$

where T_H is the absolute temperature at which the engine receives heat (high temperature) and T_L is the absolute temperature at which the engine rejects heat (low temperature) after performing work. Absolute temperatures are determined by adding 273° to a reading in °C or 460° to a reading in °F. Temperatures on the absolute scales are in degrees kelvin (K) for centigrade-size degrees, and in degrees Rankine (°R) for Fahrenheit-size degrees.

Example Problem 16.9 A steam engine is designed to accept steam at 300°C and exhaust this steam at 100°C. What is its maximum possible efficiency?

Solution

$$\text{Carnot efficiency} = 1 - \frac{T_L}{T_H}$$

$$= 1 - \frac{100 + 273}{300 + 273}$$

$$= 1 - \frac{373}{573}$$

$$= 35\%$$

We have learned that all the energy put into a system does not end up producing useful work. According to the second law, a certain amount of energy is unavailable for productive work. That is not the entire story; in fact, it gets worse. The available energy promised by the Carnot engine does not perform an equivalent amount of work because of losses incurred during the transfer of energy from one form to another. An automobile engine converts chemical energy in the form of gasoline to mechanical energy at the axle; however, some of the energy is lost through bearing friction, incomplete combustion, cooling water, and other thermodynamic and mechanical losses.

An engineer designing a device to convert heat into work must also be concerned with the overall efficiency of a proposed system. Equation 16.9 can be written to include the overall efficiency of an entire plant as

$$\text{Overall efficiency}\,(\eta) = \frac{\text{useful output}}{\text{total input}} = \frac{W_{\text{cycle}}}{Q_{\text{in}}} \qquad (16.11)$$

From Equation 16.10, it is clear that for a given process the maximum (Carnot) efficiency can be increased by lowering the exhaust temperature T_L and/or increasing the input temperature T_H. In theory this is true, but practical design considerations must include available materials for construction of the heat engine. The engineer thus attempts to obtain the highest possible efficiency using existing technology. Examples of overall efficiency are from 17 to 23 percent for automobile engines (gasoline), 26 to 38 percent for diesel engines, and 20 to 33 percent for turbojet aircraft engines. Thus, in the case of the gasoline automobile engine, for every 80 L (21 gal) tank of gasoline, only 20 L (5.3 gal) ends up moving the automobile.

Care must be exercised in the calculation and use of efficiencies. To illustrate this point, consider Figure 16.6, which depicts a steam power plant operating from the burning of fossil fuel for steam generation to driving a turbine attached to an electric generator. Efficiencies of each stage or combinations of stages in the power plant may be calculated by comparing energies available before and after the particular operations. For example, combustion efficiency can be calculated as 0.80/1.00, or 80 percent. The turbine efficiency is 0.33/0.50, or 66 percent. The overall power plant efficiency up to the electric generator is 0.33/1.00, or 33 percent. By no means is the 33 percent a measure of the efficiency of generation of electricity for use in a residential home. There will be losses in the generator and line losses in the transmission of the electricity from the power plant to the home. The overall efficiency from fuel into the boiler at the power plant to the electric oven in the kitchen may run as low as 25–30 percent.

Figure 16.6

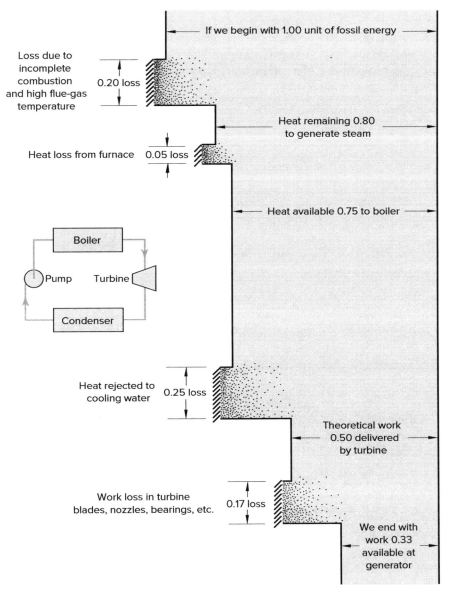

Energy losses in a typical steam power plant.

It is interesting to note that the cycle is complete when the oven converts electricity back into heat, which is where the entire process began.

16.7 Power

Power is the rate at which energy is transferred, generated, or used. In many applications it may be more convenient to work with power quantities rather than energy quantities. The SI unit of power is the watt (one joule per second), but many problems will have units of horsepower (hp) or foot-pound-force per second (ft · lbf/s) as units, so conversions will be necessary.

Example Problem 16.10   A steam power plant produces 3 500 net hp at the shaft. The plant uses coal as fuel (12 000 Btu/lbm). Using the overall efficiency presented in Figure 16.6 (33 percent), determine how many metric tons of coal must be burned in a 24-h period to run the turbine.

Solution   From Equation 16.11,

$$\text{Total input} = \frac{\text{useful output}}{\text{overall efficiency}}$$

$$= \frac{3\,500 \text{ hp}}{0.33} \times \frac{2\,546.1 \text{ Btu}}{1.0 \text{ hp} \cdot \text{h}}$$

$$= 2.7(10^7) \text{ Btu/h}$$

The amount of coal needed for one day of operation is therefore

$$\text{Coal required} = \frac{2.7(10)^7 \text{Btu}}{1 \text{ h}} \times \frac{1 \text{ lbm}}{12\,000 \text{ Btu}} \times \frac{1 \text{ kg}}{2.205 \text{ lbm}} \times \frac{1 \text{ t}}{10^3 \text{kg}} \times \frac{24 \text{ h}}{1 \text{ day}}$$

$$= 24 \text{ t/day}$$

Example Problem 16.11   Estimate the area in acres required for an array of solar cells to collect and provide enough electrical energy for a community of 4 500 people in a central Arizona town. Assume a solar cell conversion efficiency of 8 percent.

Solution   This example requires some assumptions in order to obtain a meaningful result.

1. Each home consumes about 13 000 kWh of electricity on average each year.
2. An average of three people live in each home.
3. The sun shines an average of 8 h/d.
4. The typical solar heat transfer rate is 1.0 kW/m². Equation 16.11 may be used.

$$\text{Efficiency} = \frac{\text{useful output}}{\text{total input}}$$

$$\text{Input} = \frac{\text{output}}{\text{efficiency}}$$

Output:

# of homes in town = 4 500/3 = 1 500

# of kWh needed for town/year = 13 000 × 1 500 = 19 500 000 kWh/year

# of kWh needed for town/day = 19 500 000/365 = 53 425 kWh/day

Input:

Input = (area)(solar heat-transfer rate) = area × 1.0 kW/m²

Input/8 h day = area × 1.0 kW/m² × 8 h = 8 kWh/m² × area

Input = area (8.0 kW/m²)

Therefore, the area can be computed for an 8 h day as follows

$$\text{Area} = \frac{m^2}{8.0 \, k \, Wh} \times \frac{53 \ 425 \ kWh}{0.08}$$

$$= 83 \ 476 \ m^2 = 898 \ 500 \ ft^2 = 20.6 \ \text{acres}$$

16.8   Refrigeration Cycles

For many years a measure of efficiency commonly used in the refrigeration and air-conditioning fields has been the *energy efficiency ratio,* abbreviated EER. In essence, a refrigerating machine is a reversed-heat engine; that is, heat is moved from a low-temperature region to a high-temperature region, requiring a work input to the reversed-heat engine. The expression for efficiency of a reversible-heat engine is

$$\text{Refrigeration efficiency} = \frac{\text{refrigerating effect}}{\text{work input}} \qquad (16.12)$$

Refrigeration efficiency is also called *coefficient of performance* (CP). The numerical value for CP may be greater than 1.

More recently, the U.S. Department of Energy has developed a testing method that rates performance of a unit over a wide range of operating conditions. The new rating system is called the seasonal energy efficiency ratio (SEER).

Industrial-size refrigeration units are measured in tons of cooling capacity. The ton unit originated with early refrigerating machines and was defined as the amount of refrigeration produced by melting 1 ton of ice in a 24-h period. If the latent heat of ice is taken into account, then a ton of refrigeration is equivalent to 12 000 Btu/h. Home-size units are generally rated in British thermal units per hour of cooling capacity.

The EER takes into account the normal designations for refrigerating effect and work input and expresses these as power rather than energy. Thus, EER is the ratio of a refrigerating unit's capacity to its power requirements:

$$\text{EER} = \frac{\text{refrigerating effect, Btu/h}}{\text{power input}} \qquad (16.13)$$

Example Problem 16.12   Compare the costs of running two 36 000 Btu/h air-conditioning units (3-ton) an average of 8 h/d for 1 month if electricity sells for $0.10/kWh. One unit has an EER of 8 and a second has an EER of 10.0.

Solution

$$EER = \frac{refrigerating\ effect}{power\ input}$$

$$8 = \frac{36\ 000\ Btu/h}{power\ input} \quad 10 = \frac{36\ 000\ Btu/h}{power\ input}$$

Power input = 4 500 Btu/h   Power input = 3 600 Btu/h

1 watt = 3.414 4 Btu/h

Power input = 1 054.36 W   Power input = 1 317.95 W

$$\frac{Dollars}{month} = \frac{1.317\ 95\ kW}{1} \times \frac{8\ h}{1\ day} \times \frac{30\ day}{1\ month} \times \frac{0.10\ dollars}{1\ kWh}$$

= $25.30 for a 10 EER unit

= $31.63 for an 8 EER unit

Problems

Potential and Kinetic Energy

16.1 A new flexible-fuel vehicle (FFV) is traveling at 75 mph on I-10 in Arizona. The vehicle has a mass of 2 875 lbm. Determine its kinetic energy in kJ.

16.2 An SUV weighs 2 345 kg and has a kinetic energy of 835 kJ. Determine its velocity in miles per hour (mph).

16.3 A Chevrolet Silverado with a mass of 6 555 lbm is being driven on a mountain road 6 250 ft above sea level ($g_L = 31.0$ ft/s²) at 55 mph. Determine the total energy possessed by the vehicle using sea level as the datum for potential energy. Express the answer in joules.

16.4 A Ford Ranger with a mass of 2 825 kg is traveling at a velocity of 55 mph down a mountain road in Colorado. The brakes fail and the driver elects to use a "runaway" truck tramp to stop the pickup. What distance in feet will it travel if the ramp has a 25 percent upward incline? Neglect air and road friction ($g_L = 32$ ft/s²).

16.5 A bobsled with two passengers, total mass of 245 lbm, races down a hillside that maintains a constant 32 percent slope. Neglecting air and snow friction, what will be the speed (mph) of the bobsled, when it has traveled 145 ft alone the slope. ($g_L = 32.2$ ft/s²)?

16.6 A new military aircraft, the Superhornet, with a weight of 5 150 lbm is traveling 1 350 mph at an altitude of 28 550 ft ($g_L = 30.5$ ft/s²). What is the total energy in joules? How many 50-ton tanks at sea level have an equivalent amount of energy, if they have an average ground speed of 35 mph?

16.7 A cliff diver, mass 185 lbm, dives from a 155 ft cliff into the sea. Gravitational constant = 32.2 feet per second squared. Neglecting air friction:
  (*a*) What is the diver's total energy in joules at the following heights: 100 ft, 50 ft, surface of the water?
  (*b*) What is the diver's velocity in mph at the first contact with the water?

16.8 During the World Series a ball is hit straight up from the batter's box and reaches a height of 295 ft. Neglecting air friction, what speed (mph) will the baseball attain if it is caught by the catcher at the same height it was hit?

Work

16.9 A father pulls his children in a wagon for 25 minutes covering 5 550 ft on a level sidewalk. He pulls with an average force of 25 lbf at an angle of 45 degrees to the sidewalk.
  (*a*) How much work is done (in ft · lbf)?
  (*b*) What is the average horsepower required?

16.10 How much work in N · m is done when raising a mass of 655 kg to an altitude of 145 m above the surface of the Moon? Assume g_L on surface of the Moon is equal to 1.634 meters per second squared.

16.11 If the mass in Problem 16.10 fell back to the surface of the Moon, with what velocity, in ft/s, would it strike the surface?

Pressure and Force

16.12 Air in a piston–cylinder configuration is heated until an external force of 1 225 lbf is required to hold the piston stationary. If the piston diameter is 2.55 inches, what is the pressure exerted by the air normal to the piston face (in lbf/ft^2)? (See Figure 16.5.)

16.13 The piston-cylinder arrangement in Problem 16.12 was designed and rated with an internal pressure of 6.45 MPa. Prior to shipping, the cylinder is tested by increasing the internal pressure to 3.0 times the design pressure (safety factor of 3.0). What maximum force in newtons must be applied to the piston to hold it stationary during the test?

Closed Systems

16.14 If 11 250 ft · lbf of work is done by a closed system while 145 Btu of heat is added, what is the change in internal energy (in joules) of the system?

16.15 During a process, 23.5 MJ of heat is added to a closed system. If the internal energy is increased by 42.5 MJ, how much work in Btu was done? Is the work done on or by the system?

16.16 In an adiabatic process, 102 kJ of work is done on 25 kg of water. Express the change in internal energy (Btu) per pound of mass of fluid. *Hint: u2 − u1 = U2 − U1/m* (kJ/kg). Lowercase denotes energy per unit mass.

Cycles

16.17 A V-6 internal combustion engine burns fuel at the rate of 5.5 gallons per hour. The fuel has a heating value of 42.7 kJ/mL. Calculate the useful output to the power train (in kilowatts) if the overall efficiency is 35 percent.

16.18 Compute the Carnot efficiency of a heat engine operating between 455 and 75°F.

16.19 An inventor claims to have developed a power cycle capable of delivering a net work output of 395 kJ for an energy input by heat transfer of 985 kJ. The system receives its heat transfer from a fossil fuel at 235°C and rejects heat at 55°C. Is this a reasonable claim? Why or why not?

16.20 Heat is delivered to a Carnot engine at the rate of 285 kJ/s and heat is rejected at a rate of 8.35 (10^3) Btu/min to a 32°C low-temperature reservoir. What is the temperature (in °C) of the high-temperature source? *Hint: $Q_{in} − Q_{out}$* = Work (useful output).

16.21 A gasoline engine is used to drive an electric generator. To operate the engine 10.8 L/h of gasoline with a heating value of 45 MJ/L is burned. The engine delivers 55 kW to an electric generator that produces 110 amps at 240 volts DC. Determine:
  (*a*) engine efficiency
  (*b*) generator efficiency
  (*c*) overall efficiency

16.22 An electric motor with an efficiency of 73 percent drives a water pump. What input power is required of the motor (in kilowatts) to pump 21 725 gals of water from a lake to a storage tank 65 ft above the lake surface in 4.0 hours?

16.23 A pump with an efficiency of 65 percent has an output capacity of 25×10^3 ft · lbf/s and is used to deliver a grain-slurry mixture. An electric motor with an efficiency of 85 percent drives the pump. Determine:
   (*a*) the input horsepower to the pump
   (*b*) the power, in kilowatts, required for the motor.

16.24 An 85 percent efficient electric motor has a useful output of 0.75 hp and it drives a 68 percent efficient water pump.
   (*a*) How much power, in watts, does the motor require?
   (*b*) How much water, in gallons, could this combination lift 7.5 ft in one hour?

16.25 A heating value of 90 TJ has been measured from the fission of 1.0 kg of U-235.
   (*a*) How many gallons of water would need to be stored on a hillside 225 ft above sea level to provide an energy equivalence?
   (*b*) If the heating value of 1.0 kg of coal is 25 MJ, how many short tons of coal would need to be consumed to provide the heating equivalence of 1.0 kg U-235?

16.26 Estimate the number of households that could receive electric energy from 35 kg of U-235. Assume the average household requires 17 000 kWh per year, that the conversion of U-235 to electricity is 68 percent efficient, and that the energy equivalent of U-235 is 10^8 MJ/kg.

16.27 Using the data given in Problem 16.26, determine the surface area (in hectares) of solar collectors operating at an efficiency of 12 percent to supply electric energy to the same households. Assume an average of 8 hours of sunlight per day and a transfer rate of one kW per square meter.

16.28 A one-ton window air conditioner (12 000 Btu/h) is installed in a mobile home. If all the following appliances were operating for one hour, what fraction of the unit's capacity would be needed to remove the heat generated by four 150 W lamps, six 100 W lamps, two 75 W lamps, a 500 W refrigerator, an 900 W oven, and four people watching TV (120 W)? How many kilowatt-hours of electric energy are used during each hour for these conditions? What is the hourly cost to the mobile home owner if electricity costs $0.10/kWh? *Note:* The average heat output of a person at rest is 480 Btu/h.

16.29 Develop a spreadsheet and produce a table of values that represents the solar collector area, in acres, needed to supply electric energy for cities with populations of 5 000, 20 000, 50 000, 100 000, and 1 000 000. Provide results for conversion efficiencies from 5 to 15% in increments of 1 percent. Use the same assumptions as used in Example Problem 16.11. Interpolate the data to determine collector area for the city in which you attend college.

16.30 Develop a spreadsheet that will determine the average monthly cost of operating 215 individual air-conditioning units in a manufacturing facility. Each unit is rated at 24 000 Btu/h. Consider EER values from 7.0 to 11.0 in increments of 0.5 and prepare a table of monthly costs versus EER. The electrical rate structure is as follows:

First 5 000 kWh = 11.0¢/kWh

Next 15 000 kWh = 8.5¢/kWh

Over 20 000 kWh = 8.0¢/kWh

Assume that the units run an average of eight hours per day on weekdays and 10 hours on Saturdays (closed Sunday). Use a 31-day month beginning on a Monday.

CHAPTER **17**

Electrical Theory*

Chapter Objectives

When you complete your study of this chapter, you will able to:

- Compute the equivalent resistance of resistors in series and in parallel
- Apply Ohm's law to a resistive circuit
- Determine the power provided to a DC circuit and the power used by circuit components
- Use Kirchhoff's laws to solve resistive networks
- Utilize mesh currents to solve resistive networks

17.1 Introduction

Electricity is universally one of our most powerful and useful forms of energy. It affects our world in many useful ways. It affects our lives through communication systems, computer systems, control systems, and power systems. Certainly electrical engineers, but to some extent all engineers, must understand how to design, analyze, and maintain such systems.

Electrical and computer engineering are very large and diverse fields of study. This chapter provides an introduction to one small aspect called *circuit theory*. It is important to the study of engineering because many products or systems that are designed involve the application of the electrical theory. This area that is fundamental to computer and electrical engineers is also important to all engineering disciplines.

Circuit theory does many things for us. (1) It provides simple solutions to practical problems with sufficient accuracy to be useful. (2) It allows us to reduce the analysis of large systems to a series of smaller problems that we can conveniently handle. (3) It provides a means of synthesizing (i.e., building up) complex systems from basic components.

In this chapter we will review a number of the elementary concepts of electricity that were first learned in physics. We also will introduce and apply some fundamental circuit-analysis equations such as Ohm's law and Kirchhoff's laws. Applications, however, will be restricted to those involving steady-state direct current (DC).

---

*Users will find Appendix A and E useful reference material for this chapter.

17.2 Structure of Electricity

Matter consists of minute particles called molecules. Molecules are the smallest particles into which a substance can be divided and still retain all the characteristics of the original substance. Each of these particles will differ according to the type of matter to which it belongs. Thus a molecule of iron will be different from a molecule of copper.

Looking more closely at a molecule, we find that it can be divided into still smaller parts called atoms. Each atom has a central core, or nucleus, that contains both protons and neutrons. Moving in a somewhat circular motion around the nucleus are particles of extremely small mass called electrons. In fact the entire mass of the atom is practically the same as that of its nucleus since the proton is approximately 2.0×10^3 times more massive than the electron.

To understand how electricity works, bear in mind that electrons possess a negative electric charge and protons possess a positive electric charge. Their charges are opposite in sign but numerically the same magnitude. The neutron is considered neutral, being neither positive nor negative.

The typical atom in its entirety has no net electric charge because the positive charge of the nucleus is exactly balanced by the negative charge of the surrounding electron cloud. That is, each atom contains as many electrons orbiting the nucleus as there are protons inside the nucleus.

The actual number of protons depends on the element of which the atom is a part. Hydrogen (H) has the simplest structure, with one proton in its nucleus and one orbital electron. Helium (He) has two protons and two neutrons in the nucleus; and since the neutrons exhibit a neutral charge, there are two orbital electrons (see Figure 17.1). More complex elements have many more protons, electrons, and neutrons. For example, gold (Au) has 79 protons and 118 neutrons, with 79 orbital electrons. As the elements become more complex, the orbiting electrons arrange themselves into regions, or "shells," around the nucleus.

The maximum number of electrons in any one shell is uniquely defined. The shell closest to the nucleus contains a maximum of two electrons, the next eight, and so on. There are a maximum of six shells, but the last two shells are never completely filled.

Figure 17.1

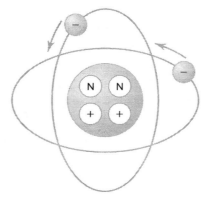

Schematic representations of a helium atom.

Atoms therefore can combine by sharing their outer orbital electrons and thereby fill certain voids and establish unique patterns of molecules.

Atoms are extremely minute. In fact, it is difficult to imagine the size of an atom, since a grain of table salt is estimated to contain 10^{18} atoms. However, it is possible to understand the size relationship between the nucleus and the orbital electrons. Assume for purposes of visualization that the diameter of the hydrogen nucleus is a 1.0 mm sphere. To scale accurately the electron and its orbit, the electron would revolve at an average distance of 25 m from the nucleus. Although the relative distance is significant, this single electron is prevented from leaving the atom by an electric force of attraction that exists because the proton has a positive charge and the electron has an opposite but equal negative charge.

How closely the millions upon millions of atoms and molecules are packed together determines the state (e.g., solid, liquid, or gas) of a given substance. In solids, the atoms are packed closely together, generally in a very orderly manner. The atoms are held in a specific lattice structure but vibrate around their nominal positions. Depending on the substance, some electrons may be free to move from one atom to another.

17.3 Static Electricity

History indicates that the Greeks were the first to have a word for electricity. They discovered that after rubbing certain items together, the materials would exert a force on one another. It was concluded that during the rubbing process, the bodies were "charged" with some unknown element, which the Greeks called electricity. For example, they concluded that by rubbing silk over glass, electricity was added to the substance. We realize today that during the process of rubbing, electrons are displaced from some of the surface atoms of the glass and are added to the surface atoms of the silk. The branch of science concerned with static, or stationary, charged bodies is called electrostatics.

The charge of an electron can be measured, but the value is extremely small. A large unit, the coulomb, has been selected to denote electric charge. Charles Augustin Coulomb (1736–1806) was the first individual to measure an electric force. In recognition of his work, the SI unit of charge is called the *coulomb*. A coulomb is defined in terms of the force exerted between unit charges. A charge of one coulomb will exert on an equal charge, placed one meter away in air, a force of about 8.988×10^9 N. The magnitude of this force is very large, equivalent to the weight of 15 million people. Because of the large size of this unit of measure, the charge on a proton is only $+1.6 \times 10^{-19}$ C.

17.4 Electric Current

Earlier we noted that electrons are prevented from leaving the atom by the attraction of the protons in the nucleus. It is entirely possible, however, for an electron to become temporarily separated from an atom. These free electrons drift around randomly in the space between atoms. During their random travel many of them will collide with other atoms; when they do collide with sufficient force, they dislodge electrons from those atoms. Since electrons are frequently colliding with other atoms, there can be a continuous movement of free electrons in a solid. If the electrons drift in a particular direction instead of moving randomly, there is movement of electricity through the solid. This continuous movement of electrons in a direction is called an electric current. If the electron drift is in only one direction, it is called direct current (DC). If the electrons periodically reverse direction of travel, then we have alternating current (AC).

The ease with which electrons can be dislodged by collision as well as the number of free electrons available varies with the substance. Materials in which the drift of electrons can be easily produced are said to be good conductors; those in which it is difficult to produce an electron drift are good insulators. For example, copper is a good conductor, whereas glass is a good insulator. Practically all metals are good conductors. Silver is a very good conductor but it is expensive. Copper and aluminum also are good conductors and are commonly used in electric wire.

17.5 Electric Potential

Both theory and experimentation suggest that like charges repel and unlike charges attract. Consequently, to bring like charges together, an external force is necessary, and therefore work must be done. The amount of work required to bring a positive charge near another positive charge from a large distance is used as a measure of the electric potential at that point. This amount of potential is measured in units of work per unit charge or joules per coulomb (J/C). By definition, one joule per coulomb is one volt, a unit of electric potential.

Devices such as electric batteries or generators are capable of producing a difference in electric potential between two points. Such devices are rated in terms of their ability to produce a potential difference, and this difference in potential is measured in volts (V). When these devices are connected to other components in a continuous circuit, electric current flows. You also could think of batteries as devices that change chemical energy to electric energy whereas generators convert mechanical energy to electric energy.

17.6 Simple Electric Circuits

When electric charge and current were initially being explored, scientists thought that current flow was from positive to negative. They had no knowledge of electron drift. By the time it was discovered that the electron flow was from negative to positive, the idea that current flow was from positive to negative had become so well established that it was decided not to change the convention. See Figure 17.2.

When battery or generator terminals are connected to a conducting material, the battery or generator creates a potential difference across the load measured as a voltage. It follows that the random movement of the negatively charged electrons will have a drift direction induced by this potential difference. The resulting effect will be the movement of electrons away from the negative terminal of the battery or generator. Electrons will travel in a continuous cycle around the circuit, reentering the battery or generator at its positive terminal.

Figure 17.2

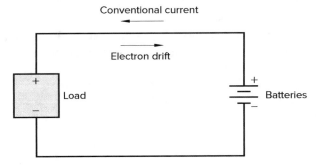

Conventional current

Electron drift

Load

+

Batteries

A simple DC electric circuit.

The speed by which any individual electron moves is relatively slow, less than 1 mm/s. However, once a potential difference is connected into a circuit, the "flow" of electrons starts almost instantaneously at all points. Individual electrons at all locations begin their erratic movement around the circuit, colliding frequently with other atoms in the conductor. Because electron activity starts at all points practically simultaneously, electric current appears to travel about 3×10^8 m/s.

Electric current is really nothing more than the rate at which electrons pass through a given cross section of a conductor. The number of electrons that migrate through this cross section is gigantic in magnitude in that approximately 6.28×10^{18} electrons pass a point per second per ampere. Since this number is very large, it is not convenient to use the rate of electron flow as a unit of current measurement. Instead, current is measured in terms of the total electric charge (coulomb) that passes a certain point in a unit of time (second). This unit of current is called the ampere (A). That is, one ampere equals one coulomb per second (C/s).

17.7 Resistance

Another critical component of circuit theory is *resistance*. George Simon Ohm (1789–1854), a German scientist investigating the relation between electric current and potential difference, found that, for a metal, the current in the conductor was directly proportional to the potential difference across the conductor. This important relationship has become known as Ohm's law, which is stated as:

At constant temperature, the current I *in a conductor is directly proportional to the potential difference between its ends,* E.

The ratio *E/I* describes the "resistance" to electron flow and is denoted by the symbol *R:*

$$R = \frac{E}{I} \tag{17.1}$$

and is called Ohm's Law. It is more often presented as

$$E = IR$$

This is one of the simplest but most important relations used in the electric circuit theory. A conductor has a resistance R of one ohm (Ω) when the current I through the conductor is one ampere (A) and the potential difference E across it is one volt (V).

When a specific value of resistance is required in a circuit, a resistor is used. Resistors come in many sizes and tolerances. Resistance and tolerance values of resistors are marked on the body of the resistors with coded color bands.

The reciprocal of resistance is called *conductance* (G):

$$G = \frac{1}{R} \tag{17.2}$$

Conductance is measured in siemens (S).

Example Problem 17.1 The current in an electric aircraft instrument heater is measured as 2.5 A when connected to a battery with a potential of 60.0 V. Calculate the resistance of the heater.

Solution

$$R = \frac{E}{I}$$

$$= \frac{60.0}{2.5}$$

$$= 24\ \Omega$$

17.8 DC Circuit Concepts

A considerable amount of information about electric circuits can be presented in a compact form by means of circuit diagrams. Figure 17.3 illustrates three typical symbols that are used in such diagrams.

Circuits may have resistors that are connected either end to end or parallel to each other. When resistors are attached end to end, they are said to be connected in series, and the same current flows through each. When several resistors are connected between the same two points they are connected in parallel.

Figure 17.3

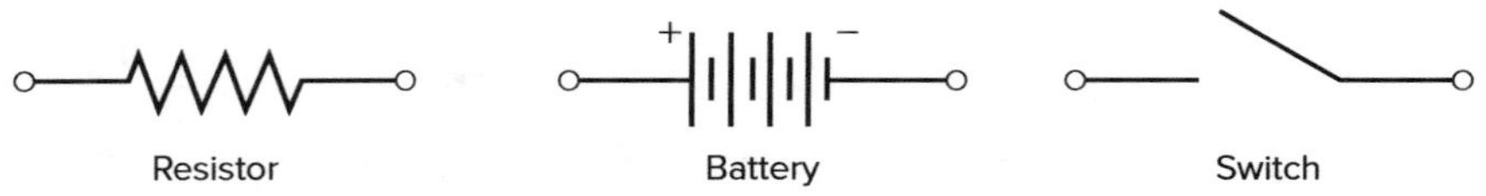

Resistor   Battery   Switch

Symbols.

Figure 17.4

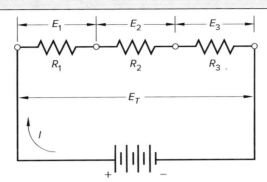

Series circuit.

For the series circuit illustrated in Figure 17.4, there will be a potential across each resistor, since a potential must exist between the ends of a conductor if current is to flow. This potential difference E is related to current and resistance by Ohm's law. For each unknown voltage (potential), we can write

$$E_1 = IR_1$$

$$E_2 = IR_2$$

$$E_3 = IR_3$$

Since the total voltage drop E_T across the three resistors is the sum of the individual drops, and since the current is the same through each resistor, then

$$E_T = E_1 + E_2 + E_3$$

$$= IR_1 + IR_2 + IR_3$$

$$= I(R_1 + R_2 + R_3)$$

or

$$R_1 + R_2 + R_3 = \frac{E_T}{I}$$

Since E_T is the total potential difference across the circuit and I is the circuit current, then the total resistance must be

$$R_T = \frac{E_T}{I}$$

Therefore

$$R_T = R_1 + R_2 + R_3 \qquad (17.3)$$

This total resistance R_T is sometimes called the equivalent resistance R_E.

These steps demonstrate that when resistors are connected in series, their combined resistance is the sum of their individual values.

Figure 17.5

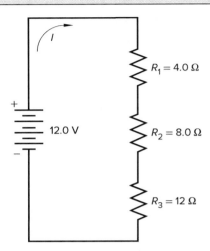

Example Problem 17.2   The circuit in Figure 17.5 has three resistors connected in series with a 12.0 V source. Determine the line current I and the voltage drop across each resistor (E_1, E_2, and E_3).

Solution   For resistors in series

$$R_T = R_1 + R_2 + R_3$$
$$R_T = 4.0 + 8.0 + 12$$
$$= 24 \ \Omega$$

Ohm's law gives

$$E = IR$$
$$I = \frac{E_T}{R_T} = \frac{12.0}{24} = 0.50 \ A$$

Then

$$E_1 = 0.50(4.0)$$
$$= 2.0 \ V$$
$$E_2 = 0.50(8.0)$$
$$= 4.0 \ V$$
$$E_3 = 0.50(12)$$
$$= 6.0 \ V$$

Check: $E_T = 12.0 = 2.0 + 4.0 + 6.0$

When several resistors are connected between the same two points, they are said to be in parallel. Figure 17.6 illustrates three resistors in parallel.

Figure 17.6

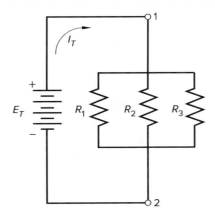

Parallel circuit.

The current between points 1 and 2 divides among the various pathways formed by the resistors. Since each resistor is connected between the same two points, the potential difference across each of the resistors is the same.

In analyzing the problem, we let I_T be the total current passing between the points 1 and 2 with I_1, I_2, and I_3 representing the branch currents through R_1, R_2, and R_3, respectively.

Using Ohm's law we can write

$$I_1 = \frac{E_T}{R_1}, I_2 = \frac{E_T}{R_2}, I_3 = \frac{E_T}{R_3}$$

or

$$I_1 + I_2 + I_3 = E_T\left(\frac{1}{R_1} + \frac{1}{R_2} + \frac{1}{R_3}\right)$$

But we know that

$$I_T = I_1 + I_2 + I_3$$

Applying Ohm's law to total circuit values reveals that

$$I_T = \frac{E_T}{R_T}$$

Therefore,

$$\frac{E_T}{R_T} = E_T\left(\frac{1}{R_1} + \frac{1}{R_2} + \frac{1}{R_3}\right)$$

or

$$\frac{1}{R_T} = \frac{1}{R_1} + \frac{1}{R_2} + \frac{1}{R_3} \qquad (17.4)$$

This equation indicates that when a group of resistors are connected in parallel, the reciprocal of their combined resistance is equal to the sum of the reciprocals of their separate resistances.

Figure 17.7

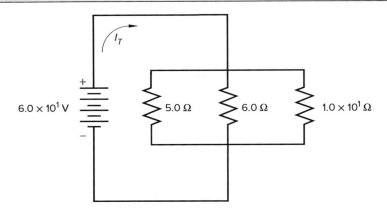

Example Problem 17.3   In Figure 17.7 three resistors are connected in parallel across a 6.0×10^1 V battery. What is the equivalent resistance of the three resistors and the line current?

Solution   For resistors in parallel:

$$\frac{1}{R_T} = \frac{1}{R_1} + \frac{1}{R_2} + \frac{1}{R_3}$$

$$= \frac{1}{5.0 \times 10^0} + \frac{1}{6.0 \times 10^0} + \frac{1}{1.0 \times 10^1}$$

$$= \frac{28}{6.0 \times 10^1}$$

$$R_T = \frac{6.0 \times 10^1}{28}$$

$$= 2.1 \ \Omega$$

From Ohm's law

$$E = IR$$

$$E_T = I_T R_T$$

So that

$$I_T = \frac{E_T}{R_T}$$

$$= (6.0 \times 10^1) \frac{2.8 \times 10^1}{6.0 \times 10^1}$$

$$= 28 \ \text{A}$$

Figure 17.8

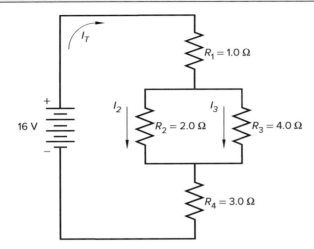

Electric circuits may involve combinations of resistors in parallel and in series. The next example problem demonstrates a solution of that nature.

Example Problem 17.4   Determine the line current I_T, the circuit equivalent resistance R_E, and the voltage drop E_4 across the resistor R_4 for the circuit in Figure 17.8. What resistance should be substituted for R_1 to reduce the line current by one-half?

Solution

Ohm's law: $E = IR$

Resistors in series: $R_T = R_1 + R_2 + \ldots + R_N$

Resistors in parallel: $\dfrac{1}{R_T} = \dfrac{1}{R_1} + \dfrac{1}{R_2} + \ldots + \dfrac{1}{R_N}$

For parallel resistors R_2 and R_3

$$\frac{1}{R_T} = \frac{1}{R_2} + \frac{1}{R_3}$$

$$= \frac{1}{2.0} + \frac{1}{4.0}$$

For series resistors

$$R_E = R_1 + R_T + R_4$$

$$= 1.0 + \frac{4.0}{3.0} + 3.0$$

$$= \frac{16}{3.0}$$

$$= 5.3\ \Omega$$

Then the line current is

$$E_E = I_T R_E$$

$$I_T = \frac{E_E}{R_E}$$

$$= 16\left(\frac{3.0}{16}\right)$$

$$= 3.0 \text{ A}$$

and the voltage drop across R_4 is

$$E_4 = I_T R_4$$

$$= 3.0(3.0)$$

$$= 9.0 \text{ V}$$

If we reduce the line current by one-half, the new line current is $3.0/2 = 1.5$ A. The new equivalent resistance then must be

$$R_E = \frac{E_t}{I_T} = \frac{16}{1.5} = 10.667 \ \Omega$$

But

$$R_E = R_{new} + R_T + R_4$$

so the resistor replacing R_1 is

$$R_{new} = R_E - R_T - R_4 = 10.667 - \frac{4.0}{3.0} - 3.0 = 6.3 \ \Omega$$

17.9 DC Electric Power

Consider the following illustration of a simple DC circuit. A common household lantern, as illustrated in Figure 17.9, is represented by a section view (*a*) and a circuit diagram (*b*). As the switch is closed, current (*I*) flows through the bulb producing light and heat. Both light and heat are forms of energy, thus the chemical energy stored in the battery is converted first to electrical energy and then to light (useful energy) and heat (waste energy).

The rate at which energy is consumed by the bulb is a product of the voltage and current.

$$\text{Power } (P) = E(I) \tag{17.5}$$

Voltage (*E*) is in volts (V) or joules/coulomb (J/C) and current (*I*) is in amperes (A) or coulombs/second (C/s). The units of power, therefore, are joules/second or watts (W) (after James Watt, 1736–1819). Using Ohm's law, we can express power in the following alternative forms:

$$\text{Power } (P) = \frac{E^2}{R} \tag{17.6}$$

Figure 17.9a

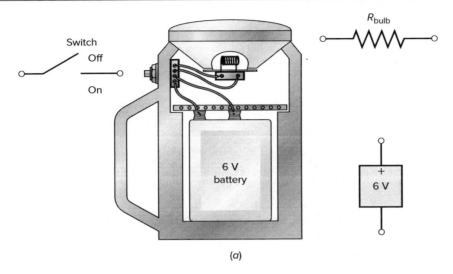

(a)

Household lantern.

Figure 17.9b

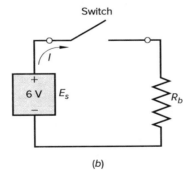

(b)

Schematic diagram.

$$\text{Power } (P) = I^2 R \tag{17.7}$$

If the rate of energy production or consumption (power) is constant, then the total energy produced or consumed can be computed from

$$\text{Energy} = (\text{Power})(\text{Time}) = EIt \tag{17.8}$$

and is expressed in units of joules (J).

Example Problem 17.5   The lantern in Figure 17.9 contains a lamp with a measured resistance of 2.0 Ω. When the switch is closed, what is the power consumed by the lamp?

Solution

$$P = \frac{E^2}{R}$$

$$= \frac{(6.0)^2}{2.0}$$

$$= 18 \text{ W}$$

Example Problem 17.6   A gallon of gasoline has the potential energy of approximately 131.8 MJ. Assume that a gasoline engine is driving a generator and the generator is supplying electricity to a 100 W lamp. The overall efficiency (from gasoline to electrical energy) of the engine-generator set is 20%.

(*a*) How long will the lamp provide light from one gal of gasoline?
(*b*) If the system operates at 120 volts, what is the lamp current?
(*c*) How much electric charge passes through the lamp in 10 seconds?

Solution

(*a*) Electrical energy produced from 1 gal of gasoline is

$$131.8 \times 10^6 \text{ J} \times 0.2 = 26.36 \times 10^6 \text{ J}$$

From the equation:

$$\text{Energy} = (\text{power})(\text{time})$$

$$\text{time} = \frac{26.36 \times 10^6 \text{ J}}{100 \text{ J/s}} = 0.263\,6 \times 10^6 \text{ s} = 73 \text{ hr, } 13 \text{ min, } 20 \text{ s}$$

(*b*) $I = \dfrac{P}{E} = \dfrac{100 \text{ W}}{120 \text{ V}} = 0.833 \text{ A}$

(*c*) $0.833 \text{ A} = 0.833 \text{ C/s or } 8.33 \text{ C in } 10 \text{ s}$

17.10   Terminal Voltage

Figure 17.10 is a basic circuit in which there can be different sources of electric potential. The storage battery and the electric generator are two familiar examples.

The potential does work of amount E in joules per coulomb on charges passing through the voltage source from the negative to the positive terminal. This results in a difference of potential E across the resistor R, which causes current to flow in the circuit. The energy furnished by the voltage source reappears as heat in the resistor.

Current can travel in either direction through a voltage source. When the current moves from the negative to the positive terminal, some other form of energy (such as mechanical or chemical energy) is converted into electric energy. If we were to impose a

Figure 17.10

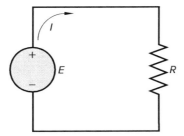

Basic circuit.

higher potential in the external circuit—for example, forcing current backward through the voltage source—the electric energy would be converted to some other form. When current is sent backward through a battery, electric energy is converted into chemical energy (which can be recovered in certain types of batteries; that is, charge the battery). When current is sent backward through a generator, the device becomes a motor.

A resistor, on the other hand, converts electric energy into heat no matter what the direction of current. Therefore, it is impossible to reverse the process and to regain electric energy from the heat. Electric potential always drops by the amount IR as current travels through a resistor. This drop occurs in the direction of the current.

In a generator or battery with current flowing negative to positive, the positive terminal will be E volts above the negative terminal minus the voltage drop due to internal resistance between terminals. There always will be some energy converted to heat inside a battery or generator no matter which direction the current flows.

When a battery or a generator is driving the circuit, the internal current passes from the negative to the positive terminal. Each coulomb of charge gains energy E from chemical or mechanical energy but loses IR in heat dissipation. The net gain in joules per coulomb can be determined by $E - IR$.

For a motor or for a battery being charged, the internal current passes from the positive to the negative terminal. Each coulomb loses energy E and IR. The combined loss can be determined by $E + IR$.

In the case of a motor, the quantity E is commonly called back-emf (the electromotive force, or potential), since it represents a voltage that is in a direction opposite the current flow.

Figure 17.11 shows a circuit wherein a battery is being charged by a generator. E_G, E_B, R_G, and R_B indicate the potentials and internal resistances, respectively, of the generator and battery. Each coulomb that flows around the circuit in the direction of the current I gains energy E_G from the generator and loses energy E_B in the form of chemical energy to the battery. Heat dissipation is realized as IR_G, IR_1, IR_B, and IR_2.

17.11 Kirchhoff's Laws

To analyze a DC circuit network that consists of more than simple elements in series or parallel, we will use Kirchhoff's network laws. These laws recognize the conservation of current at a node and potential drop in a closed loop and state these concepts

Figure 17.11

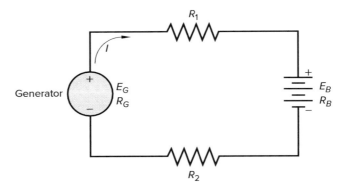

Generator charging a battery.

in algebraic form. Thus a network solution requires that one write these algebraic equations and then solve the resulting set of simultaneous, linear, algebraic equations. Kirchhoff's current law:

> *The algebraic sum of all of the currents coming into a node (junction) in a network must be zero.*

Kirchhoff's voltage law:

> *The algebraic sum of the voltages (potential drops) around any closed loop in a network equals zero.*

In applying Kirchhoff's laws, an algebraic sign must be provided with each current and voltage to indicate its direction. When writing Kirchhoff's current law equations, a positive direction for current flow must be defined, either current flow into a junction is positive, or current flow out of a junction is positive. Either convention may be used, but the convention must be consistent throughout the circuit. If a resultant current is negative, that will indicate the actual current is in the opposite direction that was assumed.

When writing Kirchhoff's voltage equations, the voltage rise or drop across an element must have a polarity in accordance with the assumed current, mainly that current enters the positive end of a resistor and the negative end of a battery or generator as indicated in Article 17.10. It must then be defined whether a voltage rise or a voltage drop is positive. Common convention is that rises are considered positive and drops are considered negative, but either may be used. A computation resulting in a negative voltage indicates the actual polarity is the opposite of that assumed.

Example Problem 17.7   Given the circuit illustrated in Figure 17.12, determine the currents I_x, I_y, and I_z.

Figure 17.12

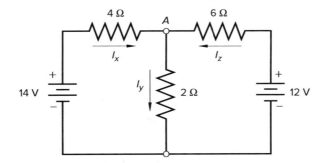

Application of Kirchhoff's laws.

Solution   From Kirchhoff's current law we can write (at point A)

$$I_y = I_x + I_z$$

Applying Kirchhoff's voltage law around the left loop in a clockwise fashion beginning at A, we find

$$-I_y(2) + 14 - I_x(4) = 0$$

Likewise, Kirchhoff's voltage law for the right loop applied counterclockwise from A gives

$$-I_y(2) + 12 - I_z(6) = 0$$

We then have three equations in I_x, I_y, and I_z which yield

$$I_x = 2\ A$$

$$I_y = 3\ A$$

$$I_z = 1\ A$$

To check the solution, write voltage drops in the left loop

$$-(3)(2) + 14 - (2)(4) = 0$$

and in the right loop.

$$-(3)(2) + 12 - (1)(6) = 0$$

As a further check, write voltage drops around the entire outside loop, moving clockwise from A

$$(6)(1) - 12 + 14 - (2)(4) = 0$$

Example Problem 17.8   A 220 V generator is driving a motor drawing 8.0 A and charging a 170 V battery. Determine the back-emf of the motor (E_m), the charging current of the battery (I_2), and the current through the generator (I_1). See Figure 17.13.

Figure 17.13

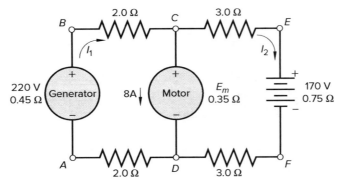

Application of Kirchhoff's laws.

Solution   Since the current through the motor is given as 8.0 A, we can see by applying Kirchhoff's current law to junction C that $I_1 = I_2 + 8.0$.

Kirchhoff's voltage law dictates that we select a beginning point and travel completely around a closed loop back to the starting point, thereby arriving at the same electric potential.

Applying Kirchhoff's voltage law to the circuit $ABCDA$ in Figure 17.13:

$$(E_{A-B})_{emf} + (E_{A-B})_{loss} + (E_{B-C})_{loss} + (E_{C-D})_{emf} + (E_{C-D})_{loss} + (E_{D-A})_{loss} = 0$$

By applying correct algebraic signs according to the established convention, we get the results given in Table 17.1.

Substituting the values from Table 17.1, we find that the equation becomes

$$220 - 0.45(I_1) - 2.0(I_1) - E_m - 0.35(8.0) - 2.0(I_1) = 0$$

Substituting $I_1 = I_2 + 8.0$ and simplifying, we get

$$-4.45I_2 - E_m + 181.6 = 0$$

This equation cannot be solved because there are two unknowns. However, a second equation can be written around a different loop of the circuit. For loop *DCEFD*

$$(E_{D-C})_{emf} + (E_{D-C})_{loss} + (E_{C-E})_{loss} + (E_{E-F})_{emf} + (E_{E-F})_{loss} + (E_{F-D})_{loss} = 0$$

From this we can develop Table 17.2 and therefore we have a second equation:

$$E_m + 0.35(8.0) - 3.0I_2 - 170 - 0.75I_2 - 3.0I_2 = 0$$
$$E_m - 6.75I_2 - 167.2 = 0$$

Solving these two equations simultaneously, we obtain the following results:

$$I_2 = 1.3 \text{ A}$$
$$E_m = 1.8 \times 10^2 \text{ V}$$

Then

$$I_1 = I_2 + 8.0 = 1.3 + 8.0 = 9.3 \text{ A}$$

Table 17.1 Voltage summation for loop *ABCDA*

Symbols	Quantities	Notes
$(E_{A-B})_{emf}$	+220 V	Potential of generator
$(E_{A-B})_{loss}$	$-0.45\,I_1$	Loss in generator
$(E_{B-C})_{loss}$	$-2.0\,I_1$	Loss in line
$(E_{C-D})_{emf}$	$-E_m$	Back-emf of motor
$(E_{C-D})_{loss}$	$-0.35(8.0)$	Loss in motor
$(E_{D-A})_{loss}$	$-2.0\,I_1$	Loss in line

These values can be checked by writing a third equation around the outside loop, *ABCEFDA:*

$$(E_{A-B})_{emf} + (E_{A-B})_{loss} + E_{B-C} + E_{C-E} + (E_{E-F})_{emf} + (E_{E-F})_{loss} + E_{F-D} + E_{D-A} = 0$$

Using values from Tables 17.1 and 17.2, we obtain

$$+220 - 0.45(I_1) - 2.0\,(I_1) - 3.0\,(I_2) - 170 - 0.75\,(I_2) - 3.0\,(I_2) - 2.0\,(I_1) = 0$$

With $I_1 = 9.3$ A and $I_2 = 1.3$ A, we have

$$+220 - 0.45(9.3) - 2.0(9.3) - 3.0(1.3) - 170 - 0.75(1.3) - 3.0(1.3) - 2.0(9.3) = 0$$
(within roundoff error)

By the preceding procedure, a set of simultaneous equations may be found that will solve similar problems, provided the number of unknowns is not greater than the number of circuit paths or loops.

The following general procedure is outlined as a guide to systematically applying Kirchhoff's laws.

1. Sketch a circuit diagram and label all known voltages, currents, and resistances. Show + and − signs on potentials.
2. Indicate a current direction in each branch of the circuit. If the direction is not known, choose a direction. A negative current solution will indicate that the current is flowing in the opposite direction to the direction assumed.
3. Assign symbols to all unknown currents, voltages, and resistances.
4. Apply Kirchhoff's voltage law to circuit loops and Kirchhoff's current law at junctions to obtain as many independent equations as there are unknowns in the problem.

Table 17.2 Voltage summation for loop *DCEFD*

Symbols	Quantities	Notes
$(E_{D-C})_{emf}$	$+E_m$	Back-emf of motor
$(E_{D-C})_{loss}$	$+0.35(8.0)$	IR rise in motor
$(E_{C-E})_{loss}$	$-3.0\,I_2$	Loss in line
$(E_{E-F})_{emf}$	-170 V	Drop across battery
$(E_{E-F})_{loss}$	$-0.75\,I_2$	Loss in battery
$(E_{F-D})_{loss}$	$-3.0\,I_2$	Loss in line

Figure 17.14

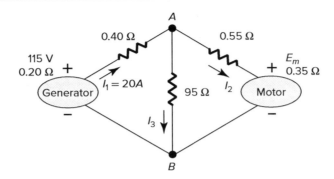

5. Solve the resulting set of equations.
6. Check results from Kirchhoff's voltage law written on a loop that was not used earlier.

Example Problem 17.9   A 115-V generator provides energy for a 95-Ω resistive load and a motor. See Figure 17.14. Determine the currents through the motor and resistive load and the back-emf of the motor and power consumed by the resistive load.

Solution   Apply Kirchhoff's current law at point A.

$$20 - I_2 - I_3 = 0$$

Applying Kirchhoff's voltage law to the left loop, moving clockwise from B, we have

$$115 - (0.20)(20) - (0.40)(20) - 95(I_3) = 0$$

Kirchhoff's voltage law for the right loop, moving clockwise from A, gives

$$-(0.55)(I_2) - E_m - (0.35)(I_2) + 95(I_3) = 0$$

The left loop equation can be solved for I_3:

$$I_3 = (115 - (0.20)(20) - (0.40)(20))/95 = 1.084\ 2 \text{ A}$$

Then the current equation gives

$$I_2 = 20 - I_3 = 20 - 1.0842 = 18.915\ 8 \text{ A}$$

E_m can be found from the right loop equation:

$$E_m = 0.95(I_3) - (0.55)(I_2) - (0.35)(I_2)$$

$$= (95)(1.084\ 2) - (0.55)(18.915\ 8) - (0.35)(18.915\ 8)$$

$$= 85.974\ 8 \text{ V}$$

Write Kirchhoff's voltage law for the outside loop as a check (clockwise from B):

$$115 - 0.20(20) - 0.40(20) - 0.55(18.915\ 8) - 85.974\ 8 - 0.35(18.915\ 8)$$

$$= 9.8 \times 10^{-4} \text{ (should be zero, okay within roundoff error)}$$

Power consumed by the resistive load is

$$P = 95\,I_3^2 = 95(1.084\,2)^2 = 111.671\,5 \text{ W}$$

The results considering significant figures then are

Current through the motor $= I_2 = 19$ A

Current through the resistive load $= I_3 = 1.1$ A

Back-emf of the motor $= E_m = 86$ V

Power consumed by the resistive load $= P = 1.1 \times 10^2$ W

17.12 Mesh Currents

Individual elements or components can be connected to form unique circuits. The interconnectivity of each element can be described in terms of nodes, branches, meshes, paths, and loops.

A node is a specific point or location within a circuit where two or more components are connected.
A branch is a path that connects two nodes.
A mesh is a loop that does not contain any other loops within itself.

A mesh current is defined as a current that exists only in the perimeter of the mesh. Mesh currents are selected clockwise for each mesh. A mesh current is considered to travel all the way around the mesh.

Notice that Figure 17.15 is the same circuit diagram as Figure 17.12 without specific values. Referring to Figure 17.15, we can apply Kirchhoff's voltage law in the direction of the mesh currents around the two meshes expressing voltages across each component in terms of the mesh currents, I_a and I_b.

$$E_1 - I_a R_1 - (I_a - I_b) R_3 = 0$$

and

$$-E_2 - (I_b - I_a) R_3 - I_b R_2 = 0$$

Figure 17.15

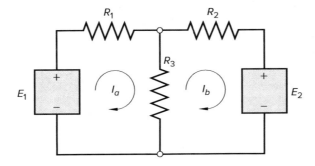

Application of mesh analysis.

Collecting and rearranging these two equations give us

$$E_1 - I_a (R_1 + R_3) + I_b R_3 = 0$$

and

$$-E_2 + I_a R_3 - I_b (R_3 + R_2) = 0$$

By comparing Figures 17.12 and 17.15, the branch currents can be expressed in terms of the mesh currents:

$$I_1 = I_a \qquad (I_1 \text{ is the current through } R_1, \text{ to the right in Fig. 17.15})$$

$$I_2 = I_b \qquad (I_2 \text{ is the current through } R_2, \text{ to the left in Fig. 17.15})$$

$$I_3 = I_a - I_b \qquad (I_3 \text{ is the current through } R_3, \text{ downward in Fig. 17.15})$$

Once we know the mesh currents, we know the branch currents, and once we know the branch currents, we can compute any voltage.

Example Problem 17.10   Substitute the specific values given in Figure 17.12 into the mesh current equations and verify the answers obtained in Example Problem 17.7.

Solution   Writing Kirchhoff's voltage law for the two loops gives

$$E_1 - I_a (R_1 + R_3) + I_b R_3 = 0$$

$$-E_2 + I_a R_3 - I_b (R_3 + R_2) = 0$$

Substituting values we see that

$$14 - 6I_a + 2I_b = 0$$

$$-12 + 2I_a - 8I_b = 0$$

Thus

$I_b = -1$ A (meaning that mesh current I_b is counterclockwise rather than clockwise as first assumed)

and

$I_a = 2$ A (meaning that mesh current I_a is clockwise as assumed)

Therefore,

$I_1 = 2$ A (to the right in the diagram)

$I_2 = -(-1) = 1$A (to the left in the diagram)

$I_3 = 2 - (-1) = 3$A (downward in the diagram)

Example Problem 17.11   Solve Example Problem 17.9 using mesh currents.

Figure 17.16

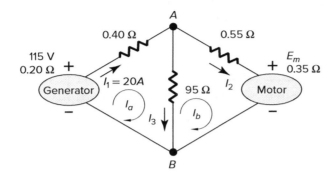

Solution Apply Kirchhoff's voltage law in the direction of the mesh currents I_a and I_b around the two meshes. See Figure 17.16.

$$115 - 0.20I_a - 0.40I_a - 95(I_a - I_b) = 0$$

and

$$-0.55I_b - E_m - 0.35I_b - 95(I_b - I_a) = 0$$

Collecting terms

$$115 - 95.6I_a + 95I_b = 0$$

$$-E_m - 95.9I_b + 95I_a = 0$$

But $I_a = I_1 = 20A$

Therefore,

Then
$$I_b = -\left[\frac{115 - 20(95.6)}{95}\right] = 18.915\ 8 \cong 19\ A$$

$$E_m = 95(20) - 18.915\ 8(95.9) = 85.974\ 8 \cong 86\ V$$

Current through the resistive load is

$$I_a - I_b = 20 - 18.915\ 8 = 1.084\ 2 \cong 1.1\ A$$

Power consumed by the resistive load is

$$P = 95(I_a - I_b)^2 = 95(20 - 18.915\ 8)^2 = 111.671\ 5 \cong 1.1 \times 10^2\ W$$

Problems

17.1 What is the average current through a conductor that carries 5 500 C during a 5.0 min time period?

17.2 How many coulombs are supplied by a battery in 36 h if it is supplying current at the rate of 1.5 A?

17.3 Assuming that the current flow through a conductor is due to the motion of free electrons, how many electrons pass through a fixed cross section normal to the conductor in 1 h if the current is 1 650 A?

17.4 Five 1.5-V batteries in series are required to operate an 8.0 W portable radio. What is the current flow? What is the equivalent circuit resistance?

17.5 When the leads of an impact wrench are connected to a 12.0 V auto battery, a current of 15 A flows. Calculate the power required to operate the wrench. If 75 percent of the power required by the wrench is delivered to the socket, how much energy in joules is produced per impact if there are 1 100 impacts per minute?

17.6 A small vacuum cleaner designed to be plugged into the cigarette lighter of an auto has a 12.6-V DC motor. It draws 4.0 A in operation. What power must the auto battery deliver? What size resistor would consume the same power?

17.7 A portable electric drill produces 1.2 hp at full load. If 85 percent of the power provided by the 9.6-V battery pack is useful, what is the current flow? How much power goes into waste heat?

17.8 A DC power supply of 95 V is connected across three resistors in series. $R_1 = 12\ \Omega$, $R_2 = 15\ \Omega$, $R_3 = 25\ \Omega$.
  (a) Draw the circuit diagram.
  (b) Determine the equivalent resistance of the three resistors.
  (c) What is the current through the power supply?
  (d) What is the voltage drop across each resistor?

17.9 Three resistors—15, 35, and 55 kΩ—are connected in series to a 75-V ideal DC voltage source.
  (a) Draw the circuit diagram.
  (b) Determine the equivalent circuit resistance.
  (c) Calculate the line current.
  (d) Find the voltage drop across each resistor.
  (e) Compute the power consumed by each resistor.

17.10 An ideal 6.0-V supply is connected to three resistors wired in parallel: $R_1 = 12\ \Omega$, $R_2 = 16\ \Omega$, $R_3 = 1.0$ kΩ.
  (a) Draw the circuit diagram.
  (b) Calculate the equivalent circuit resistance.
  (c) Find the current through the voltage supply.
  (d) Determine the current through each resistor and the power consumed by each.

17.11 A battery has a measured voltage of 14.2 V when the circuit switch is open. The internal resistance of the battery is 0.35 Ω. The circuit contains resistors of 15.5, 13.7, and 135 Ω connected in parallel.
  (a) Draw the circuit diagram.
  (b) Calculate the equivalent circuit resistance as seen by the battery.
  (c) Find the current flow through the battery when the switch is closed.
  (d) Compute the current through the 15.5-Ω resistor and the power consumed by it.
  (e) Calculate the rate at which heat must be removed from the battery if it is to maintain a constant temperature.

17.12 Given the circuit diagram and the values in Figure 17.17, determine the current through the 15-Ω resistor and voltage drop across it. Find the fraction of the power produced by the battery that is consumed by the 25-Ω resistor.

17.13 In Figure 17.18, determine the current and the potential at points *S, T, U,* and *V* when $R_1 = 8.5\ \Omega$, $R_2 = 5.7\ \Omega$, $E_G = 120$ V, $R_G = 0.25\ \Omega$, $E_B = 24$ V, and $R_B = 0.15\ \Omega$.

17.14 A 155-V generator in Figure 17.19 is charging a 110-V battery and driving a motor. Determine the charging current of the battery and the back-emf of the motor. Assume no internal resistances in the generator, motor, and battery.

17.15 A 115-V generator and a 26-V battery are in parallel with a motor. The current through the motor is 12 A. Determine the back-emf of the motor and current through the battery (see Figure 17.20).

Figure 17.17

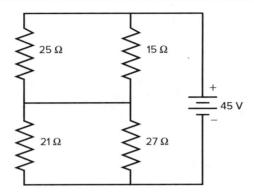

Figure 17.18

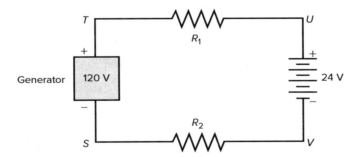

Figure 17.19

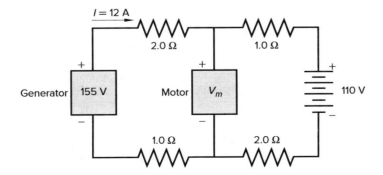

Figure 17.20

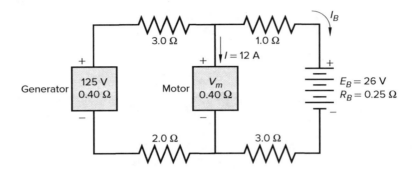

Figure 17.21

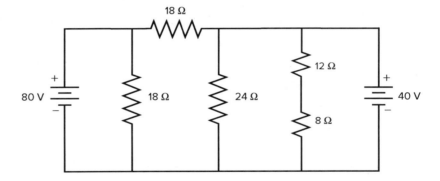

17.16 Figure 17.21 shows a resistance circuit driven by two ideal (no internal resistance) batteries. Determine

(*a*) The currents through each resistor.

(*b*) The power delivered to the circuit by the 80-V battery.

(*c*) The voltage across the 24-Ω resistor.

(*d*) The power consumed by the 12-Ω resistor.

17.17 An ideal 14-V generator and an ideal 12.6-V battery are connected in the circuit shown in Fig. 17.22.

(*a*) For $R_A = 3.0\ \Omega$ and $R_B = 4.0\ \Omega$, compute the current through each circuit component (resistors, battery, and generator). Is the battery being charged or discharged?

(*b*) With $R_B = 1.0\ \Omega$, find the current through the battery for $0.50\ \Omega \le R_A \le 10.0\ \Omega$ with $\Delta R_A = 0.50\ \Omega$. Plot the battery current versus R_A with R_A as the independent variable. Repeat the process with $R_B = 5.0$ and $10.0\ \Omega$, placing all three curves on the same graph. *Note:* Prepare a computer program and/or work as a team if approved by your instructor.

Figure 17.22

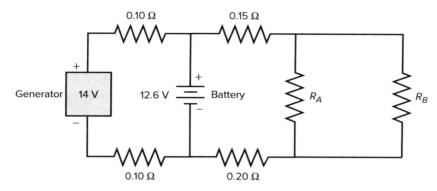

Figure 17.23

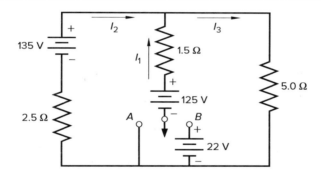

Figure 17.24

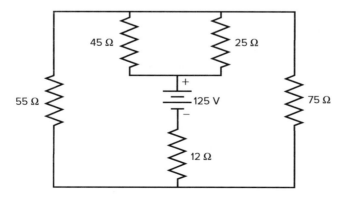

17.18 For the circuit shown in Figure 17.23:

    (*a*) Calculate the currents I_1, I_2, and I_3 when the switch is placed at *A*. How much power is consumed by each of the three resistors?

    (*b*) Repeat the problem with the switch placed at *B*.

17.19 Compute the current through each resistor and the battery shown in Figure 17.24.
Determine the power supplied by the battery and the power consumed by the 25-Ω resistor.

Figure 17.25

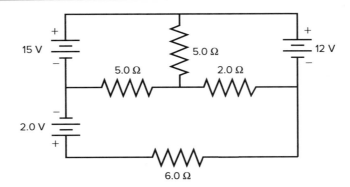

Figure 17.26

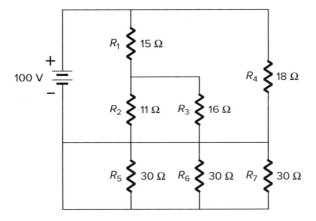

17.20 Determine the current through each component of the circuit in Figure 17.25. Find the power delivered to the 2.0-V battery, the voltage across the 2.0-Ω resistor, and power consumed by the 6.0-Ω resistor.

17.21 With reference to Figure 17.26, calculate the equivalent resistance of the circuit. Also calculate

(*a*) The current through R_3.

(*b*) The voltage across R_6.

17.22 With reference to Figure 17.27, the power consumed by R_3 is 20 W. Find the value for *R*. Repeat this exercise for values of power consumed by R_3 of 2, 4, 6, 8, 10, 12, 14, 16, and 18 W. *Note:* Prepare a computer program and/or work as a team if approved by your instructor.

17.23 With reference to Figure 17.28, the internal resistances of the generator, motor, and battery are 0.25 Ω, 0.75 Ω, and 0.35 Ω respectively. If the back-emf of the motor is measured as 60 V, calculate

(*a*) Current supplied by the generator.

(*b*) Current drawn by the motor.

(*c*) Charging current of the battery.

(*d*) Power converted to heat in the motor.

(*e*) If the back-emf of the motor is 50 V, what are the values of (*a*) through (*d*)?

Figure 17.27

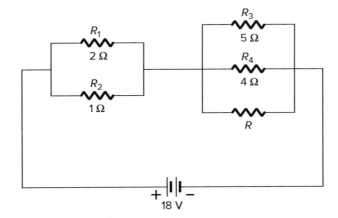

Figure 17.28

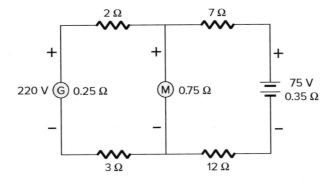

Figure 17.29

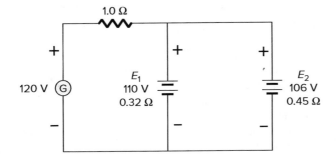

Figure 17.30

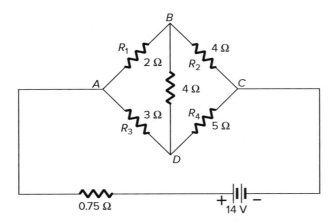

Figure 17.31

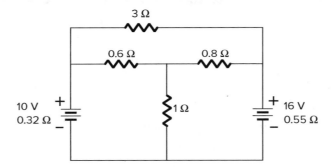

17.24 In the circuit shown (Fig. 17.29) the generator G is used to charge two storage batteries E_1 and E_2. Calculate
(a) The charging current for both batteries.
(b) Total power loss in all resistors.
(c) Power delivered by the generator.
(d) Efficiency of the charging system.
(e) How do the values of (a) through (d) change if the line resistor is 10 Ω rather than 1.0 Ω?

17.25 In the circuit of Figure 17.30, calculate (assuming mesh currents)
(a) The voltage drop V_{BD}.
(b) Current through R_1.
(c) Power dissipated in R_4.
(d) Repeat parts (a) through (c) for battery voltages of 2, 4, 6, 8, 10, and 12 V. Plot the results and interpret the curves. *Note:* Prepare a computer program and/or work as a team if approved by your instructor.

17.26 Find the power delivered by the batteries in the circuit of Fig. 17.31. Find the current through the 1-Ω resistor. What is the voltage across the 0.8-Ω resistor? (Assume mesh currents.)

Figure 17.32

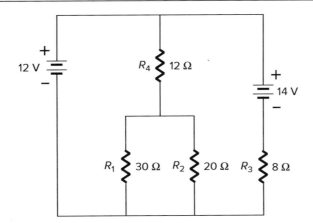

Figure 17.33

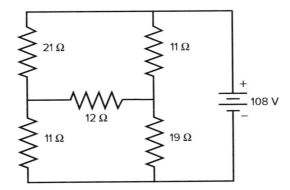

17.27 In the circuit of Figure 17.32, calculate (assuming mesh currents)

    (a) Current through R_1.

    (b) Voltage across R_2.

    (c) Power dissipated in R_3.

    (d) Power supplied by the batteries.

    (e) Repeat parts (a) through (d) with the 12-V battery replaced by one of 10 V and then by one of 14 V. Next, with the 12-V battery as shown in the diagram, replace the 14-V battery by one of 12 V and then by one of the 16 V. *Note:* Prepare a computer program and/or work as a team if approved by your instructor.

17.28 In the circuit shown in Figure 17.33, calculate (a) the current through the 12 Ω resistor, (b) the voltage across the 19 Ω resistor, (c) the current supplied by the battery, (d) the power consumed by the 21 Ω resistor, (e) the total power provided to the circuit by the battery, and (f) repeat parts (a) through (e) for batteries of 100, 102, 104, 106, and 110 V, respectively. *Note:* Prepare a computer program and/or work as a team if approved by your instructor.

Figure 17.34

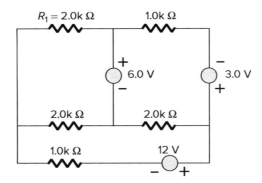

17.29 For the circuit in Figure 17.34, compute the power supplied to the circuit by each of
the batteries and the power consumed by each of the resistors. Repeat for values of
$R_1 = 3.0$ kΩ through 10.0 kΩ with increments of 1.0 kΩ. Plot the power consumed by R_1
as the resistance changes. Discuss the result. *Note:* Prepare a computer program and/or
work as a team if approved by your instructor.

CHAPTER **18**

Flowcharts

18.1   Introduction

Programming languages such as FORTRAN, C++, Visual Basic, and so forth can be used to custom prepare solutions to certain problems. This approach can be a time-consuming process and it requires much skill and experience to be an effective programmer. If spreadsheets and math calculation packages cannot do the job, you may be forced to program a solution. It is effective to program a solution if the solution is a unique application where commercial software is not likely to be available or if the solution is to be used repetitively without need for changing the programming code.

Custom-solutions may be necessary, but they are likely to be expensive in initial preparation and are not very flexible. They can be difficult to maintain since the original programmer may no longer be available and most engineering programmers are not good at thorough documentation of a program such that someone else readily can understand the process and make needed modifications.

18.2   Flowcharting

An algorithm (solution to a problem) can be described in terms of text-like statements (called pseudocode) or graphically in a form known as a *flowchart*. A flowchart provides a picture of the logic and the steps involved in solving a problem.

As you develop a flowchart, it is advantageous to think in terms of the big picture before focusing on details. For example, when designing a house, an architect must first plan where the kitchen, bathrooms, bedrooms, and other rooms are to be located before specifying where electric, water, and sewer lines should be placed. Similarly, a flowchart is designed by working out large blocks to assure that global logic is satisfied before deciding what detailed procedure should be used within each large block.

A set of graphical symbols is used to describe each step of the flowchart (see Figure 18.1). Although there are many *flowchart symbols* in general use, we will only define a small subset that is generic in nature; that is, each symbol does not denote any particular device or method for performing the operation. For example, a general *input/output* symbol is used that does not suggest that the input or output method is a document, tape, disk storage, or display. The symbol only means that communication with the software should occur by using whatever device or method is available and appropriate. However, when coding the input or output process, the programmer will have to be specific about the method or device.

Figure 18.1

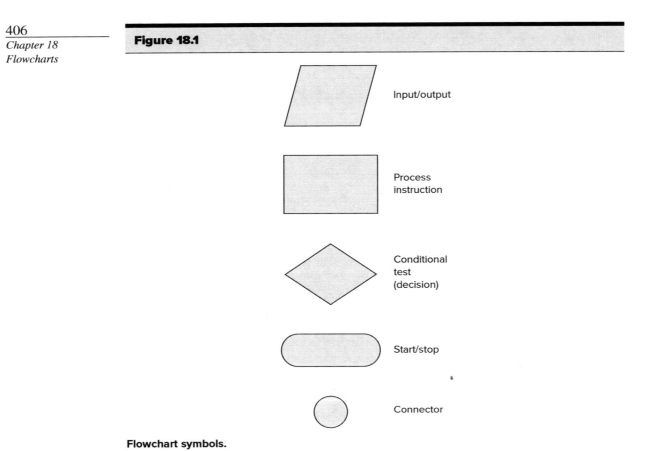

Flowchart symbols.

Three general structures are used in algorithm, or flowchart development: the *sequential structure*, the *selection structure*, and the *repetition structure*. The latter two have some variations that will be illustrated in the following paragraphs.

A *sequential structure* defines a series of steps that are performed in order, beginning at the start position and proceeding sequentially from operation to operation until the stop symbol is reached. No decisions are made and no step or series of steps is repeated. A sequential structure is shown in Figure 18.2. Dashed lines in this flowchart and others described later simply mean that repeated symbols have been omitted. A simple example of a sequential structure is shown in Figure 18.3 where values are input, a calculation is done, and the results are output.

The fundamental *selection structure* is illustrated in Figure 18.4. It contains a conditional test symbol that asks a question with a yes/no (true/false) answer or states a condition with two possible outcomes. Thus, based on the outcome of the decision, one of the two sets of operations will be performed. Each branch of the selection structure may contain as many operations as are necessary. There may be one operation or several in a branch, or even no operations in one of the branches. With this structure, flow proceeds through one or the other of the branches and continues on into a later section of the flowchart. Therefore, during a single pass through the structure one of the branches is not used.

Figure 18.2

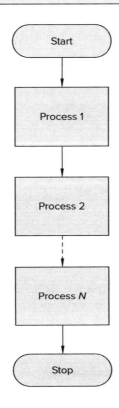

Simple sequence.

Figure 18.3

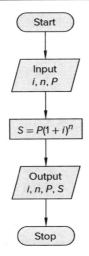

Sequence for future worth calculation.

Figure 18.4

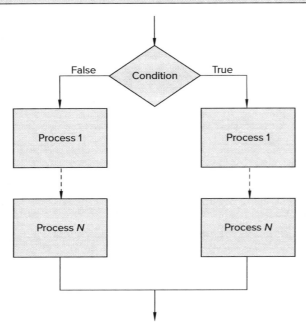

Selection structure.

Figure 18.5

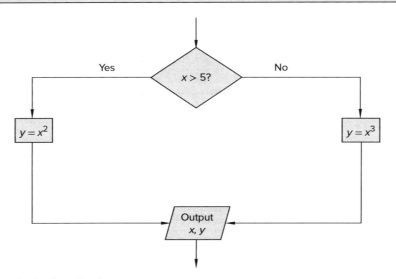

Example of selection structure.

Figure 18.5 is a simple illustration of a selection structure. Here a variable, x, which has been defined prior to this flowchart segment, is compared to the number 5. If x is greater than 5, the variable, y, is defined as x-squared. Both x and y are then output and control moves to whatever elements are next in the flowchart. If, however, in the decision block, x is not greater than 5, y is defined as x-cubed and then the output occurs.

Figure 18.6

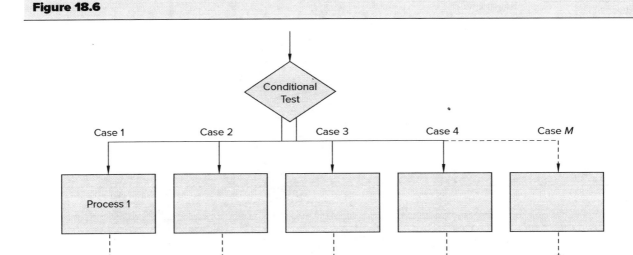

Cases labeled: Case 1, Case 2, Case 3, Case 4, Case *M*

Generalized selection structure (case structure).

Thus depending on the value of x at this point in the flowchart, y will be defined as either x-squared or x-cubed.

A somewhat generalized version of the selection structure is shown in Figure 18.6. Here the decision or condition at the top of the structure has more than two outcomes, called cases. Each outcome or case can have a unique set of steps to be performed. This structure is useful, for example, in a sorting procedure where one is treating data differently with each of several defined ranges of values.

A computation for the buckling load of a slender column is depicted in Figure 18.7. The buckling load depends on the end conditions of the column described as both ends fixed (F-F), one end fixed and one end hinged (F-H) or both ends hinged (H-H). This case structure segment examines the previously defined end condition and sets a variable n to 1, 2, or 4 and then computes the buckling load FB. The buckling load also depends on the modulus of elasticity E, the cross-sectional area A, the length L, and the least moment of gyration r, all of which would have to be input or defined prior to reaching this segment. Output of variables could then occur after the calculation.

The *repetition structure* (looping structure) consists of a step or series of steps that are performed repeatedly until some condition (perhaps a specified number of repetitions) is satisfied, at which time the next step after the loop is executed. Two common repetition structures are presented, one where the conditional test is performed as the last step of the structure and one where the test is the first step of the structure.

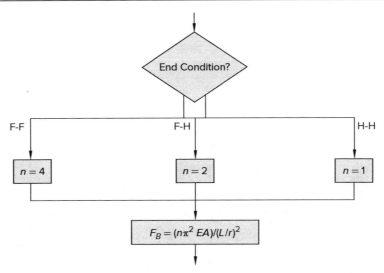

Figure 18.7

Case structure for slender column.

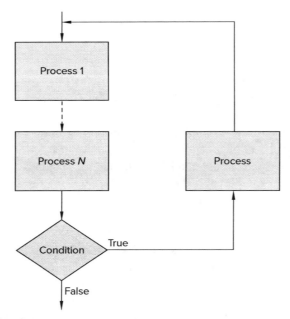

Figure 18.8

Repetition structure with conditional test last.

The repetition structure where the conditional test is the last step is illustrated in Figure 18.8. One or more processes are placed in the forward section of the structure. The conditional test can be reversed; that is, the true and false flow lines can be interchanged depending on the nature of the condition to be tested. There may be no need for the process block in the reverse loop based on the action in the process blocks in the forward section. You may or may not include the reverse-process block as your logic dictates. Frequently, the reverse-loop block performs the action of a counter. Operations such as $X = X + 1$ or $Z = Z + 5$ might appear here. These are not algebraic equations since they are clearly not mathematically correct. They are instructions to replace the current value of X by a new value 1 greater or to replace Z by $Z + 5$. Therefore, they can count the number of times through the loop, as does X, or can increment a variable by a constant, as in the case of Z. Negative increments also are possible so that you can count backward or decrement a variable.

Figure 18.9 is an example of a repetition structure where the test is last. This segment computes and outputs the surface area A and the volume V of spheres ranging from a radius R of 1 to 10 units.

Figure 18.10 shows the repetition structure where the conditional test is performed first. Again, the true and false branches can be reversed to match the chosen conditional test. As many process blocks as desired may be used. One of them could be a counter or incrementing block.

The flowchart segment in Figure 18.11 does the same thing as the segment in Figure 18.9, but is arranged such that the test is first rather than last.

Several selection structures or repetition structures can be combined by a method called *nesting*. In this way one or more loops can be contained within a loop. Similarly, a selection structure can be placed within another selection structure. Figure 18.12 shows an example of how a nested loop might appear. The inner loop is performed until condition 2 is satisfied; then control returns to the decision block for condition 1. In each pass, through the outer loop the inner loop will be repeated until condition 2 is satisfied. Eventually, condition 1 will be satisfied and flow will pass to the next part of the flowchart.

Figure 18.9

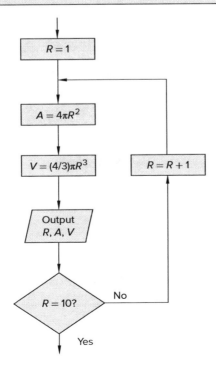

Example of test last.

Figure 18.10

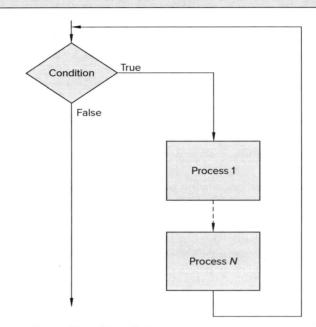

Repetition structure with conditional test first.

Figure 18.11

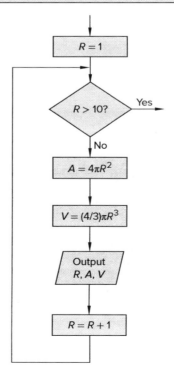

Example of test first.

Figure 18.12

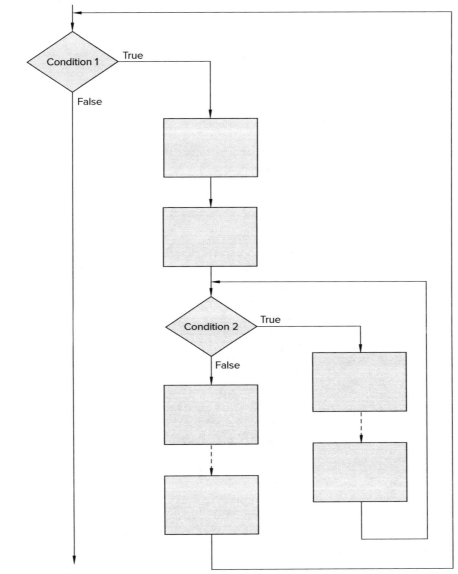

Nested repetition structure (nested loop).

Examples of various combinations of the structures just discussed can be seen in the problems that follow.

Example problem 18.1   Construct a flowchart for calculating the sum of the squares of the even integers from $N1$ to $N2$.

Procedure   For purposes of this example, $N1$ and $N2$ will be restricted to even integers only and $N2 > N1$. We could use the sequential structure shown in Figure 18.13.

Figure 18.13

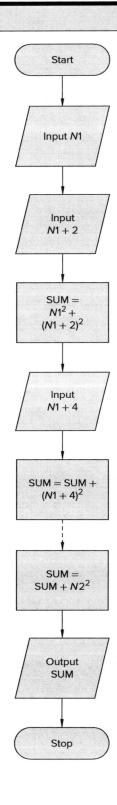

Figure 18.14

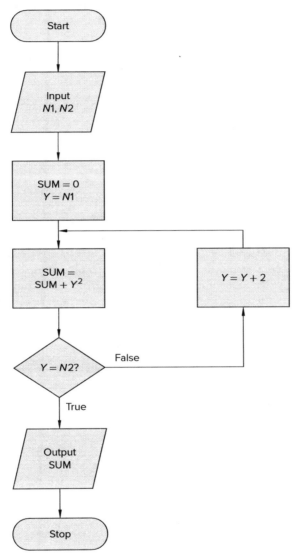

This flowchart will result in a variable called SUM as the desired value; SUM is then output. Because of the repetitive nature of the steps, it is far more convenient to use a repetition structure as seen in Figure 18.14.

Study Figure 18.14 carefully; several important flowcharting concepts are introduced there. First, the flowchart is useful for any pair $N1$, $N2$ as long as each is an even integer and $N2 > N1$. (The flowchart also will work for $N1$ and $N2$ as odd integers, although that is not specified in this problem.) Second, there are two variables, SUM and Y, that will take on numerous values. They must be initialized outside the repetition structure. If the process block containing SUM $= 0$ and $Y = N1$ was inside the loop, SUM and Y would be reset to their initial values each time through the loop and the decision block ($Y = N2$?) could never be satisfied, thereby creating an infinite loop.

The difference between initializing a variable and inputting a variable is important. As a general rule: *Variables that must have initial values but whose values will not change from one use of the flowchart to another (one run of the resulting program to another) should be placed in a process block. Variables that you wish to change from one run to another should be placed in an input block.* This provides you with the necessary flexibility of reusing the flowchart (or program) without having to input the variables that do not change from run to run.

Example problem 18.2   Draw a flowchart that will calculate the future sum of a principal (an amount of money) for a given interest rate and the number of interest periods. Allow the user to decide if simple or compound interest is to be used and to compute as many future sums as desired.

Procedure   For simple interest $S = P(1 + ni)$, and for compound interest $S = P(1 + i)^n$, where $S =$ future sum, $P =$ principal amount, $i =$ interest rate per period, and $n =$ number of interest periods. One possible flowchart is given in Figure 18.15. The user is asked to input $T = 0$ for simple interest and $T = 1$ for compound interest. A decision block checks on P before performing any further calculation. If $P < 0$ (a value not expected to be used), the process terminates. Thus, using a unique value for one of the input variables is one method of terminating the processing. A logical alternative would be to construct a counter and to check to see if a specified number of variable sets has been reached.

The connector symbol has been used to avoid drawing a long flow line in this example. A letter or number (the letter A was used in this case) is placed in the symbols to define uniquely the pair of symbols that should be connected. Connector symbols also are used when a flowchart occupies more than one page and flow lines cannot physically connect portions of the flowchart.

Example problem 18.3   The sine of an angle can be approximately calculated from the following series expansion.

$$\sin x \cong \sum_{i=1}^{N} (-1)^{i+1} \left[\frac{x^{2i-1}}{(2i-1)!} \right]$$

$$= x - \frac{x^3}{3!} + \frac{x^5}{5!} - \frac{x^7}{7!} + \cdots + (-1)^{N+1} \left[\frac{x^{2N-1}}{(2N-1)!} \right]$$

where x is the angle in radians. The degree of accuracy is determined by the number of terms in the series that are summed for a given value of x. Prepare a flowchart to calculate the sine of an angle of P degrees and cease the summation when the last term in the series calculated has a magnitude less than 10^{-7}. Of course, an exact answer for the sine of the angle would require the summation of an infinite number of terms. Include the procedure for evaluating a factorial in the flowchart.

Figure 18.15

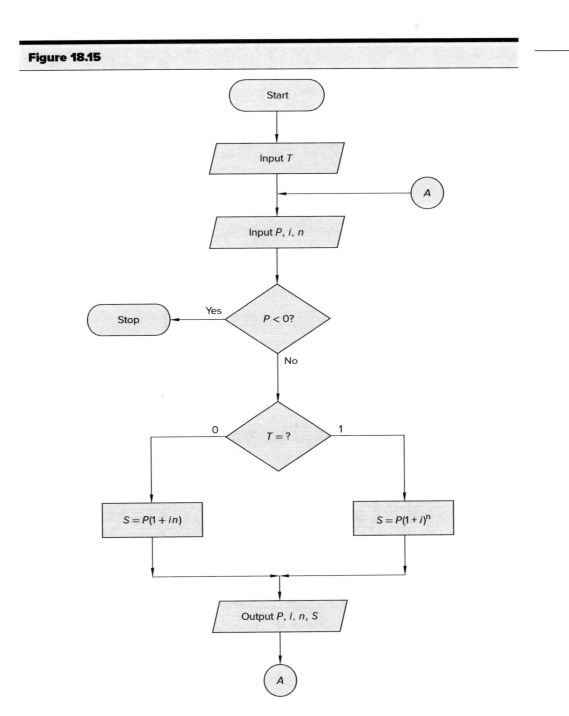

Procedure   One possible flowchart is shown in Figure 18.16. We will discuss several features of this flowchart, after which you should track on paper the first three or four terms of the series expansion to make sure you understand that the flowchart is correctly handling the problem. Note that the general term has been used in the

Figure 18.16

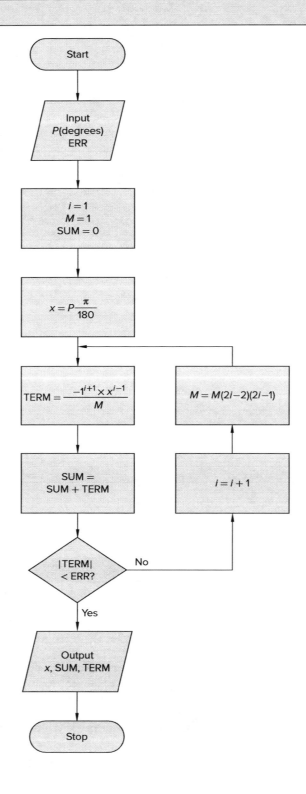

loop and that specific values of each variable are calculated in order to produce the required term each time through the loop:

1. The magnitude of the quantity controlling the number of terms summed is called ERR. It is input so that a magnitude of other than 10^{-7} can be used in a future run.
2. i denotes the summation variable and is initialized as 1.
3. M represents $(2i - 1)!$ and is initialized as 1 (its value in the first term of the series).
4. SUM is the accumulated value of the series as each term is added to the previous total. It is initialized as 0.
5. The angle is input in degrees and then immediately converted to radians by multiplying by $\pi/180$.
6. TERM is the value of each term beginning with $(-1)^{1+1} \{x^{2(1)-1}/[2(1) - 1]!\}$ or simply x. The factor $(-1)^{i+1}$ causes TERM to alternate signs.
7. SUM is equal to $0 + x$ the first time through the procedure.
8. The absolute value of TERM is now checked against the control value ERR to see if computations should cease. Note that the absolute value must be used because of the alternating signs. If a "no" answer is received to this conditional test, the appropriate incrementing of the variable must be undertaken.
9. i is increased by 1. This time though i becomes 2 since it was initialized as 1.
10. M becomes $(1)(2 \times 2 - 2)(2 \times 2 - 1) = 1 \times 2 \times 3 = 3!$
11. Following the flowchart directions, we now return to the evaluation of TERM with the new value of i.

    $$\text{TERM} = (-1)^{2+1}x^{2(2)-1}/3! = -x^3/3!$$

12. SUM then becomes $x - x^3/3!$. TERM is again tested against ERR.
13. The process repeats until the magnitude of the last term is less than ERR (10^{-7} in this case). Then the value of x, sin x, and the value of the last term are reported to make certain that the standard of accuracy has been attained.
    You should check several terms for a given value of x and then repeat the process for different angles. You will note that as the size of the angle varies, the number of terms required to achieve the standard of accuracy also varies. For example, when using a value of $P = 5°$, the third term of the series is about $4(10^{-8})$, less than the 10^{-7} requirement. But for $P = 80°$ the third term is approximately $4.4(10^{-2})$. It requires seven terms of the series before the magnitude of the last term becomes less than 10^{-7}.

The preceding examples should give you some insight into the construction of a flowchart as a prelude to writing a computer program or to using other software tools. The mechanisms for calculating, testing, incrementing, looping, and so on vary with the computational device and the programming language or software tool. A flowchart, however, should be valid for all computer systems and software tools because it graphically portrays the steps that must be completed to solve the problem.

Problems

18.1 Draw a flowchart to solve for P when $P = RQ + K + R^K$.
18.2 Draw a flowchart to solve for M when $M = 3B + BE/F$.
18.3 Draw a flowchart to calculate the sum of the areas of circles whose radii are 2, 3, 4, and 5 cm.

18.4 Draw a flowchart to calculate cos X when

$$\cos x = 1 - \frac{x^2}{2!} + \frac{x^4}{4!} + \cdots$$

correct to six decimal places. X = angle, in radians, and N is a positive integer.
HINT: The general term of the series is

$$(-1)^{N+1} \frac{x^{2N-2}}{(2N-2)!}$$

18.5 Draw a flowchart to simulate the required courses in your curriculum.

18.6 Draw a flowchart to calculate the sum of all the numbers between 0 and 99 whose square roots are integers.

18.7 Draw a flowchart to calculate the value of y when

$$y = \sum_{x=2}^{100} \frac{e^x}{\ln x}$$

18.8 Draw a flowchart to calculate the compound interest accumulated by P dollars at i percent annual interest:

(*a*) Compounded annually

(*b*) Compounded daily

HINT: Sum $= P(1 + i)^n$, where i is the interest rate per period and n is the number of periods.

18.9 Draw a flowchart to calculate the temperature in kelvins when the Fahrenheit temperature is known.

18.10 A group of engineers have an office pool for football games of their alma mater. The winner is the one that ends the season with the fewest demerits. Demerits are awarded after each game on the following basis: three demerits for each one point that one errs in guessing the correct difference in the final scores of the two teams; and one demerit for each point one is incorrect in the final score of each team. [For example: One engineer predicts the home team to win 14 to 7, but the final score is home team 10, visitors 21. Demerits $= (11 + 7)3 + (14 - 10) + (21 - 7) = 72$ demerits.] Draw a flowchart describing this pool.

18.11 Draw a flowchart to calculate the sum of the squares of the even integers between 0 and 15.

18.12 Draw a flowchart to depict the process of buying a car from a used-car lot.

18.13 Draw a flowchart that shows the process of a blackjack (21) dealer. Assume that the dealer has already completed dealing to the players, has one card himself, and is ready to complete the deal to himself. The rules are that he must draw a card if he has less than 16 points and cannot draw if he has 16 or more points.

18.14 Draw a flowchart to arrange a list of 20 numbers in descending order.

18.15 Draw a flowchart that selects from a list of numbers only numbers whose square root is an integer.

18.16 Draw a flowchart to calculate the present worth of a sinking fund. The formula is

$$\text{Present worth} = A \frac{(1 + i)^n - 1}{i(1 + i)^n}$$

18.17 Given two points with coordinates (x_1, y_1) and (x_2, y_2), draw a flowchart to calculate the length of the line connecting the two points.

18.18 Do the same as in Problem 7.17 except design the flowchart to calculate the direction of the line. Specify the output as an angle. Assume that the line goes from (x_1, y_1) toward (x_2, y_2).

18.19 Draw a flowchart to convert a Roman numeral to an Arabic number.

Figure 18.17

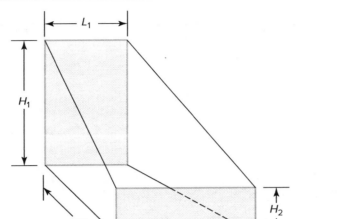

18.20 The prismoidal formula is

$$U = (A_1 + 4A_m + A_2) \frac{W}{6}$$

where

A_1 = area of one end
A_2 = area of other end
A_m = area at midpoint

Construct a flowchart to calculate the volume of a solid figure such as the one shown in Figure 7.9.

18.21 Draw a flowchart to solve the quadratic equation $Ax^2 + Bx + C = 0$ for x. Account for all possible solutions.

18.22 The area A of a triangle can be found by $A^2 = s(s - a)(s - b)(s - c)$, where a, b, c = sides of triangle and $s = \frac{1}{2}(a + b + c)$. Draw a flowchart to calculate the area of a triangle by this formula.

18.23 Draw a flowchart to determine if three given lengths can form a triangle.

18.24 Suppose I have chosen a number between two limits, say 0 and 100. Your task is to guess the number. All I will report is that your guess is too high, too low, or correct. Draw a flowchart of your process if each successive guess is midway between your last guess and the current upper or lower extreme value. (If your first guess is 40 and I say, "too low," your next guess is 70 and I say, "too high," your third guess should be 55.) Use only integers.

CHAPTER

4

Communication Skills

Information Transfer
Developing Effective Communication Skills

"Your success as an engineer will be directly proportional to your ability to communicate!"

—Dr. Charles K. Alexander,
Author of *Fundamentals of Electric Circuits*

COMMUNICATION SCENARIO

"A few years ago, when I was a policy fellow in Washington, DC, I received a call at 8:30 AM from a colleague who gave me a 'top priority' project: prepare a one-page policy paper that would be used to brief a congressman during a ten-minute car ride from his Capitol Hill office to a noon meeting at the White House. The brief was to focus on policy challenges in global neglected diseases. 'The brief is due at 10:00 AM,' my colleague repeated and abruptly hung up. Thirty panicked seconds later, I had Google open on my browser and was (over)confident that I would be able to accomplish the task."

(Guruprasad Madhavan, Biomedical Engineer and Program Officer, National Academy of Sciences)

This scenario, prepared by Guruprasad (Guru) Madhavan, demonstrates how important it is to develop good communication skills early in your career. After we discuss the fundamentals of communication, we will discover the rest of Guru's story at the end of this chapter.

4.1 Introduction

Do you think all you need to be a successful engineer is the ability to learn and apply technology? If your answer is yes, the following paradox may change your mind. Engineers must have knowledge and skills to apply technology, but success is directly proportional to their ability to apply nontechnical skills. If your answer is no, then you are already aware of the importance of nontechnical skills.

LEARNING OBJECTIVES

By using the information and exercises in this chapter you will be able to

- Understand why communication skills are so important to your career success.

- Increase comprehension by improving your reading skills.

- Organize and structure written documents.

- Develop and use professional writing skills to establish your credibility.

A review of the Table of Contents makes it clear that this entire book is based on improving your nontechnical skills. We discuss one of the most important of these skills in this chapter, and that is communication.

> *"Communication is a learned skill. Most people are born with the physical ability to talk, but we must learn to speak well and communicate effectively. Speaking, listening, and our ability to understand verbal and nonverbal meanings are skills we develop in various ways. We learn basic communication skills by observing other people and modeling our behaviors based on what we see. We also are taught some communication skills directly through education, and by practicing those skills and having them evaluated."*
>
> **(Wikipedia)**

We start with an overview of the basic fundamentals of communication you will need to be successful. Unlike some resources that only discuss communication, this chapter includes exercises to help you learn how to use engineering tools to enhance your communication skills. When you are a good communicator, you will reach higher levels of success in school and in your working career.

4.2 Why Effective Communication Is Important to You

Think about it. What value is technical knowledge if you can't share it with others in a practical way so they can understand and use it?

When you are an engineer, you may sit in a cubicle with your computer or in a laboratory and discover important ideas and information. Unless you take the next step and communicate what you know to other people, nothing will change. You can feel good about what you know, but how does that make a difference in the world? Your knowledge becomes valuable only when you transmit it to others.

> *"Effective communication is an important skill set that is often overlooked. The technical ability to understand problems and provide solutions is the backbone of a company's core capability to compete in today's challenging business environment. Engineers who are able to explain their ideas and solutions in both written and verbal formats are generally more respected by their peers and competitors. This additional recognition provides more opportunities to choose your assignments and control your fate."*
>
> **(Ted Tracy, Electrical Engineer and Regional Manager)**

4.3 The Communication Process

Various ways to communicate follow a similar pattern:

- One person (sender) has information (message) to transmit to other people (receivers).
- The sender decides how the message will be transmitted.
- The message is sent.
- The receiver hears or reads the message.
- The receiver processes the message.
- The receiver may or may not give feedback to the sender.

4.4 The Four Basic Types of Communication

The four basic types of communication are reading, writing, listening, and speaking. In this chapter, we discuss the value of reading and writing and their importance as communication skills for students and practicing engineers. Listening and speaking are covered in other chapters.

> *"My recommendation is to master the 'soft skills' of reading, writing, listening, and speaking, since these are absolutely needed to further one's career. As you advance, you will be communicating with people who have less and less of a technical background, so know your audience and direct your communications to the level of the audience."*
>
> **(Howard Wolfman, PE, Electrical Engineer and Principal, Lumispec Consulting)**

You may be surprised to learn that we are involved in reading and writing for only about one-fourth of our communication activities, as indicated in Figure 4.1. However, our ability to read and write effectively has a major impact on our ability to communicate.

TYPICAL COMMUNICATION TIME INVESTMENT

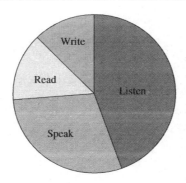

Figure 4.1
Typical communication time use.

4.5 Reading

First, let's put reading in perspective. As you consider the many electronic vehicles for delivering information, you might be tempted to think printed information on paper or in books is becoming obsolete. After all, you can search everything on the Internet, right?

Although there are new and different ways to obtain information, printed information will be used for many years. It may be on paper or in an electronic book or on another device, but printed information will be available in some form for a long time.

You have different reasons to read printed information. When you read for pleasure, you can relax with little concentration and just be entertained. When you read to gain important information related to your education and work, it requires more effort on your part. So, the way you read depends on what you are reading and what you want to gain from doing so.

4.5.1 Speed Reading

You may be acquainted with an interesting method of reading called speed reading. This method is often used to read section subtitles and the first sentence of each paragraph as a fast way to review material. The first sentence usually identifies the paragraph topic and can give an outline of the overall information. So, speed reading can be used to obtain an overview of information to identify areas for more detailed review.

4.5.2 Casual Reading

Casual reading is used to gain a general understanding of material. Because you want to understand and retain some of the information when involved in casual reading, your reading pace is slower than when speed reading. This slower pace makes it possible to think about information and how it relates to other topics. Casual reading is often used in reading fiction and less technical materials.

4.5.3 Comprehensive Reading

The third reading style is comprehensive reading, and this takes more concentration so your pace is much slower. This is the best way to obtain information when reading textbooks and other technical material. A logical way to use comprehensive reading is to break the process into a few basic steps.

Start with the big picture before reading details. Big pictures include the book's table of contents, introduction statements in book chapters, and report summaries. A good example is the outline at the beginning of each chapter of this book under the heading of **Learning Objectives.**

After you identify the big picture, the most effective way to understand information is to read at a slow pace, and to think about information and how it relates to your current knowledge. Comprehensive reading results in a greater level of retention.

Reading technical books is much like listening to class lectures. In class, you take notes of the most important concepts to help you understand and remember them. You can use a similar approach when reading books to learn and understand important information.

Book notes, like lecture notes, enhance comprehension.

As demonstrated by the student making notes while reading a textbook in Figure 4.2, you can enhance your learning process when reading textbooks by writing notes about major ideas and identifying areas that need further explanation. Use your notes to ask

Figure 4.2
Writing notes during comprehensive reading.

questions during lectures on the same topics. By the way, asking questions in class is an excellent way to expand your ability to understand and use information from your textbooks.

Reading skills are important because you need to keep up with the rapid change in technology. You will be more successful when you develop the ability now, as a student, to read printed and electronic information with good comprehension.

4.6 Writing

> *"As an engineering student, I know written communication is an integral skill that is responsible for a successful transfer of information, a stimulating exchange of ideas, and the development of a professionally enriching network. After all, no matter how profitable or unique a new idea may seem to be, without the open and effective streams of communication, it will be impossible to convey its importance and significance to others."*
>
> **(Vladislava Cuznetova, student at Cleveland State University)**

When you are given an assignment to write something, how do you feel? Do you think writing is a difficult task? Do you have a "mental block" and find it hard to get started. If writing is a challenge for you, I have good news. You can apply the principles of project management, as outlined next, to "engineer" your writing tasks and become a good writer and communicator.

PROJECT MANAGEMENT PROCESS

1. Preplanning
2. Planning
3. Organizing
4. Modeling
5. Completing project

Project management details are discussed in another chapter. However, you can start developing your project management skills now by applying them to writing. Let's use a typical laboratory report as an example of how project management steps can be applied.

4.6.1 Preplanning

Start with the big picture.

You might be surprised that there is a step before planning. Successful project managers do not get involved in project details until they define the big picture. This is called preplanning because it is based on developing an overall perspective before designing the project.

To see the big picture in a writing project, start by answering the following questions:

- Who will read what I write?
- Why would they be interested in my information?
- How will they use this information?
- How much information do they need?
- What writing style is best for them?
- What is the deadline to complete this writing project?

Preplanning is primarily identifying your readers and determining why they will read your material. By focusing on the reader, you gain a better idea of what to include and how much detail is appropriate. Then, you can use the proper tone and structure the content to be most effective for the reader.

HEAT TREATMENT AND HARDNESS

The objectives of this experiment are to become familiar with metallographic practices and to learn how to analyze mechanical properties. This was done by examining the correlation of heat treating steel and the resulting properties of hardness and strength.

Figure 4.3
Introduction of laboratory report.

Figure 4.3 is an example of a student's introduction to a laboratory report. The reader is the instructor, so the introduction outlines the objective of the experiment and gives an overview of what was done. The instructor is interested in the report because it was an assignment and the report evaluation results will be applied to the student's grade for the course.

The amount of information should be sufficient to describe the experiment in a clear and concise way to help the instructor evaluate the report. The writing style is somewhat formal and follows the format provided by the instructor. The deadline is established in the assignment.

4.6.2 Planning

After answering preplanning questions, the next step is to make an outline. A good approach is to use word processing software and identify major sections. Select information to fit the objective, as determined in the preplanning step. Most readers are busy, so they need to know enough facts to comprehend your message, but not so much that it becomes "information overload."

As you consider what is important to readers, you can expand the content and increase your credibility by researching various sources of information relating to your topic. When you reference information from others, you demonstrate that you have researched a variety of sources and included more than your own thoughts.

So, where do you start your research? Your first thought may be the Internet. This can be a good source of information as long as you recognize the source may, or may not, be credible. The Internet can save you time by identifying where information can be found.

University and public library reference sections are excellent sources of information. In addition, librarians can save you time by directing your search to appropriate sources. During your search, consider the credibility of the source as well as the information.

Textbooks, technical journals, and published articles typically are reviewed by peers, so they are based on facts and should be reliable sources. Most professional societies have electronic and printed libraries and you can find information relating to articles on their websites.

As you collect information, record the source so this can be added to your reference list as you develop your report. Reference information includes the author, title or content description, and publication. A correct format for references is shown in the following examples:

Smith, J. M., and Van Ness, Hendrick, *Introduction to Chemical Engineering Thermodynamics,* 7th ed. New York: McGraw-Hill, 2005.

Alexander, Charles K., and Sadiku, Matthew N. O., *Fundamentals of Electric Circuits,* 4th ed. New York: McGraw-Hill, 2009.

Reference information is placed at the end of written reports in a Bibliography Section just before the Index.

4.6.3 Organizing

The third step, organizing, is one of the most important. Engineers typically use logical thinking to solve problems, and a logical approach makes it easy to organize written material. In addition, the use of computers adds a very efficient way to prepare and organize an outline.

Using outline identification symbols will help you place information in the correct area of a well-organized document. Outlines save time, because the structure is established before details are added. Two typical outline formats are shown in Figure 4.4.

	Roman Numerals, Letters, Numbers	Decimals		
Major parts	I, II, III	1	2	3
1st subparts	A, B, C	1.1	2.1	3.1
2nd subparts	1, 2, 3	1.1.1	2.1.1	3.1.1
3rd subparts	a, b, c	1.1.1.1	2.1.1.1	3.1.1.1

Figure 4.4
Typical outline formats.

```
┌─────────────────────────────────────────────┐
│          LABORATORY REPORT OUTLINE            │
│  I.   Introduction                            │
│         A.  Objective                         │
│         B.  Method of Application             │
│         C.  Summary of Results                │
│  II.  Experimental Procedure                  │
│         A.  Equipment and Use                 │
│         B.  Outline of Experiment Steps       │
│  III. Discussion                              │
│         A.  Data summary                      │
│         B.  Name and Values of Variables      │
│         C.  Analysis Process                  │
│         D.  Errors                            │
│               1.  Physical Phenomena          │
│               2.  Instrument Limitations      │
│  IV.  Conclusions                             │
│         A.  Results                           │
│         B.  Analysis                          │
│         C.  Recommendations                   │
└─────────────────────────────────────────────┘
```

Figure 4.5
Sample outline.

A good example of an outline structure is shown for the sample laboratory report in Figure 4.5 Notice that the first step in organizing is to identify the major parts to be included and their location in the report. Unless you are given a specific format, think about your readers and place information in a logical flow so it is easy for them to follow and understand.

4.6.4 Modeling

An important step in building a physical product is to make a model, determine if it needs to be changed or refined, and make appropriate corrections before completing the final product. A similar approach can be used in developing your written document.

The outline is a model and provides a roadmap by defining where to place information. Add details in each section of the outline. Consider how much and what information is appropriate, based on the preplanning results. When you have completed all sections, you have a working model to review and revise.

An example of how details are added to the laboratory report outline in Section I, Subsection C, Summary of Results, is shown in Figure 4.6.

```
┌─────────────────────────────────────────────────────────┐
│              LABORATORY REPORT SAMPLE                     │
│                                                           │
│   I. Introduction                                         │
│                                                           │
│      C. Summary of Results                                │
│                                                           │
│   When carbon steel was heated to a temperature above     │
│   1,400° F, the structure was altered and an iron phase   │
│   change occurred. The rate of cooling affected the final │
│   microstructure of the steel.                            │
│                                                           │
│   If cooling is slow, the iron carbide is forced out of   │
│   solution and the gamma iron returns to alpha iron. The  │
│   resulting formation consists of a series of plates of   │
│   iron carbide interspersed with plates of ferrite.       │
│   This is known as pearlite, and slow cooling produces    │
│   coarse pearlite.                                        │
│                                                           │
│   Faster cooling rates cause closer spacing of plates and │
│   the result is medium or fine pearlite, depending on the │
│   rate of cooling. Hardness increases from coarse to fine │
│   pearlite.                                               │
│                                                           │
└─────────────────────────────────────────────────────────┘
```

Figure 4.6
Information in a typical section of the laboratory report.

Up to this point, we have been discussing how to select and organize ideas into a written format. When you have included all appropriate information, the next step is to fine-tune the document. This can be done by using spelling and grammar checking software and by reading drafts.

Spelling and Grammar   While content is important, you also need to consider how your written work is packaged. You can establish a professional image by using correct writing principles and an interesting writing style. These will eliminate barriers that could distract readers. Correct English grammar, such as subject/verb agreement and proper punctuation, is the foundation for good writing.

Start by running spelling- and grammar-checking software to identify misspelled words, errors in punctuation, subject/verb agreement, and other grammatical errors. Make corrections and then read your work on the computer screen. Test your model by reviewing the structure, and if necessary, rearrange information for better continuity. Think about how your readers will use information and make it easy for them to follow.

Word Selection   As indicated in Figure 4.7, software checks spelling but not word selection. Figure 4.8 shows the corrected version.

```
┌─────────────────────────────────────────────┐
│ I all ways used my spell checker to bee sure│
│ there are know errors. It's alright two take │
│ advantage of these resource.                 │
│                                              │
│ You're reports will help your go farther than│
│ you ever though you could bye spelling all   │
│ works properly.                              │
└─────────────────────────────────────────────┘
```

```
┌─────────────────────────────────────────────┐
│ I always use my spell-checker to be sure     │
│ there are no errors. It's all right to take  │
│ advantage of this resource.                  │
│                                              │
│ Your reports will help you go further than   │
│ you ever thought you could by spelling all   │
│ words properly.                              │
└─────────────────────────────────────────────┘
```

Figure 4.7
Incorrect word selections.

Figure 4.8
Correct word selections.

FREQUENTLY MISUSED WORDS	
WORD	MEANING
Already	Completed earlier
All ready	Completely prepared
Amount	Sum or total
Number	Units that can be counted
Can	Have ability or power to do something
May	Have permission to do something
Continually	Repeated, interrupted action
Continuously	Uninterrupted action
Effect	Noun – result
Effect	Verb – to make happen
Affect	To influence
Farther	Distance
Further	Time or quantity
Imply	To suggest or indicate
Infer	To deduce from evidence
Lie	To recline
Lay	To put or place
That	Defines or restricts (one of two or more)
Which	Additional information without defining or restricting

Figure 4.9
Sample of frequently misused words.

It is easy to use words incorrectly if you do not understand their precise meaning. Technical terms are typically not a problem. But many common words are used improperly and can create barriers. If readers have to stop and think about what a word means, they can become distracted from the content of your message.

You can improve word selection by understanding the meaning of words. An easy way to start is to review commonly misused words in Figure 4.9.

Sentence Structure   Improve your writing style by using interesting sentence and paragraph structures. For most technical writing, sentences should be short and written with a variety of simple, compound, and complex sentence structures.

Use a variety of sentence structures.

Good writing style increases reader interest and comprehension. Use a sentence to express a complete thought. To be an effective writer, use a mix of simple, compound, and complex sentences to add variety. We can demonstrate different sentence types with a few examples.

Simple sentences contain one subject and one predicate. A sample of a simple sentence is

New computer software is user-friendly.

In contrast, a compound sentence expresses two or more independent but related thoughts of equal importance. These are joined by a comma followed by or, and, or but. Compound sentences are a merger of two or more simple sentences or independent clauses that deal with the same basic topic. A sample of a compound sentence is

New computer software is user-friendly, and it is much easier to install on most personal computers.

A complex sentence expresses one independent thought and one or more subordinate thoughts (dependent clause) that relate to it, separated by a comma. The subordinate thought cannot stand alone and typically is placed at the start of the sentence. A sample complex sentence is

Although computer software changes frequently, recent software is user-friendly.

Selection of the type of sentence structure should match the relationship of ideas. If you have two ideas of equal importance, they should be expressed as two simple sentences or in one compound sentence. However, if one of the ideas is less important, it can be placed as a dependent clause in a complex sentence.

Long sentences are usually more difficult to understand than shorter ones because the reader has to work harder to follow the large amount of information. So, it is better to break long sentences into two or more sentences. Articles written in the magazine, *Reader's Digest,* are excellent examples of simple, but effective, sentence structures.

Paragraph Structure   Proper paragraph structure also impacts reader comprehension. A paragraph should cover only one main idea, and this idea should be introduced in a topic sentence.

A paragraph covers one main idea.

Typically, a topic sentence is the first one in the paragraph; however, it can also be included within the paragraph or even as the last sentence. The balance of the paragraph should include one or more sentences to support and expand the main idea. If sentences do not support or relate to the main topic, they should be placed in a new paragraph.

As in the case of sentences, shorter paragraphs are usually easier to follow and understand. The use of concise statements and a limited number of supporting sentences will result in paragraphs of reasonable lengths.

Transition Statements   Transition statements help readers move from one thought to the next. Transitional words, phrases, and sentences are tools for readers to see how different ideas relate to each other either within a paragraph or between two paragraphs.

Use transition statements to link paragraphs.

You can use transition words and transition sentences to build continuity. These connections can be established in the last sentence of a paragraph to link to the

RELATIONSHIP	TRANSITION WORD EXAMPLES
Comparison	in comparison, still, similarly, likewise
Contrast	conversely, whereas, nevertheless, however, but
Repetition	that is, in other words, as has been stated
Illustration	for example, in particular, in this case, for instance
Additional detail	furthermore, in addition, besides, first, second, finally
Relationship	therefore, because, accordingly, thus, consequently, so
Time sequence	formerly, after, when, meanwhile, sometimes
Summary	in summary, to sum up, in brief, to conclude, in conclusion

Figure 4.10
Transition statements.

following paragraph, or they can be included in the first sentence of the next paragraph. Sample transition statements are shown in Figure 4.10.

Transition examples are shown in bold in the following paragraphs:

EXAMPLE 4.1

The purpose of this research project is to increase system efficiency of existing technology. Using variations of fluid piping designs increased the efficiency of the hydraulic system from point A to point B by 10%. **Before recommending the use of these design changes, one additional comparison should be made.**

The initial cost for the most efficient design was 15% higher than previous designs. This may be acceptable if operating cost savings offset the first cost within 3 years.

EXAMPLE 4.2

However, if initial cost is the most important factor for consideration, it may be more acceptable to consider the application of new technology. Some systems, using synthetic fluids, have entered the market with relatively low first costs.

EXAMPLE 4.3

In summary, the original purpose of this study may be too narrow to produce practical results. Additional studies are recommended.

4.6.5 Completing the Project

"The most valuable of all talents is that of never using two words when one will do."

(Thomas Jefferson, third president
of the United States of America)

To complete your writing project, print a draft and review the overall structure by reading it aloud. Are topics and subtopics appropriate? Are various topic areas related, and do they fit into the overall story? Is the content written concisely without extra, unneeded words?

Prevent barriers by using common words and eliminating unnecessary ones.

As a result of the fact that four of our astute committee members could not be present at our last scheduled meeting time on today, June 25 at 9:00 AM, the liberty was taken to cancel that assemblage. It is, therefore, planned to consider the same agenda items at the newly scheduled aggregation, which will convene the forthcoming Friday morning, June 27 at 9 AM. Therefore, it is my personal decision that this same committee meeting will be convened in accordance with the previously established agenda which I have repeated herein for your convenience to review before the meeting and to help you be better prepared to discuss agenda items in significant detail at the meeting on Friday.

Figure 4.11
Wordy message.

Because four members could not attend our last meeting, I rescheduled it to 9 AM next Friday. We will use the same attached agenda.

Figure 4.12
Concise message.

Think about readers as you review your final draft. Does your message create a barrier like the wordy example in Figure 4.11, or is it concise and easy to understand like Figure 4.12? Are the length and variety of sentences appropriate to generate reader interest? Are paragraphs easy to read? Did you use appropriate transitions to enhance the flow of information?

The final step is to make corrections from the last review, use your spell-checker one more time, and print the final product. If you have worked hard and followed each step of the draft process, you will have a very professional and effective written document.

A CONVERSATION WITH GURUPRASAD MADHAVAN

Guru, the scenario you described in the beginning of this chapter is a little overwhelming. How did you handle this challenge to prepare something so important so quickly?

Answer

"My work in public policy not only gives me the opportunity to look at issues differently, but also challenges me to communicate better.

In this situation, as I was looking at the Internet, I was blindsided with hundreds of thousands of results. After 45 minutes of research online for credible information—mind it I hadn't written a word for the brief yet—I realized I was pedaling at the same location without moving forward. I detached myself from the computer, changed my research strategy, and started calling experts in this area for guidance. Their suggestions helped me to frame the topic and start writing. Alas, the time was already 9:45 am. I felt I needed at least an extra hour to chisel the issues.

I called my colleague and said, 'I blew it! I don't think I'll be able to finish the brief by 10:00.' She chuckled and revealed that this was a training exercise to help me get adapted to the realities of the business as part of my 'startup' package in public policy.

My colleague and I later had coffee together to go over what I had developed during the exercise. I learned a lot about improving both my writing and storytelling skills under pressure."

Although this turned out to be a test run for you, how do you typically prepare for briefings? What nontechnical skills do you use?

Answer

"If I hadn't started making phone calls to experts, I'd have woefully failed in my research. I had to achieve an escape velocity to overcome my fear and shyness in calling world leaders in the subject. Engineers can learn a great deal from talented journalists who are renowned for asking thoughtful questions to elicit thoughtful answers to help build a thoughtful story.

Engineers, in general, are competent in tackling complex data and models, but that skill alone is not sufficient in an overwhelmed society with ultra-short attention spans. More impressive to me than data-dense reports filled with charts, graphs, and numbers is a story line that's well thought out, buttressed with relevant data, and presented in an accessible and engaging style. Always remember: Stories stick.

This experience has bolstered my interests in telling stories supported by solid research findings. It is these factually accurate stories, coupled with objective persuasive skills that help create actionable policies."

What advice would you share with students?

Answer

"Read, for example,*The Economist, The New Yorker, Foreign Policy, Scientific American,* and other magazines, books, and guides. Search for talented writers whose working style will inspire you to sharpen your research, writing, and storytelling skills.

Also focus on reading broadly beyond your subject area, including areas in the arts, design, business, health, finance, economics, law, psychology, sociology, humanities, policy, history, government, and international development. As 21st-century engineers, our challenges are far more crosscutting and complex than they have been in the past."

(Guruprasad Madhavan, Biomedical Engineer and Program Officer, National Academy of Sciences)

4.7 Conclusion

We have discussed two of the four communication processes, reading and writing, in this chapter on communication. Other chapters will cover listening and speaking. All four communication processes are very important to help us receive and deliver information.

We also discussed how we use different reading styles when reviewing printed and electronic messages. These included speed reading for a quick overview, casual reading for pleasure, and comprehensive reading when we need to understand and use information.

In our discussion of written communication, we identified the most important principles of keeping a focus on the reader, using good organization, and providing documentation to add credibility to our technical documents. Writing should be based on proper English grammar and professional writing techniques. Written documents can last a long time, so we should prepare them in a correct and professional way to establish a positive image.

Although applying correct and concise writing skills takes effort and time, it results in many benefits. Professional writing will enhance your credibility and will encourage others to understand the value of your ideas. This, in turn, will open many doors of opportunity for advancement and increased career success.

"I have witnessed throughout my career, many brilliant engineers that border on the line of genius. Unfortunately, some of these sharpest minds were not considered to be promotable because of a deficiency in communication skills. As an engineering student, spend the extra time and effort on your lab reports and writing assignments. It will pay off in ways that at this point you can only imagine."

(Ted Tracy, Electrical Engineer and Regional Manager)

Ted Tracy's comments summarize the value of good communication skills. Many engineers fail to reach high levels of success, not because they lack technical skills, but because they cannot communicate with other people. So, take Ted's advice and use the many opportunities you have as a student to develop effective communication skills. This will pay big dividends throughout your life and career.

END OF CHAPTER REVIEW QUIZ

Select the most appropriate answer to the following statements.

1. The best way to prepare to be a successful engineer is to
   a. Study hard and earn good grades.
   b. Balance technical skills with nontechnical skills.
   c. Learn how to apply technical skills.
   d. Develop good writing skills.

2. The four basic types of communication are
   a. Reading, writing, listening, and speaking.
   b. Talking to friends, listening to speakers, text messaging, and talking on a cell phone.
   c. Writing reports, sending e-mails, preparing resumes, and sending cover letters.
   d. Turning in homework, asking questions in class, reading textbooks, and taking tests.

3. The major parts of the communication process are
   a. Learning how to write and speak.
   b. The three types of reading—speed, casual, and comprehensive.
   c. One person sends a message, others receive and process the message, and others may give feedback to the person sending the message.
   d. To take notes when reading textbooks, ask questions in class, and listen to answers.

4. Speed reading is an effective way to
   a. Quickly obtain an overview of written material.
   b. Study for a test.
   c. Read books for pleasure.
   d. Read the chapter in a textbook just before class to prepare for the lecture.

5. Comprehensive reading is a good way to
   a. Read the textbook before class.
   b. Prepare for a laboratory experiment.
   c. Study material in preparation for a test.
   d. Accomplish all of the above.

6. The best result of writing notes when reading a textbook is
   a. It makes sure you read the entire book.
   b. It will help you identify questions to ask in class for more information.
   c. It provides evidence you can use to show your instructor you read the book.
   d. To slow your reading speed and help you understand all the details of a text.

7. When starting a writing project, the first step is to
   a. Make an outline of the material.
   b. Write the first paragraph of each part of the written document.
   c. Write the first draft and use spell-checking software to correct errors.
   d. Identify readers, establish the writing objective, and decide what to write.

8. The most efficient method of preparing a formal report is to
   a. Start with preplanning activities to see the big picture.
   b. Make an outline and arrange information in a logical structure.
   c. Use drafts to review and revise information.
   d. Accomplish all of the above.

9. The best way to eliminate barriers when writing is to
    a. Use outline identification symbols so readers know where information is located.
    b. Use spell-checking software to eliminate misspelled words.
    c. Write concisely and use the correct tone for the reader.
    d. Use tables to show detailed information.
10. Learning to write well is important because it
    a. Delivers your information to others in a way they can understand and use it.
    b. Helps you communicate more effectively with people.
    c. Is evidence of your knowledge and leads to greater career success.
    d. Is all of the above.

EXERCISES TO DEVELOP AND ENHANCE YOUR SKILL SET

Exercise 4.1   This is a reading exercise. Evaluate comprehension by using three reading methods to review the excerpts from the Introduction section of the *Fundamentals of Electric Circuits* book, Chapter resource 4.1, as follows:

1. Speed Reading
   - Read the seven paragraphs in 30 seconds. (Hint: If you have not been trained in speed reading, look at the first sentence in each paragraph and quickly move down the page to obtain a visual image of content.)
   - Without looking at the excerpts again, write a summary of what you have just read.
2. Casual Reading
   - Read the paragraphs again in 5 minutes, but do not take notes as you read.
   - Without looking at the excerpts again, write a summary of what you have just read.

3. Comprehensive Reading
   - Read the paragraphs a third time in 5 minutes and take notes as you read.
   - Without looking at the excerpts again, use your reading notes and write a third summary.

Class discussion (or your study team if it is not discussed in class):

1. Compare the content of all three summaries.
   - When would speed reading be appropriate?
   - If you were preparing for a test, which method would you choose?
   - What method would you use if details are not important and you only need a general understanding of material?
2. Use notes from this exercise and class (or study team) discussion to complete the homework assignment.

Exercise 4.2 This is an exercise in developing paragraphs. Review the information shown below and determine where new paragraphs should start.

People, equipment, space, and energy are a company's resources. They are expensive, and you want to use them effectively. Productivity is a measure of resource use, and is the ratio of output over input. To increase productivity, you need to increase output, reduce input, or a combination of the two. The location of services like restrooms, locker rooms, cafeterias, tool cribs, and any other service will affect employee productivity and, therefore, the employees' utilization or effectiveness. It is said that you can run pipe and wire, but you cannot run people. Providing convenient locations for services will increase productivity. Equipment can be very expensive, and the operating costs must be recovered by charging each part produced on that machine a portion of the cost. The more parts run on one machine, the lower is the unit cost that each part must carry. So to achieve the second supporting objective, namely, to reduce cost, you must strive to get as much out of each machine as possible. Calculate how many machines are required in the beginning for maximum machine use. Remember, machine location, material flow, material handling, and workstation design all affect equipment usage. Space is also costly, thus designers need to promote effective use of space. Good workstation layout procedures will include everything required to operate that workstation, but not extra space. Normally, planners can do a good job of using floor space, but there are also other spaces for consideration. Basements are a good place for utility tunnels, walkways between buildings, under-the-floor conveyors for material delivery or trash removal, and tanks for storage. Overhead spaces may also be usable. These can be used for overhead conveyors, pallet racks, mezzanines, shelves or bins for storage, balcony offices, pneumatic delivery systems, dryers, ovens, and so on.

Exercise 4.3 This is an exercise in preparing a written report.

Prepare a written report based on notes from Exercise 4.1 and turn in your report at the beginning of class on a date assigned by your instructor. Prepare your report as follows:

Reading Exercise Report

Prepared by _____

Application of Reading Methods

Speed Reading
Identify when speed reading would be appropriate.
Discuss the value of speed reading for your personal use.

Casual Reading
Identify typical uses of casual reading.
Discuss the value of casual reading for your personal use.

Comprehensive Reading
Identify when comprehensive reading would be appropriate.
Discuss the value of comprehensive reading for your personal use.

Evaluation of Reading Exercise

Write at least three paragraphs to compare results of each reading method as they relate to comprehension and retention of content.

Use a separate paragraph to discuss how you plan to use what you learned in this exercise in future classes and other reading experiences.

Exercise 4.4   This is an exercise to enhance your writing skills. Prepare a written report on the courses you are taking this semester and how you plan to learn new skills or enhance skills associated with each course.

Organize your report with section titles and a logical flow of information. Use proper sentence and paragraph structure and English grammar. Check spelling and grammar with appropriate software and correct errors before submitting report.

Your report should be one to two pages (400 to 800 words) in length.

Step 1:

Prepare your report using the process outlined in this chapter. Give an electronic copy of your report to your instructor no later than the established due date for this step.

Step 2:

If assigned by your instructor, visit the University Writing Center and request them to review your report and suggest how you can improve your writing skills. Work with their staff to revise and prepare a final report. Give an electronic copy of your final report to your instructor no later than the established due date for this step.

If your writing skills are evaluated with codes on your printed report, use Chapter resource 4.2, Writing skills reference, for an explanation of each code.

END OF CHAPTER RESOURCES

Chapter resource 4.1

Excerpts from the Introduction of the Fourth Edition of *Fundamentals of Electric Circuits,* by Dr. Charles K. Alexander and Dr. Matthew N. O. Sadiku:

Electric circuit theory and electromagnetic theory are the two fundamental theories upon which all branches of electrical engineering are built. Many branches of electrical engineering, such as power, electric machines, control, electronics, communications, and instrumentation, are based on electric circuit theory. Therefore, the basic electric circuit theory course is the most important course for an electrical engineering student, and always an excellent starting point for a beginning student in electrical engineering education. Circuit theory is also valuable to students specializing in other branches of the physical sciences because circuits are a good model for the study of energy systems in general, and because of the applied mathematics, physics, and topology involved.

In electrical engineering, you are often interested in communicating or transferring energy from one point to another. To do this requires an interconnection of electrical devices. Such interconnection is referred to as an *electric circuit,* and each component of the circuit is known as an *element.*

A simple electric circuit consists of three basic elements; a battery, a lamp, and connecting wires. Such a simple circuit can exist by itself; it has several applications, such as a flashlight, a search light, and so forth.

An example of a complicated circuit would be a radio receiver in which there are several elements with many connecting paths. Although a radio receiver seems complicated, this circuit can be analyzed using the techniques covered in this book. Our goal in this text is to learn various analytical techniques and computer software applications for describing the behavior of a circuit.

Electric circuits are used in numerous electrical systems to accomplish different tasks. Our objective in this book is not the study of various uses and application of circuits. Rather our major concern is the analysis of the circuits. By the analysis of a circuit, we mean a study of the behavior of the circuit: How does it respond to a given input? How do the interconnected elements and devices in the circuit interact?

We commence our study be defining some basic concepts. These concepts include charge, current, voltage, circuit elements, power, and energy. Before defining these concepts, we must first establish a system of units that we will use throughout the text.

As electrical engineers, we deal with measurable quantities. Our measurement, however, must be communicated in a standard language that virtually all professionals can understand, irrespective of the country where the measurement is conducted. Such an international measurement language is the International System of units (SI), adapted by the General Conference on Weights and Measures in 1960. In this system, there are six principal units from which the units of all other physical quantities can be derived. Quantities and units are length (meter), mass (kilogram), time (seconds), electric current (ampere), thermodynamic temperature (Kelvin) and luminous intensity (candela).

Chapter resource 4.2

Writing Skills Reference	
Code	Comments
GT	Use requested title and/or sub-titles for added clarity
GF	Use 11 or 12 point font for professional appearance
GP	Use page break to prevent splitting bullet points or paragraphs between pages
PB	Use parallel construction of bullets (start all with a noun or all with a verb, but do not mix)
SS	Work on sentence structure–a sentence expresses a complete thought
SL	Replace long, run-on sentences with two or more shorter sentences
SR	Reduce number of sentences that start with the same word
PS	Improve paragraph structure (typically, a paragraph has a topic sentence and supporting sentences)
PL	Break long paragraphs into two or more shorter paragraphs for added clarity
DS	Double space between paragraphs and single space within paragraph
SV	Review principles of subject/verb agreement
PT	Review correct use of punctuation
AR	Review correct use of articles (a, an, the)
AF	Review correct use of "affect" and "effect"
IT	Review correct use of "it's" and "its"
TN	Review correct use of "than" and "then"
TR	Review correct use of "their" and "there"
TO	Review correct use of "to" and "too"
WH	Review correct use of "who" and "whom"
WD	Improve word selection for clarity and reader interest
SP	Run Spellchecker and make corrections

5

Professional Presentation Skills

Information Transfer
Developing Professional Presentation Skills

"Effective presentation skills are key elements towards a successful engineering profession."

—Marius Marita, PE, Electrical Engineer
and Advanced Engineer at FirstEnergy Corporation

PROFESSIONAL PRESENTATION SCENARIO

"My path down a 24-year career has been full of professional presentations that started with a single opportunity during my senior year in college. That single experience was not only career-changing but also life-changing. My speaking experiences have allowed me to progress in my career from a college student to project engineer, project manager, operations manager, product line manager, to a general manager running a division in a major company. Writing and presentation skills can be directly related to the opportunities I have been able to accept over my 24-year career."

(John J. Paserba, General Manager, Gas Circuit Breaker Divison, Mitsubishi Electric Power Products, Inc.)

Some of your most important opportunities to prepare for career success are found outside of your formal classes. This was true for John Paserba, and during our conversation with him at the end of this chapter, we will learn how this single event at Gannon University changed his life.

5.1 Introduction

The purpose of this chapter is to focus on the important nontechnical skills you need to develop and deliver professional presentations. Although written communication continues to expand with the use of portable electronic devices, it is likely you will have many opportunities to give presentations to audiences of peers, managers, clients, and community groups. In addition, you may be involved in Web-based conferences and seminars.

LEARNING OBJECTIVES

By using the information and exercises in this chapter you will be able to:

- Appreciate why the ability to speak before an audience is important to career success.

- Use the fundamental principles of public speaking for your presentations.

- Learn how to plan and deliver effective presentations for different types of audiences.

- Prepare and use effective visuals.

- Build confidence and deliver outstanding professional presentations.

- Participate effectively in team presentations.

- Minimize the fear of public speaking by gaining speaking experience.

Your ability to communicate ideas and project details in live presentations before an audience or in Web-based settings has a significant impact on your career success. Many technical professionals have excellent information, but if they cannot effectively deliver this to others during presentations and group discussions, they will fail to achieve desired results.

In addition to discussing the principles of public speaking, this chapter uses exercises to show you how to use engineering tools to enhance your presentation skills. This approach will save you time, reduce stress and fear, and help you deliver effective and professional presentations.

5.2 Public Speaking

Next to listening, the greatest amount of time in communicating is speaking. You may be reasonably comfortable in informal conversations with friends and peers. But, when you stand before a group of people and speak, you may feel some anxiety, as demonstrated in Figure 5.1.

Many engineers and other technical professionals are uncomfortable when involved in public speaking, at least until they have gained experience by giving several presentations. Some have said they fear speaking before a live audience more than death. This sounds rather severe, but indicates the need to build confidence by improving speaking skills.

As professional engineers, the authors of this book have delivered several thousand lectures and other presentations. It is easy for us to give presentations now, but the first few were difficult. Our engineering experience helped us develop speaking skills, and we will show you how you can use the same skills to become an effective speaker.

This practical approach, developed by engineers for engineers, should be easy for you to use. As engineering students, you can relate to this structured process to develop and deliver professional presentations. This will save you time in preparing visuals, and help you build public speaking confidence.

Figure 5.1
Fear of public speaking.

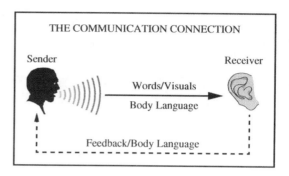

Figure 5.2
The communication loop.

"A great engineering design or analysis may be rejected if it is hidden behind a poor presentation. Every project that an engineer works on will require the approval of another party. If that party does not understand the benefit that will be received from the associated cost, then the project will never proceed. As a result, the ability to give a good presentation is a critical skill for an engineer to possess."

(Paul Kruger, Electrical Engineer in an electric utility industry)

As illustrated in Figure 5.2, communication is more than just sending a message. The message needs to be delivered in an appropriate style so that receivers process information as they listen. Receivers may also give important feedback.

Effective speakers are good communicators. They understand and use the principles of public speaking. The secret to successful speaking techniques is to adapt principles to personal styles. Speaking style includes interaction with visuals and the audience, and the use of your voice to vary delivery levels and speed.

The principles of public speaking are planning and preparation, practice, and professional presentation.

5.3 Planning and Preparation

Professional presentations require sufficient time for planning. An effective speaker will invest a minimum of twenty-five to thirty times the amount of time involved in actually delivering a presentation to develop, rehearse, and become familiar with information and visuals. The planning process should be started early and include sufficient time to develop and rehearse the presentation.

Start planning activities by identifying your audience. Because the audience has a great impact on your ability to deliver your message effectively, you should design your presentation to fit their needs and level of technical expertise. If necessary, ask questions to determine who will be in the audience and why they are interested in your topic.

5.3.1 Identifying Specific Audience Needs

To save preparation time and be more effective with audiences, you should think about why your information is important to various audiences and then determine the best way to communicate your message. Typical audiences in your future may include:

- Supervisors and peers
    - Are interested in technical information and many facts
    - Understand technical terms
    - Understand detailed sketches, graphs, and diagrams
    - Ask technical questions
    - Are comfortable with longer, detailed presentations
    - Relate to informal presentations and animation to demonstrate processes
- Senior management
    - Are less interested in technical information
    - May not understand technical terms
    - Can be overwhelmed with too much detail
    - Focus on economics and what technology can do for the bottom line
    - Usually ask nontechnical questions
    - Are extremely busy and have limited time to listen to presentations
    - Want brief, concise, and more formal presentations
    - Are not impressed with excessive animation in PowerPoint presentations
- Clients
    - Can have a combination of technical and nontechnical backgrounds
    - Want to know some technical detail
    - Are interested in how the project helps them and their bottom line
    - May ask both technical and nontechnical questions
    - Want brief but informative presentations
    - Are not impressed with excessive animation in PowerPoint presentations
- General public and other nontechnical audiences
    - Are less interested in technical information
    - May not understand technical terms and usually ask nontechnical questions
    - May be overwhelmed with too much detail
    - Want brief, concise presentations
    - May or may not be impressed with animated PowerPoint presentations

A classroom audience is similar to supervisors (instructor) and peers (students). Senior design project presentations may also include supervisors, peers, and clients (visiting industrial representatives). Students who attend professional society meetings are peers.

All presentations are important, and you should strive to deliver your message in the most appropriate way for each type of audience. However, presentations to senior management are the most critical and you should plan them very carefully. Senior managers expect you to be informative, clear, and concise and to end on time. Remember, your career future often depends on your ability to have a positive impact on senior management.

Start your preparation by making an outline of major points. Use a word processor to structure the presentation and arrange ideas for a logical flow of information. Continue by adding details to each section of the outline. Prepare introduction and summary sections after the main body of the presentation has been completed.

Select the type of presentation and visuals that will be most appropriate for the audience. Use major points of the outline to structure visuals. Then, use visuals to practice your presentation.

After preparing visuals, rehearse by talking aloud about information covered in each visual. Think more about overall concepts than specific words.

Time rehearsals, and adjust the amount of information to fit the amount of time allocated for your presentation. A general rule for time use during the presentation is to allocate 10% for an introduction, 80% for the main presentation, and 10% for the summary.

5.3.2 Preparing Effective Visuals

You can use a variety of visuals, depending on the audience and type of meeting. Options for visuals include black/white boards, flip charts, DVDs, and PowerPoint. Most visuals are prepared before the meeting and provide an outline for the discussion. Our discussion will focus on PowerPoint visuals, but you can apply many of the same ideas to other media as well.

Content   In addition to knowing what to say, the next most important point is to support your comments by preparing visuals that are easy for the audience to see and understand. It is better to use a few, common words on a PowerPoint word visual instead of sentences, paragraphs, or long quotations. Your audience will remember more of what you say when they see key words and you provide additional details in your comments.

Use the KISS principle to prevent barriers.

A general rule for all visuals is the KISS principle, "*Keep it simple, student.*" A common mistake is to clutter visuals with too much written information or detailed sketches and diagrams. Your audience can understand visuals more quickly when you limit the amount of information on each one. A good example is shown in Figure 5.3. This is much easier to read and understand than Figure 5.4. Unfortunately, too many visuals look somewhat like Figure 5.4 and are too busy for the audience to read and understand.

MULTI-MEDIA COMPUTERS

◆ Dynamic Visuals
◆ Convenient To Use
◆ Flexible For Changes
◆ Interesting For Audience
◆ Professional Image
◆ Portable For Travel

Figure 5.3
Effective word visual content.

MULTI-MEDIA COMPUTERS

- Dynamic visuals that can be prepared before the presentation and that will be a good guide for the speaker to use during the discussion and questions
- Convenient to use because they are easy to carry and easy to show to the audience so they can follow the words being said
- Flexible for changes in that you can make corrections or changes just before the presentation to be more current and appropriate for the audience
- Interesting for audience to see something while you are talking about the details of each topic as you proceed through the presentation
- Professional image that demonstrates that you know how to use PowerPoint and can deliver your message in a modern way for your audience to see
- Portable for travel because you can take these in your computer or you can just save the message on an USB memory stick, CD, or other memory system
- Expensive to own but this is usually worth the cost because it makes it much easier to prepare and deliver your message in a professional way
- Available everywhere and audiences are familiar with this type of presentation visual support so will be happy to see your visuals
- Reliable but some older systems for projection may not be compatible and require you to change the resolution of your computer to fill the screen
- Effective for presentations because the audience can read more details as you are talking about each topic
- Common to most speakers and most speakers know how to use this media
- Very useful tool to help you deliver many details about your presentation and you do not need to have a lot of visuals to tell your story-art equipment and also that you are up-to-date with all the
- Sign of professional speaker, especially when you put a great deal of information on each visual to show how much you know about your topic
- Demonstrates state-of-the wonderful electronic presentation systems
- Expected by most audiences because they have seen many PowerPoint presentations and always expect to be entertained in addition to hearing the story
- Can be distracting if a lot of animation is used to add emphasis and to direct your audience to each part of the presentation
- Needs a projector but these are usually very easy to get and most hotels and companies have several of these available at all times
- Provide excellent notes for speaker if you can see what is on the very busy visual and then use this to help you remember what to say and when to say it
- Can also be used as an eye test by your audience to help them determine if they need to get new glasses or if their present glasses are fine
- Although you can put a lot of information on one visual, you eventually run out of space and have to go to the next visual

Figure 5.4
Ineffective word visual content.

Format for Presentations to Live Audiences   When preparing PowerPoint visuals to be projected on a screen in front of a live audience, use dark colors and simple designs for backgrounds. A long series of white backgrounds tend to cause eye fatigue. Also, when presentations are video-recorded, white backgrounds reduce camera shutter openings and images of speakers are often too dark. Dark backgrounds provide excellent contrast when you select white, yellow, and other light colors for words, graphs, and other figures.

As indicated in Figure 5.5, 44-point, white, Arial fonts are appropriate for titles. Most titles should be limited to one or two lines so they do not take up too much space. When you use all capital letters and add bold and shadow features, words are easier to read.

When using bullet points, we recommend 40-point, yellow, Arial fonts, with bold and shadow features for the first level of information. Second-level bullets can be 36-point white or other light color Arial fonts. Continue using bold and shadow features and capitalize the first letter of each word for all bullets. Avoid third-level bullets because they are small and difficult to see.

Minimize information overload by limiting bullet points to six lines of information under the title. If information does not fit in six lines, you can make a series of visuals with the same title.

Pictures and graphs are an excellent way to enhance visual presentations. Select pictures with limited details so your audience can quickly understand them. Graphs should be simple and uncluttered. For added clarity, use the power of 10 for large values on the X and Y axes. Select appropriate graph styles so the entire audience can easily understand the information.

Charts and graphs with properly selected colors are most effective. Subconscious minds tend to remember graphic relationships longer than columns of numbers. The large amount of information in Figure 5.6 is a barrier to the message. The graph in Figure 5.7 is easy to understand and is more effective.

You can use block diagrams, similar to the sample in Figure 5.8, to introduce more complicated information and data. These can be animated to demonstrate the flow of activities or processes. Block diagrams give your audience the big picture and prepare them for details. Then, you can talk about details of each block area with additional visuals after showing the overall process.

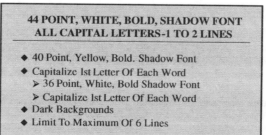

Figure 5.5
Effective word visual for projection on a screen.

RESULTS OF OIL CIRCUIT BREAKER TESTS AT CLOVERDALE SUBSTATION									
123.456	124.456	132.222	133.432	150.002	108.322	98.566	108.322	96.666	111.222
144.332	99.003	100.110	98.752	99.332	100.000	102.224	103.333	102.444	108.662
123.456	124.456	132.222	133.432	150.002	108.322	98.566	108.322	96.666	111.222
133.466	133.486	122.226	132.422	148.001	146.522	133.333	132.222	131.112	130.220
123.456	124.456	132.222	133.432	150.002	108.322	98.566	108.322	96.666	111.222
144.332	99.003	100.110	98.752	99.332	100.000	102.224	103.333	102.444	108.662
133.466	133.486	122.226	132.422	148.001	146.522	133.333	132.222	131.112	130.220
123.456	124.456	132.222	133.432	150.002	108.322	98.566	108.322	96.666	111.222
144.332	99.003	100.110	98.752	99.332	100.000	102.224	103.333	102.444	108.662
123.456	124.456	132.222	133.432	150.002	108.322	98.566	108.322	96.666	111.222
144.332	99.003	100.110	98.752	99.332	100.000	102.224	103.333	102.444	108.662
123.456	124.456	132.222	133.432	150.002	108.322	98.566	108.322	96.666	111.222
133.466	133.486	122.226	132.422	148.001	146.522	133.333	132.222	131.112	130.220
123.456	124.456	132.222	133.432	150.002	108.322	98.566	108.322	96.666	111.222
144.332	99.003	100.110	98.752	99.332	100.000	102.224	103.333	102.444	108.662
133.466	133.486	122.226	132.422	148.001	146.522	133.333	132.222	131.112	130.220
123.456	124.456	132.222	133.432	150.002	108.322	98.566	108.322	96.666	111.222
144.332	99.003	100.110	98.752	99.332	100.000	102.224	103.333	102.444	108.662
133.466	133.486	122.226	132.422	148.001	146.522	133.333	132.222	131.112	130.220
123.456	124.456	132.222	133.432	150.002	108.322	98.566	108.322	96.666	111.222
144.332	99.003	100.110	98.752	99.332	100.000	102.224	103.333	102.444	108.662
133.466	133.486	122.226	132.422	148.001	146.522	133.333	132.222	131.112	130.220
123.456	124.456	132.222	133.432	150.002	108.322	98.566	108.322	96.666	111.222
144.332	99.003	100.110	98.752	99.332	100.000	102.224	103.333	102.444	108.662
123.456	124.456	132.222	133.432	150.002	108.322	98.566	108.322	96.666	111.222
144.332	99.003	100.110	98.752	99.332	100.000	102.224	103.333	102.444	108.662
123.456	124.456	132.222	133.432	150.002	108.322	98.566	108.322	96.666	111.222
133.466	133.486	122.226	132.422	148.001	146.522	133.333	132.222	131.112	130.220

Figure 5.6
Ineffective data visual.

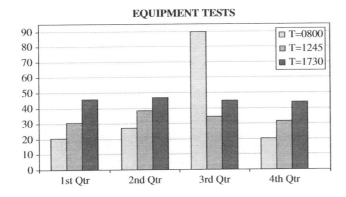

Figure 5.7
Effective data visual.

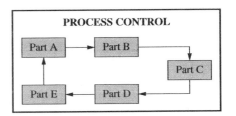

Figure 5.8
Sample block diagram.

Format for Web-Based Presentations   Most of the principles relating to visual format for live audiences also apply to Web-based situations. This is certainly true for the amount of information and size of fonts.

However, because Web-based visuals are usually viewed on computer screens, you can use colors that may not be effective on a large screen in live audience presentations. For example, black on white word sides and graphs with white backgrounds can be effective on electronic screens. This does not result in eye fatigue because the screen is much smaller. You can also use as many as eight lines of bullets in Web-based visuals. Figure 5.9 shows examples of Web-based visuals that will be easy to read and understand.

Animation   PowerPoint software includes a variety of visual animation and special effects. Some of these can be incorporated into presentations to add interest and emphasize major points. However, you should resist the temptation to make your presentation too entertaining. This is a frequent complaint from technical audiences because it tends to distract from the message.

When giving presentations to live audiences, you have the option of using a pointer or laser to interact with visuals on a screen. We discuss the pros and cons of pointers in the section on professional presentations.

A more professional approach to visual interaction is to develop visuals with overlays and progressive bullets. While animation should not be overdone, it offers an excellent way to emphasize major points of your presentation and keep audiences in step with your comments.

Progressive bullets help audiences follow your discussion point by point and prevent them from jumping ahead of your comments to additional bullets on the visual. Overlays of arrows, box outlines, shading, and other effects can be used to emphasize various parts of a visual.

Typically, progressive bullets and overlays are most effective with live audiences. It may be more difficult to control animation in Web-based presentations, especially during team presentations if only one team member controls transitions and animation.

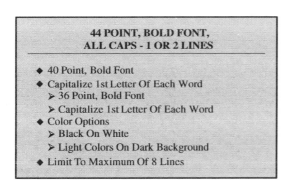
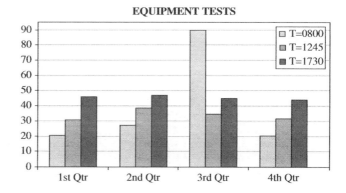

Figure 5.9
Appropriate Web-based visuals.

The number of visuals is a personal choice. If one visual is on the screen more than 30 to 60 seconds, it may become boring. On the other hand, the visual should be on the screen long enough for the audience to fully understand its content. When visuals are simple, the audience needs less time to comprehend the message.

General Comments Relating to Visual Preparation   To make your presentations more interesting, include pictures and graphs along with word visuals. Digital cameras are a convenient way to take pictures of events and projects. "A picture is worth a thousand words" applies to presentations. Pictures add variety and help your audience to be more attentive during your presentation.

Preparing computer visuals can be time consuming. A reasonable amount of animation can be included if development of the program starts early. So, start your preparation of visuals early and consider how you can make them more effective to help you deliver your message.

Because computer visuals offer a multitude of options, it is easy for the audience to focus on an "entertaining" delivery and miss the content of the message. Pictures should have a direct relationship to the message and add to the presentation without becoming a distraction. It is more important to keep visuals easy to understand than it is to entertain with special effects.

5.3.3 Practice

You can develop a more professional presentation by investing a significant amount of time to rehearse your presentation. One proven technique is to practice what to say with each visual. You can build speaking confidence by scheduling time for several practice sessions.

If you rehearse aloud you can practice projecting your voice and developing a smooth delivery. Effective speaking style is developed by being confident, by using positive body language such as looking at the audience and using natural gestures. Improve your delivery by including variations in your voice level and speed, and by eliminating time fillers such as uh, you know, and next between sentences. Use your practice sessions to develop a speaking style that will be interesting and that will encourage the audience to listen and enjoy your presentation.

Practice delivering general ideas instead of memorized words.

Practice talking about the content of each visual without memorizing specific words. If you memorize a presentation, it is easy to forget what to say if you are nervous when you stand in front of an audience. Instead, use the information on visuals to help you remember what to discuss, and then just talk about overall concepts of each topic.

5.3.4 Presentation—Delivering the Message

Now, let's discuss the major part of any presentation—delivery.

Presentations can either build a positive image for you or result in negative impacts on your career. It all depends on how you deliver your message. You can demonstrate your knowledge and enhance your image by making your presentations more professional. And the good news is that you can improve your presentations skills now by taking advantage of many opportunities to practice while you are in school.

Presentations to Live Audiences

Introduction

When starting a presentation, your introduction should establish a connection with the audience. You can do this by standing near the audience, establishing good eye contact, and giving appropriate comments in your introduction. Audiences are usually more interested in what you have to say and how it relates to them than they are in you. So, use introductory comments to explain why your message is important to them. The introduction should take about 10% of your total presentation time.

Eliminating Barriers

The effectiveness of any presentation is significantly improved by eliminating barriers between you and the audience. Barriers include a variety of ineffective presentation visuals and poor speaking styles that cause the audience to lose interest and think about something else.

> Eliminate barriers between you and the audience.

Many barriers can be eliminated by good planning and by preparing visuals that are easy to read and understand. When you use visuals for notes, you can focus on the audience and increase eye contact and voice projection. Properly designed visuals also increase audience interest and become a bridge to the presentation content and not a barrier.

Dress appropriately for the audience. If the audience focuses more on how you look than what you say, it can be a barrier and distract from your message. You can dress more casually for peer presentations, but should use business attire for senior management and clients. It is usually better to dress casually for most community and nontechnical audiences.

While it is good to interact with visuals to help the audience focus on what is being discussed, some interaction can also become a barrier. For example, if you use a pointer and face the screen with your back to the audience as you point to the visual, this becomes a major barrier. Your eye contact and audience focus will disappear and your voice will be projected to the screen. This can be avoided by placing the pointer in your hand next to the screen, pointing to a specific area on the screen, and then looking at the audience to discuss the information.

Similar barriers are associated with using a laser pointer. If you are nervous, your shaking hand will be magnified by the laser beam on the screen. In addition, you tend to face the screen and lose audience contact when pointing to the visual with a laser.

Other barriers are caused by poor speaking style or nervous movements that are often the result of limited experience. Frequently, speakers use time fillers as they are thinking about what to say. Repeating titles and bullets on the visual to the audience becomes a barrier.

```
┌─────────────────────────────────────────────────────────────┐
│                  PUBLIC SPEAKING BARRIERS                     │
│                                                              │
│  ➤ Improper dress (overdressed or too informal)              │
│                                                              │
│  ➤ Busy visuals with too much information, poor contrast     │
│    or small fonts                                            │
│                                                              │
│  ➤ Negative attitude and body language                       │
│                                                              │
│  ➤ Obvious nervous movements                                 │
│                                                              │
│  ➤ Rocking from one foot to the other or continually         │
│    waving hands                                              │
│                                                              │
│  ➤ Being stiff like a statue and not using natural gestures  │
│                                                              │
│  ➤ Hiding behind the lectern or other physical barriers      │
│                                                              │
│  ➤ Low energy level and lack of enthusiasm                   │
│                                                              │
│  ➤ Chewing gum                                               │
│                                                              │
│  ➤ Lack of eye contact with the entire audience              │
│                                                              │
│  ➤ Inappropriate level of information for specific audience  │
│                                                              │
│  ➤ Speaking too fast or too slow                             │
│                                                              │
│  ➤ Lack of voice projection to entire audience               │
│                                                              │
│  ➤ Repeating information from visuals, word for word,        │
│    to audience                                               │
│                                                              │
│  ➤ Saying "thinking time" fillers such as uh, you know,      │
│    now, and next                                            │
│                                                              │
│  ➤ Reading presentation to audience from note cards          │
│    or script                                                │
└─────────────────────────────────────────────────────────────┘
```

Figure 5.10
Typical presentation barriers.

By recognizing these barriers, you can remove them by better preparation, additional rehearsal time, practicing in front of a mirror, and speaking experience. Fortunately, you can gain this experience now, as a student, by taking advantage of speaking opportunities in classes, laboratories, and professional organizations.

Typical barriers to delivering a message are summarized in Figure 5.10. If the audience remembers any of these barriers instead of your message, you have failed to communicate effectively. Review this list before giving your next presentation, and work to eliminate barriers you may have used in previous presentations.

Using Visuals for Notes

Unless your topic is a legal document or you are representing your company before a congressional committee or other high-level audience, avoid reading to the audience. When you hide behind a lectern and read your paper word for word, your presentation will be boring and ineffective, as demonstrated in Figure 5.11. If you observe the

90   **CHAPTER 5**   Professional Presentation Skills

Figure 5.11
Boring and unprofessional delivery.

Figure 5.12
Professional delivery.

audience while reading, you will find that eyes are closing, heads are nodding, and eventually you may even hear snoring sounds.

But you may say, "There is no way I can face an audience without using notes or reading my presentation." Well, if that is how you feel, we have a very practical solution for you. You can actually use notes and be quite professional. The secret is to use your visuals for notes, as the speaker in Figure 5.12 is demonstrating.

Develop visuals to include major points that you want to discuss and practice talking about the concepts outlined on your visuals. Then, you will not need written notes, and you can build confidence by using information on your visuals to remember what to say.

> *"The presentation skills developed during my senior year at Cleveland State University helped me put together effective presentations throughout my 5-year career in power systems engineering. I am thankful for the guidance and support of my instructors who emphasized the value of good communication and showed me how to improve my public speaking skills."*
>
> (Marius Marita, PE, Electrical Engineer and Advanced Engineer at FirstEnergy Corporation)

In addition, visuals help your audience understand and remember what you say. Without visuals, retention of information is limited. Using good visuals increases retention to

TYPICAL INFORMATION RETENTION	
Presentation without visuals	10%
Presentation with good visuals	40%
Presentation with good visuals and handout materials	100%

Figure 5.13
Typical retention rates for presentations.

as much as 40%. When you distribute printed summaries of your major ideas, your audience has the opportunity to increase their retention up to 100%, as shown in Figure 5.13.

Handout materials are usually distributed after the presentation. However, if you want audience participation, such as in workshops, give worksheets to the audience at the beginning and use them as a reference during the presentation.

The use of properly selected and designed visual aids will multiply the effectiveness of your presentation. Even more importantly, when you use visuals as a guide, you will build confidence and minimize feelings of anxiety.

Presentation Summary

The last 10% of your allocated time should be used to summarize your presentation. This is an excellent way to emphasize the most important points of your subject. Your audience will remember information in your summary longer because they hear it near the end of the session.

The summary is another opportunity to show how your topic applies to the audience. Your summary is also a good way to initiate questions. This brings us to the last part of most presentations—a question-and-answer session.

Responding to Questions

An important part of most presentations is the opportunity to answer questions from the audience. So, how can you handle questions effectively and avoid being intimidated? One approach is to tell the audience during your introduction when you would like to have questions.

Questions can be asked during the presentation or at the end. Answering questions during the presentation can be time consuming and, in some cases, distracting. However, if the presentation is a workshop and you want audience participation, you can encourage the audience to ask questions during the workshop.

A second way to answer questions effectively is to think about potential questions as you prepare for the presentation and develop answers to them before the event. Then, it will be much easier for you to handle these questions if they are asked by the audience. Additional tips on handling questions are shown in Figure 5.14.

Team Presentations

Because you will probably be a member of a team when involved in large and complex projects, you may also be part of team presentations. All of the principles discussed to this point apply to team presentations as well. But, there are additional points you need to keep in mind when giving team presentations.

RESPONDING TO QUESTIONS

- Repeat or paraphrase the question to be sure you and the audience heard it correctly
- If you know the answer, give a concise reply
- If you need time to think about an answer, you can say, "That is a good question -let me think about it for a moment"
- If you don't know the answer, admit it, and then ask the person to see you after the presentation and discuss how you can provide the answer at a later date
- If you receive a question that disagrees with your comments, you can answer in a professional way by saying there can be more than one opinion and you expressed your opinion in the presentation

---

Figure 5.14
Tips for responding to questions.

In addition to delivering your part of a team presentation, if you are the first speaker, you have the responsibility to introduce the team and project. A good introduction will set the tone of the team presentation and develop audience interest and attention.

Key activities for the first speaker include

- Avoiding speaking until first looking at the audience to establish an audience connection.
- Introducing the project and team members, and identifying who will be covering the various parts of the presentation.
- Presenting appropriate details using good eye contact and voice projection.
- Completing the presentation with a brief summary of major points.
- Making an effective transition to the next speaker by giving his or her name and topic, and perhaps using a transition visual.

The transition will be most effective if the next speaker uses transition statements to bridge from the previous topic to the next. Key activities for team members who follow the first speaker are

- Starting with a brief introduction of his or her part of the presentation.
- Giving appropriate details with good eye contact and voice projection.
- Completing the presentation with a brief summary of major points.
- Making an effective transition to the next speaker.

The last speaker has an important task in addition to delivering his or her part of the team presentation. The final speaker should summarize the major points of the total team project to emphasize the most important information, and set the stage for questions from the audience.

The suggestions on how to answer questions as an individual speaker also apply to questions for teams. One additional suggestion for team members is to decide who will answer questions and how they can work together so they do not talk over each other in giving answers. In all aspects, individual parts of team presentations should be coordinated to result in one, overall presentation.

A team presentation should be a single, coordinated discussion and not a series of individual presentations.

Mechanical Problems Even with good planning, audience analysis, and preparation of visuals, mechanical or technical problems may surface during your presentation. For example, the room arrangement may be inappropriate for the audience to see the screen or lights may not be easily controlled.

Arrive early to check out equipment.

Additional problems occur when microphones do not operate properly or when projector bulbs burn out during presentations. If you are using an on-site computer instead of your own, your version of PowerPoint may not be compatible and animations may not work properly.

To prevent many of these problems, arrive early and check out as many systems as possible before your presentation. As a speaker, it is your responsibility to arrange for proper equipment to fit your needs and to minimize audience distractions. Request equipment before the meeting and then arrive early enough to practice using it before your presentation begins.

Web-Based Presentations In many respects, Web-based presentations are similar to live presentations. In both cases, the purpose is to transfer information from speakers to the audience, and to do this in a way that the members of the audience can understand and apply the message to their needs.

Many speakers fail to communicate effectively because they let barriers interfere with the delivery of their message. This is especially important for Web-based presentations because communication tools are usually limited to visuals and the speaker's voice. So, it is important to maximize the use of these tools and minimize barriers in the process.

Typical barriers for Web-based visuals are

- Too much information on a single visual.
- Each visual on the screen too long, resulting in listener distraction.
- Poor contrast between information (words, diagrams, graphs, charts, etc.) and visual background caused by poor color selection or busy backgrounds.
- Small font size that is difficult to read.
- Lack of coordinated interaction between the visual and spoken comments.

Typical barriers associated with the speaker's voice are

- Using low voice levels and lack of projection.
- Having poor-quality microphones or being too far from the microphone.
- Using time fillers.

■ Having a lack of enthusiasm and little change in voice levels to emphasize major points.
■ Using a delivery that is choppy with long pauses between visuals or major thoughts.
■ Reading the material or repeating information on the visual to the audience.

For best results, design visuals to eliminate barriers. Increase rehearsal time and practice effective interaction with visuals. Avoid memorizing specific words, but practice discussing concepts relating to each visual. To deliver professional presentations, do not read from a script or repeat titles or words from the visual for the audience.

If possible during Web-based presentations, arrange to personally advance visuals and then you can use progressive bullets, overlays, and other animation to correlate interaction of visual details with your comments. This is usually more professional than using the mouse or pointer, which can become a distraction.

Rehearse aloud to develop voice projection and a style that includes various speeds and levels. Use your voice to emphasize major points and to be more interesting and professional. Eliminate time fillers and develop a smooth delivery. Although you may not be visible in online presentations, you can use your voice to demonstrate confidence and your knowledge of the subject.

Some Additional Thoughts   A discussion of major points on how to deliver a professional presentation is a good way to finish this part of the chapter. So, here are some of the most important tips for success.

To relax, take a few deep breaths just before moving to the front of the audience. Start the presentation by standing near the audience and not behind the lectern.

Focus on *ideas* and not specific words. Deliver information without written notes and use visuals for notes. Locate your computer screen or monitor where you can easily see it and use this to view your visuals and not look at the screen behind you. Then, you can look more at the audience and less at the screen.

Prepare your presentation for the benefit of your audience and monitor their response during the presentation. When you see signals the audience is restless or bored, make changes in your delivery style.

Proper use of visuals is one of the best methods to keep your audience interested. Use a mix of words, graphs, and pictures, and include an appropriate amount of information.

Voice levels and speed can be changed to add variety to your presentation. Use style, body language, and movement to demonstrate enthusiasm.

Some forms of humor can be effective, but humor can also be risky. Keep all humorous stories short and relate them to the presentation. Never use humor that could offend someone in the audience. When in doubt, leave it out.

Finish with a summary of the most important points of the presentation. This helps your audience remember information and may encourage them to ask questions to expand the value of your presentation.

Be flexible and use only the amount of time allocated for your presentation. You may be notified of a change in your time allocation just before you are introduced, so adjust your presentation to end on time. It is always better to end early than to go over the time limit.

5.4 Value of Public Speaking Experience

When it comes to public speaking, there is really no substitute for experience. Look for opportunities to speak to a variety of audiences to gain experience and to build confidence. Use friendly environments, such as classes, laboratories, and professional organizations to practice speaking to audiences.

Professional organizations offer excellent opportunities for you to practice presentation skills. As an active member, you can volunteer to introduce a speaker or give informal presentations before an audience of your peers. You can also gain additional skills and self-confidence by leading projects or being an officer in these organizations. Other organizations, such as Toastmasters International (www.toastmasters.org), are located in most areas and offer excellent opportunities to gain speaking experience and confidence.

> *"I used to be an introvert and dreaded giving presentations. However, I knew that the ability to present ideas was an integral part of a successful engineering career. To overcome my fear I decided to participate as an officer in SWE (Society of Women Engineers). By regularly engaging in outreach events where I delivered engineering related presentations to small groups of high school students, I gradually became more confident speaking before a group.*
>
> *When our local SWE chapter hosted a national outreach event, I was able to feel comfortable delivering the opening remarks in front of a crowd of over one hundred fifty students, parents and professionals.*
>
> *Now, making presentations to corporate leaders is a regular part of my role as a Technical Advisor/Prior Art Search professional. Therefore, the public speaking experience gained through my active participation in a student organization has proved invaluable."*
>
> **(Maria Marez Baker, BEE, Technical Advisor, Electrical Arts, Frisina, LLC)**

You are encouraged to look for opportunities to speak to a variety of audiences to gain experience and to build confidence. Use friendly environments, such as your classes, laboratories, and professional organizations to practice speaking in front of an audience.

A CONVERSATION WITH JOHN PASERBA

John, I know you have given hundreds of professional presentations. How did you develop public speaking skills?

Answer

"I was a senior in college and our local IEEE (Institute of Electrical and Electronics Engineers) Student Branch was sponsoring a technical paper contest at my university supported by the local IEEE section. The contest consisted of a written paper and an oral presentation. As the date of the contest neared, the 'volunteers' for entering this contest were few. One of my professors encouraged me to enter the contest. I resisted at first but later, with proper academic encouragement (a.k.a. twisting of my arm), I agreed to enter the local contest.

I wrote a paper based on my senior design project and created a presentation. Back in those days, we used 'flip-charts' drawn by hand, as access to any computer-generated graphics programs, such as PowerPoint, was still off in the future, especially for college students. Four of us entered the contest and there were cash prizes for 1st, 2nd, and 3rd place.

I recall the evening of the contest very well. At the time, our university had a weekly 'Senior Seminar' that every graduating senior was required to attend. Normally the seminar was during the day, but, this particular week, we were all assigned to attend the evening IEEE dinner and presentation contest, so, the room was packed for the event.

The four of us presented our respective papers, and to my surprise I not only enjoyed the experience, but, I won first prize with the top cash award—a welcome addition to my sparse college income. Because I was the winner of a local contest, I was automatically invited to the IEEE Region Paper Contest, where a region consisted of several states and nearly seventy-five eligible schools with IEEE Student Branches. I updated my paper and my presentation based on the local contest experience, and traveled several hundred miles to participate in the Regional contest.

While I did not place in the top three of the Region Paper Contest, I did enjoy the experience so much that I decided when I graduated I would only take a job at a company that supported participation in a professional society (in my case, IEEE) and supported industry publications and presentations. This decision guided me in my graduate work and with the companies I interviewed with as I was nearing graduation.

When I graduated with a master's degree, I only considered taking employment with a company that offered this opportunity to publish. I was fortunate that I found such a company with which to begin my career. Later, when I moved to my second company, I pursued the same attributes of support of industry publications and presentations."

In this age of electronic communication, do you think it is important for engineers to learn how to give oral presentations in their working careers?

Answer

"There is no question in my experience that oral presentations are more important today than ever before. With e-mail, phone, text, PowerPoint, and many other media competing for people's attention, an opportunity for oral presentations can make the difference in getting your points, proposals, and ideas across to your colleagues and upper management. The key is to be brief, focused, and clear on your points. Flexibility is always critical. Multiple times

I have walked into upper management presentations and as I enter the room, I am asked 'can you make your points in one hour?' when the meeting was scheduled for two hours or more. Preparing short, crisp, concise, and on-point presentations is critical to a successful career."

To emphasize the value of public speaking skills, what are typical examples of your presentations in your work and in your professional activities?

Answer

"In twenty-four years, I have published and presented over sixty national and international technical papers in journals, conferences, and in magazines, including chapters in five *Engineering Handbook* editions. I have attended conferences and workshops and have made technical presentations around the world including in many cities in the USA and Canada as well as in Brazil, Mexico, Singapore, China, Japan, Belgium, Germany, Saudi Arabia, France, and Indonesia.

I have been invited to teach seminars and courses worldwide including the University of Pittsburgh, Pennsylvania State University, University of Wisconsin, Waseda University, Japan, Institute of Technology at Bandung, and others. Furthermore, I have been invited to speak at nearly forty colleges worldwide on engineering professionalism and career management. These presentations and others have been made to audiences from a dozen to thousands.

As a Project Manager, I had to make presentations to customers and to advisory boards on proposals for new business and for final reports on my own or my group's technical work. Later, as a Department Manager and as a Division General Manager I routinely make presentations to upper management to go over business plans (consisting of sales plans, staffing plans, operation budgets, and capital investments), and then to my employees for execution of those plans.

One of my presentations that had a high-impact occurred recently after an annual review of my business, which was presented to nearly three hundred professional, clerical, and factory attendees of my Division (I had been a Division General Manager for only 3 weeks at that time). After the 90-minute presentation, several of our factory technicians approached me and said 'I really comprehend our business and our customers and how it all comes together and the importance of my role—thank you for making it so understandable.' I'll never forget the impact of that moment—as it further emphasized the importance of professional presentations skills."

What advice do you have for students relating to professional presentation skills?

Answer

"The best advice I can give to students related to professional presentation skills aligns with my experience as an undergraduate and graduate student and a young engineer in my company when I first started: that is to take every opportunity you can to get professional speaking experience. Enter your university's paper or speaking contests and orally present your senior design project or other undergraduate projects. At your first job, if you are ever in small groups such as a seminar or workshop, volunteer to present your group's work. Your communication skills, both writing and speaking, will take you as far as your willingness to continually improve in this area."

(John J. Paserba, General Manager, Gas Circuit Breaker Divison, Mitsubishi Electric Power Products, Inc.)

5.5 Conclusion

Technical expertise is the foundation for your career. But, as John has clearly stated in our discussion with him, technical skills are only part of what you need to be a successful engineer. Success is achieved by a balance of technical and non-technical skills. And, communication is your most important nontechnical skill.

Remember, the purpose of making a presentation is to deliver appropriate information to an audience with a delivery process that makes it easy for them to understand and use the information. Effective and professional speakers chart their course early, analyze their audience, and prepare materials in time to permit adequate rehearsal before the presentation.

As noted in the beginning of this chapter, our objective is to encourage you to improve your speaking skills and to show you how you can do that. Your ability to communicate with technical and nontechnical people will be a key ingredient to help you reach higher levels of success and to make a positive impact on society. Use the principles of this chapter to develop communication skills now, and you will be better prepared to start your working career.

END OF CHAPTER REVIEW QUIZ

Select the most appropriate answer to the following statements.

1. The most important reason for you to improve your public speaking skills is
   a. To receive a better grade when assigned to give a presentation in class.
   b. To avoid being nervous when speaking before a large audience.
   c. To prepare to run for a public office such as a school board member.
   d. To deliver your ideas to others so they can understand and use them.
2. The best way to prepare to give an effective presentation before an audience is to
   a. Spend most of the night before the presentation to practice.
   b. Invest appropriate time to know your subject, make good visuals, and rehearse.
   c. Spend time to make a lot of animated visuals so the audience will enjoy your presentation.
   d. Memorize your presentation and prepare note cards to help you remember it.
3. The purpose of an introduction to a presentation is to
   a. Outline what you are going to discuss.
   b. Explain how your topic relates to the audience.
   c. Start your presentation on a positive note so the audience will be interested.
   d. Accomplish all of the above.

4. It is important to eliminate barriers between you and the audience because barriers
   a. Distract you and make it more difficult for you to remember what to say.
   b. Make it harder to recognize audience feedback.
   c. Distract the audience and cause them to lose interest in your presentation.
   d. Make the audience think you are a great speaker.

5. During your presentation, the best way to remember what to say is to
   a. Use visuals for notes.
   b. Read the presentation word for word so you don't leave out any information.
   c. Use note cards for guidance and read details from them to the audience.
   d. Look at the screen and repeat information from the visual to the audience.

6. You can reduce nervousness by
   a. Taking medicine to be more relaxed.
   b. Hiding behind a lectern so the audience can't see you.
   c. Rehearsing and using good visuals to build confidence in what to say.
   d. None of the above.

7. The most important value of summarizing your presentation at the end is
   a. To give you a way to end the presentation.
   b. To emphasize the most important points of the presentation.
   c. To use time so you don't have to prepare as much material.
   d. To discourage the audience from asking questions.

8. When answering questions the most important thing to do is to
   a. Repeat the question and answer in a concise way.
   b. Argue with someone who does not agree so you can defend your ideas.
   c. Write answers to potential questions and read the answers when the questions are asked.
   d. Answer the question by asking the audience what they think.

9. The best way to minimize mechanical problems is to
   a. Take your own audio visual equipment with you to the meeting.
   b. Discuss equipment needs several days before the event with the facility manager.
   c. Reserve equipment, arrive early, and test audio visual equipment and lighting controls.
   d. Have a someone adjust equipment during your presentation, if needed.

10. It is important to improve your presentation skills because
   a. This is a sign of a professional and can open career opportunities.
   b. You will save preparation time and reduce stress when speaking.
   c. You can make positive contributions to team project presentations.
   d. It includes all of the above.

EXERCISES TO DEVELOP AND ENHANCE YOUR SKILL SET

Exercise 5.1   Your instructor may select one of the following options for this exercise: 1) assign you to give a five-minute presentation to summarize a previous class lecture in class; 2) assign you to give a five-minute presentation to summarize a class lecture to one of your study groups. These assignments will include the use of evaluation reports.

Exercise 5.2   Change the busy and ineffective PowerPoint visual in Chapter resource 5.1 to one PowerPoint visual using bullets. Print this visual and give to your instructor on the date assigned.

Exercise 5.3   Prepare a PowerPoint presentation for the laboratory report in Chapter resource 5.2. Provide an electronic file of your PowerPoint presentation to your instructor, if assigned.

END OF CHAPTER RESOURCES

Chapter resource 5.1

Ineffective PowerPoint Visual

MULTI-MEDIA COMPUTERS

Multi-media computers offer many new tools to make visuals for presentations. These flexible tools provide opportunities for you to make presentations very dynamic. Softwere is user friendly, easy to learn, and convenient to use, and can be programmed with a variety of transitions and animation techniques. By using these format tools, you can make your presentations much more interesting for the audience. This helps you make a positive impact on your audience and results in a very professional image for you as a speaker.

Chapter resource 5.2

Laboratory Experiment to Demonstrate Ohm's Law

Introduction: This experiment was designed to prove Ohm's law by using a simple electrical circuit to measure voltage across resistors and current through resistors. The validity of Ohm's law formulas can be confirmed by comparing measured results to calculated values. Two resistors of different values were used to observe and record results of voltage and current.

Purpose: The purpose was to demonstrate that when resistance increases in a series circuit, the current decreases and equals the amount determined by Ohm's law that $I = V/R$, where I is current, V is voltage, and R is resistance.

Apparatus: A simple circuit was constructed by placing each resistor, one at a time, in series with a DC power supply. Resistor values were 1 kΩ and 3.3 kΩ. A voltmeter and an ammeter were connected at the proper locations in the circuit and used to measure voltage across the resistor and current through the resistor.

Procedure: The power supply was adjusted to create voltages across the resistor of 2, 4, 6, 8, and 10 V. At each voltage level, the current was measured. Results are tabulated in Table 1 for the 1-kΩ resistor and in Table 2 for the 3.3-kΩ resistor.

Calculated values for the five (5) voltage levels for the 1-kΩ resistor are shown in Table 1 and for the 3.3-kΩ resistor in Table 2. The difference (measured current less calculated current) is shown in the third column in both tables.

Results: As shown in Tables 1 and 2 , the differences between experiment results and calculated results using Ohm's law are small, proving that Ohm's law is correct. Differences can be attributed to small voltage drops within resistor wires.

MEASURED RESULTS			
VOLTAGE VOLTS	CURRENT (mA)		
	Measured	Calculated	Difference
0	0.00	0.00	0.00
2	2.00	2.04	−0.04
4	4.00	4.08	−0.08
6	5.98	6.12	−0.14
8	8.00	8.16	−0.16
10	9.90	10.20	−0.30

Table 1
Values for a 1-kΩ resistor.

MEASURED RESULTS			
VOLTAGE VOLTS	CURRENT (mA)		
	Measured	Calculated	Difference
0	0.00	0.00	0.00
2	0.62	0.62	0.00
4	1.22	1.23	−0.01
6	1.84	1.85	−0.01
8	2.45	2.47	−0.02
10	3.07	3.09	−0.02

Table 2
Values for a 3.3-kΩ resistor.

Conclusions: Experimental data confirmed that Ohm's law of $I = V/R$ is correct. The relationship of voltage and current is linear and current decreases when resistance increases.

CHAPTER

10

Team Building Skills

The Power of Team Building

> *"Teamwork is the fuel that helps common people to attain uncommon results."*
>
> —Jim Watson, PE, President, Watson Associates

TEAM BUILDING SCENARIO

"As the project lead of a cross-functional team, I was tasked to create a plan for a new consumer product that meets customer needs, hits cost and resource allocations, and launches on time.

Our team needed to meet an aggressive cost goal on the total solution (product, packaging, accessories, and other materials) to hit our target market price. This meant that we could not do things 'the same old way.' We had to get creative without sacrificing quality or the customer experience."

(Beth Moses, Electrical Engineer and Program Manager, Hewlett-Packard Company)

Beth Moses has outlined a team situation that is typical of many corporate projects. We will identify the principles involved in team building and then, in our discussion at the end of this chapter, learn how Beth applied many of these principles to this project.

10.1 Introduction

Engineering teams are frequently used to handle the complexity of designing large projects. This chapter is designed to prepare you to be a successful team member or leader.

Use opportunities to build team skills now.

As a student, your team building skills can be developed by your participation in laboratory teams, senior project design teams, and projects sponsored by engineering professional organizations. And, as you develop and enhance team building skills now, you will be better prepared to successfully handle team opportunities in coop or intern positions, and throughout your working career.

LEARNING OBJECTIVES

By using the information and exercises in this chapter you will be able to

- Understand and apply the principles of successful team building.

- Be prepared to participate in more challenging team projects.

- Observe and recognize personality traits in yourself and others.

- Match your personality traits to team activities.

- Recognize and use opportunities to develop team building skills for greater career success.

10.2 Team Building

Teamwork is a powerful tool for technical professionals, and teams often replace individuals as the primary unit of operation. This is especially true in the more innovative organizations in business, industry, government, research, and academia.

10.2.1 Team Definition

A team usually *is not* just

- A group of individuals who work in the same location.
- A group of individuals who work for the same person.
- A group of individuals who do the same type of work.

A successful team is more than a group of individuals.

A team *is*

- A group that shares a common assignment.
- A group that recognizes that it needs the contributions of all members.
- A group that is committed to achieving maximum results within constraints.

10.2.2 Characteristics of a Successful Team

A successful team is a unified group of individuals with special and unique talents who work together to achieve common objectives. Strong and effective teams see diversity of ideas as a good way to blend the various abilities and strengths of each individual to accomplish a greater result than just the sum of individual contributions.

Successful teams share several characteristics including:

- Clear objectives.
- Strong leadership and appropriate roles for each team member.
- Good communication, trust, and openness to new ideas.

■ Cooperation and ability to deal with conflict.
■ Ability to balance innovation, quality, and cost.

10.2.3 Team Advantages/Disadvantages

Although teams help corporations accomplish major goals, there are advantages and disadvantages when you participate in team activities. These can be summarized as follows:

Team Member Advantages

■ Work on new and more challenging projects.
■ Share resources and skills toward common goals.
■ Participate in learning experiences that enhance personal careers.
■ Practice interpersonal skills and develop leadership skills.
■ Produce greater results from synergy in group discussions.

Team Member Disadvantages

■ Need to give up freedom to operate independently.
■ Need to consider different ideas of other team members.
■ May need to sacrifice individual goals to achieve team overall goals.
■ Can be a waste of your time if poorly managed.

10.3 Team Building Process

Establishing a successful team is more than just asking a few individuals to work together on a project. Team members should be carefully selected based on their skills and knowledge and their ability to work effectively with other members of the team.

As an engineering student, you have skills that are important in team building. One good example is your ability to solve problems by a logical, step-by-step process, and this skill can be applied to a team assignment. So, let's review the basic principles of team building and see how your skills can make this a successful venture.

10.3.1 Forming

The following activities are typically included in forming a team:

> ➤ The team is formed by members meeting to become acquainted and select a leader
>
> ➤ Personal information or agendas usually remain in the background at the start
>
> ➤ Project objectives and specific goals are identified and established
>
> ➤ Important ground rules for team operation are established
>
> ➤ Roles are identified for each team member

Figure 10.1
Team forming activities.

As indicated in Figure 10.1, you can help form a more successful team by participating in defining important items associated with the project. The project objective and specific goals to accomplish that objective also need to be clarified at the beginning.

As a team member, you will be more productive when you understand your specific role, starting in the forming stage. We discuss team member roles in detail in Section 10.5. Roles during the forming stage are very important and set the tone for an effective team. You will help your team be successful when you:

- Contribute your ideas during the development of team objectives and ground rules.
- Volunteer to participate in team activities that use your strongest skills.
- Listen to others and encourage team members to work together and use teamwork skills.
- Are prepared to invest sufficient time and apply your skills to achieve objectives.

Equally important to identifying team objectives is the establishment of ground rules that set the foundation for discussion and help the team develop recommendations. Some samples of ground rules are shown in Figure 10.2.

Time invested in forming a team whose members work well together results in time saved during the project and will increase the level of harmony within the group. More importantly, a well-formed team arrives at better solutions to the project, and this can have a positive impact on personal careers for team members.

The forming stage should be accomplished at the team's first meeting. The next step, storming, takes significantly more time and often requires a series of meetings.

10.3.2 Storming

The term storming is a good indication that this part of the team process can be lively and perhaps even stressful for some members. The ability of the team to arrive at the best possible solution to the project is based on how well individuals participate in the storming stage.

Let's start with an overview of the storming stage, as shown in Figure 10.3.

TYPICAL GROUND RULES

Be on time for meetings
Let one member speak at a time
Share time use
Encourage new ideas from brainstorming
Listen to all opinions
Criticize *ideas* and *not people* who offer them
Offer solutions and not complaints
Keep team objectives in focus
Work toward an honest consensus
Support team decisions
Take responsibility for team assignments
Complete work assignments on schedule

➤ Individuals introduce their ideas and goals

➤ Members listen to other ideas and consider their value

➤ Members promote own ideas and question or challenge ideas of others

➤ Ground rules are used to minimize chaos

Figure 10.2
Typical team ground rules.

Figure 10.3
Storming activities.

When you join a team, you usually have some preconceived ideas about the project. Some of your ideas will be based on your skills and interest in specific parts of the project. Guess what? Other members will also have ideas about the project, and many of their ideas may be different from yours. Frequently, you'll be representing your area of work and your supervisor will suggest desired outcomes for the project solution.

Most team members arrive on the scene with an agenda and are motivated to influence the team decision to fulfill that agenda. In addition, you may discover that team members often have hidden agendas that reflect personal career goals.

Because team members have these different agendas, discussions will be more productive when members follow ground rules as project solutions are introduced. This is the time for each team member to propose and discuss new ideas.

You, and all other members, need to contribute so the team has the advantage of exploring many different ways to design the project. If all potential solutions are not discussed, the final decision may be less than desired. Therefore, it is important to allocate sufficient time so that many different ideas can be discussed.

The storming session is most productive through the synergy of hearing one idea and then developing a second related idea. This is called brainstorming, and is a proven way to expand options. Results of brainstorming are maximized when members do not criticize others for suggesting new ideas. Ground rules should encourage brainstorming. Time invested in introducing new ideas can produce better results, and the team should not be impatient when members want to expand the storming session.

Explore a multitude of options to arrive at the best solution.

The second important part of the storming session is for each member to defend his or her ideas and to offer documentation to support these ideas. As a member presents an idea, other members have three assignments—listen carefully, ask questions for clarification or additional information, and discuss the value of the idea. Though sometimes frustrating, this is the best method for a team to decide what should be included in their recommendations.

The storming session can be a challenging part of team building. When members are passionate about their ideas, they often see questions as criticism, and take comments to be rather personal. When this happens, the team leader needs to be a mentor, apply principles of conflict resolution, remind the team of the ground rules, and remove the personal aspect of discussions.

An important principle of the storming stage is that the team should take as much time as possible to arrive at a viable solution. One or more better solutions may be overlooked if many ideas are not offered and discussed before decisions are made. For team members who favor early decisions, this can appear to be taking too much time. However, the overall results are well worth the extra time investment in this session.

10.3.3 Conforming

To be efficient and meet reasonable time schedules for project development, the team needs to make the transition from discussing individual options to arriving at a team solution. This is called conforming because all members will likely have to make some concessions for the team to arrive at a single solution. Activities in this stage are listed in Figure 10.4. Recommendations will impact each member, so members should work hard to find the best team solution.

> Team leader takes control and moves team into a cooperative mode
>
> Hidden agendas may be disclosed to solicit support
>
> Individuals compromise to arrive at a team solution
>
> Team solution is clarified and members identify assignments

Figure 10.4
Conforming activities.

The responsibility of bringing the team to a single solution rests heavily on the team leader. Because individuals may have personal agendas, the leader needs to start this step carefully by focusing more on the concepts than the individuals who support them. This typically includes a give-and-take approach, and the process may now reveal some of the hidden agendas.

A major role of the team leader is to keep the team on track.

Eventually, the final solution is developed and all members need to agree to support team decisions. This is a time for effective communication to ensure all members understand the solution and their role in making it happen.

The team solution to the project should be put in writing and distributed to all members. This is the best way for you, and other team members, to have a clear picture of what the team decided and how each member will participate in implementing the solution.

And this brings us to the fourth and final step in team building—performing.

10.3.4 Performing

The major activities of the performing stage are shown in Figure 10.5.

> The team becomes committed to achieving goals and completing the project
>
> Members review assignments and start work in a cooperative spirit
>
> The leader reviews work progress and encourages completion
>
> Team members communicate results to appropriate management levels

Figure 10.5
Performing activities.

Attitude is important when team members reach the fourth step. If members who did not feel the team solution met their goals or the goals of their department have a negative attitude, they may not complete their team assignment well.

One way to minimize negative attitudes is for the team to develop supporting information to demonstrate why the team decision is best for all concerned. This will also help members communicate results to their departments and may prevent negative impacts on their careers.

The team leader should continue to coordinate the implementation of the project and remind members of their assignments, when needed. When each member meets the target dates for completion, everyone benefits.

Communication is an important key to success.

Communication during the implementation of the project is just as important as communication in team work sessions. The concepts discussed in the chapter on written communication can be applied to team reports and this will help to coordinate the project implementation. You can also add the project report to your records of achievement.

"Being a student leader with many different facets of my life was synonymous to being a judge at a talent show. I needed to indentify the potential and the talents possessed by fellow students who would otherwise not step forward to participate in various capacities. In no time I created a following and a culture of students with whom I studied and worked. This made it possible for me to delegate pressing issues that I could not personally attend to. For example, I formed my senior design team but made a colleague the leader of the team and our senior design team won the best senior design project of the year."

(Sedofia Gedzeh, Electrical Engineer)

You can prepare for team projects in your working career by taking advantage of opportunities to practice team building now. Some of these opportunities are laboratory classes and senior design projects. You can also practice team building when you participate in professional organization projects. These experiences can help you be a better team player in your working career.

10.4 Personality Traits

So far, we've discussed team building from the viewpoint of the team. Now, let's turn our attention to the most important part of any team—you and the other individuals involved.

Each individual is special and unique. We are different in our backgrounds, experiences, attitudes, and abilities. All of us have opportunities, challenges, disappointments, and moments of great success. Because we are unique, we respond to situations differently. And, personal differences can enhance our lives, because as we interact with others we learn new ideas and observe different personality traits.

Personality traits are not good or bad, they are just unique. The most important person for you to study and understand is you. Because you are unique, you can better relate to others if you first understand your own behavioral tendencies.

> Each individual is unique and important.

Your knowledge of your strengths and limitations provides a foundation for achieving a professional attitude and work ethic. You can maximize your strengths, minimize your limitations, and learn to be effective in interpersonal relationships. And, when you understand your personality traits, you will be able to observe similar and different traits in others.

Behavioral patterns can be identified by professional assessment and interpretation. Perhaps you have been involved in this type of assessment and are aware of your personality traits. Our discussion in this chapter is intended to help you apply your most effective skills so you enjoy your involvement in a team setting and can be most productive.

10.4.1 Personality Traits Categories

Personality traits are typically identified by looking at four basic behavioral patterns associated with how you participate in group situations. There are many different titles for the four major personality traits. For simplicity, we will use the titles in Figure 10.6.

10.4.2 Personality Trait Strengths and Limitations

An overview of typical strengths of each of the four major traits sets the foundation for discussing how personality traits impact team building. For example, *drivers* typically are good at accepting challenges and taking responsibility of making things happen.

Figure 10.6
Personality trait categories.

They can visualize the future and take control of difficult situations by solving problems. Because they question present status, they often cause problems for people who resist change.

In contrast, *influencers* love to interact with other people and are good at expressing their ideas and making positive first impressions. They are helpful, are usually active in group settings, and can be quite entertaining. They bring enthusiasm to group settings and tend to talk more than listen. Because they do not worry about details, they are often perceived as being superficial.

As indicated by their title, *specialists* enjoy operating in a well-established world. They like to stay in a comfortable environment, concentrate on their part of a project, and use specialized skills. They are patient, loyal, sincere, and honest. They appreciate security and are good listeners. Because they do not like change, they are uncomfortable in thinking outside the box.

Perfectionists concentrate on details, follow standards, and like to be 100% accurate. They are diplomatic, enjoy being supervised by others, and accept decisions by others. They appreciate compliments for their good work but can be very critical of poor work performance by others.

Most people have a mixture of these traits, but usually one or two tend to stand out in personality evaluations. In each case, we can use our traits for successful results.

10.5 Personality Trait Application to Project Teams

A basic understanding of personality traits gives insight to better observe others and to learn the best methods of interacting with those around us. When we avoid trying to change others and work to understand and appreciate their traits, we help the team achieve much greater overall results.

Fortunately, we don't need a detailed analysis of other people to observe their strongest personality traits. Strong leaders often demonstrate *driver* traits. *Influencers* bring creativity and enthusiasm to a group. Team members who are *specialists* are excellent in completing work and will remain loyal to the project. *Perfectionists* are diplomatic and produce quality work.

Based on the results of our observations, we can learn to influence others or to increase cooperation within group activities by providing an atmosphere in which others are motivated and successful. This will build a strong team.

So, how can you apply your best skills to a team setting? If you have strong *driver* traits, you can offer to set up the procedure for a laboratory experiment, lead a senior design project, or coordinate a project in a professional organization.

Or, if you have strong *influencer* traits, you can effectively verbalize the results of a team project. Your strongest asset in a team activity is your enthusiasm and creativity. If properly channeled, your creativity will add to the success of a laboratory team or other group activities.

Influencers do not like details of a project, but are excellent supporters of the team. So, if you are an *influencer*, you will be good at communicating team needs and results and should play a major role in written and oral presentations that are an important part of all projects.

Each team needs one or more *specialists*. If you have strong specialist's traits, you are a good listener and can concentrate on the tasks to be completed. You will be most effective when the procedure is well defined and is not changed.

Specialists need to identify with the overall group, and are motivated by compliments from others. If you are a *specialist*, you are not usually aggressive so you may need help in getting started on the work. Your loyalty will encourage others to complete the task, and this helps to obtain results.

Because accuracy of results is important, the team needs at least one *perfectionist*. If you fit this personality type, you will enforce procedures, and this should help the team obtain accurate results. In group planning meetings, you tend to continually check for the correct procedure and accurate information. You review plans and instructions very carefully and prevent the group from making serious mistakes. As a *perfectionist*, you will be most effective if given opportunities to be precise.

Teams perform best when members apply different personality traits.

If all team members have the same personality traits, the team will be unproductive. A team whose members are all *drivers* will spend most of their time trying to elect a leader. *Influencers* will talk all day about a variety of topics but never establish a project plan. A team of *specialists* will wait forever for someone to make assignments. And, a team of *perfectionists* will just study the assignment and take no action.

So, the most productive teams are made up of members with a variety of personality traits. For best results, assignments should match the stronger traits of each member. This does not guarantee team harmony, but supports greater success in achieving project objectives.

10.6 The Value of Diversity

Teams are excellent opportunities for you to actively participate in decision-making activities and to realize a greater sense of accomplishment. Because teams consist of individuals, team success depends on how well individuals work together. Team results are directly related to how well team members include a diversity of ideas.

If your team consists of members from a diverse background with different ideas and skills, this can be used to great advantage when members view a variety of ideas as a way to expand options. Ground rules should encourage new and different ideas and viewpoints on topics. Members should give ample time and listen and respect all ideas, especially during brainstorming activities.

"The true beauty of teamwork emerges when it offers a glimpse of creative solutions beyond the walls of your biases and preconceptions. For new teams, I've found the biggest stumbling block to achieving these insights is a failure to incorporate diversity of life experience in addition to skillset. Without this diversity, teams risk reinforcing lackluster ideas and producing mediocre outcomes. These failures often take teams by surprise, still unaware that they were working within their comfort zones the whole time."

(Joshua Brandoff, *Mathematical Programmer and IT Specialist at the Museum of Mathematics)*

Because individuals are different in attitudes, abilities, and experiences, they respond to team situations in different ways. The value of diversity is that different people have different ideas, and this expands options for the team to find the best solution to a project. Your contribution to a team will be valuable when you maximize your personality trait strengths and minimize your limitations.

A CONVERSATION WITH BETH MOSES

Beth, tell our readers how you used the principles of team building in your project introduced at the beginning of this chapter.

Answer:

"I will answer that question by indicating how we used the basic team building steps.

Forming:
Our team consisted of ten professionals ranging from software engineers to marketing managers. The members were experts with specialized skills to ensure a broad perspective across the whole customer experience. Each person brought diverse backgrounds and experiences.

As team lead, in our first meeting, I outlined the situation. . . the target customer and desired experience, project cost goal, timeline, the scope of what we could impact and fixed items that could not be changed.

Early in the project, it was important to spend time getting to know each other. We often did a 'round table' discussion that allowed each person sitting 'around the table' to share status as well as describe issues and concerns on the project. This gave each person a chance to talk and for us to better understand personality traits as well as team members' strengths.

Storming:
We identified drivers, influencers, specialists, and perfectionists on the team fairly quickly. This helped me as team leader to request tasks and activities of each team member that best matched his or her personality traits.

We spent time brainstorming and discussing ideas on how to exceed the customer's expectations, while best utilizing our team resources within the cost constraints. As team lead, I wrote the ideas on a flip chart to ensure that no idea was lost. We then performed a quick assessment of the ideas to determine impact to the customer experience, time frame required, resources needed, and cost to the solution.

This exercise involved everyone's diverse inputs and expertise to be sure that we evaluated the ideas from all angles. This step was crucial to include all members of the team, as no one person in our team had all of the answers.

Conforming/Performing:

In the end, our team determined several ways that we could deliver a better, higher-quality product by providing information in a different, more interactive way. To ensure that the customer was successful getting started with the product, we included a large, 'setup' poster with plenty of visuals to keep words and translations to a minimum. This solution helped to quickly deliver the necessary start up instructions, provide a great customer experience across many countries and cost less than previous approaches.

For more specific operating instructions, we enhanced on-screen instructions shown on the product display. By using visuals and illustrations right on the product, the customer was able to quickly access information and directions when needed in the operation of the product. Finally, we included a full written manual on the software disc. This way, the customer could read the step-by-step operating instructions on a computer and even print them out if desired.

The overall solution was a cost-effective approach and delivered a high-quality product to the consumer. In addition, we were able to leverage our resources in a new and different manner while still meeting timelines."

How would you summarize the results of your participation in this career opportunity?

Answer:

"Our team was able to find a creative solution that exceeded customer expectations while leveraging resources, achieving cost goals, and introducing to the market on time. By bringing together a diverse set of people who were focused on meeting the team's objectives, we created and delivered a successful product.

As team leader, I leveraged team members' expertise, but challenged each one to think differently to solve problems. The willingness of team members to partner with each other to create a new and better solution was the turning point.

As team lead, I also felt strongly that successes should be recognized and celebrated. Sometimes I would simply announce accomplishments during team meetings. Other times, I would bring candy or cookies to celebrate team successes (we loved this in kindergarten, why not in the workplace?). Bigger accomplishments deserved email notes to management. Finally, we celebrated major milestones with larger organization celebrations."

One final question—what advice would you share with students?

Answer:

- Early in the team formation, a team leader should provide clear team vision, objectives, time frame, and constraints. This helps align all team members to common goals and challenges.
- Bring together key team members with diverse backgrounds, expertise, and specialties.
- Spend time early forming team, getting to know the team members, understand strengths and personality traits.
- Listen to ideas and solicit inputs from those that are more quiet or shy—use the 'round table' approach where everyone in the team gets a turn to share status, successes, frustrations, and issues.
- Track, recognize, celebrate success (small and large).

(Beth Moses, Electrical Engineer and Program Manager, Hewlett-Packard Company)

10.7 Conclusion

The chapter on team building is included in this book because you will often be involved in team projects. The best way to prepare for future team projects after graduation is to use opportunities to develop and improve your teamwork skills now.

Some opportunities for you to build teamwork skills are included in your classes and laboratories. Others can be found by volunteering to be an active member of one or more professional organizations and participating in group activities.

We emphasized the value of developing nontechnical skills for team building because this will help you achieve greater career results. And, you will be more successful as a team member when you use engineering principles of logical thinking and organization.

We used engineering principles in this chapter to develop the logical steps in team building and in the application of personality traits to teamwork. So, apply a balance of technical and nontechnical skills in your future team opportunities and you will enjoy the benefits of working with others to complete successful projects.

END OF CHAPTER REVIEW QUIZ

Select the most appropriate answer to the following statements.

1. A team is
   a. A group of people who work in the same department and have common interests.
   b. Several engineers who work for the same person.
   c. A group selected to develop a project or solve a problem.
   d. All of the above.

2. A typical characteristic of a successful team is
   a. The selection of a strong leader.
   b. Good communication within the team and to stakeholders.
   c. The ability to balance many options to find a solution to a project.
   d. All of the above.

3. The most important advantage of being on a team is
   a. To get promotions by achieving the goals of your department.
   b. You can be a leader and tell others what to do.
   c. You can work on more challenging and rewarding projects.
   d. You don't have to spend as much time on routine activities in your job.

4. The biggest disadvantage of working on a team is
   a. You may need to give up some of your goals to reach a team solution.
   b. You may have to work with people you don't like.
   c. You might have to put in extra hours to keep up in your other work.
   d. You have to take notes and give a report to your supervisor.

5. You can determine your personality traits by
   a. Asking other people to tell you what they like about you.
   b. Using evaluation tools and by thinking about what you usually do best.
   c. Asking your supervisor why you are given various tasks to do.
   d. Doing all of the above.

6. The most effective skills of a person who has strong director traits are
   a. Leadership and making things happen.
   b. Thinking before deciding what to do.
   c. The ability to relax and not worry about what might happen.
   d. Getting involved in details so results are perfect.

7. People with strong influencer traits are not good at:
   a. Interacting with other people.
   b. Making a positive first impression because they talk too much.
   c. Being patient with people who like details.
   d. Showing enthusiasm for a project.

8. Specialists are important on a team because they
   a. Initiate new ideas.
   b. Are good at adapting to change.
   c. Can handle several tasks at a time.
   d. Are patient, sincere, and very honest.

9. People with strong perfectionist traits are not good at
   a. Delegating work to other team members.
   b. Concentrating on details or standards.
   c. Accepting decisions by others.
   d. Telling others when their work is not up to standard.

10. A successful team should consist of
    a. Several members with driver traits so the work will get done.
    b. Members with different personality traits to take advantage of diversity.
    c. Many members with perfectionist traits for greatest accuracy of results.
    d. All members who have strong influencer traits to have good communication.

EXERCISES TO DEVELOP
AND ENHANCE YOUR SKILL SET

Exercise 10.1   Project team exercise

Option 1: Your instructor will discuss details and assign a team project exercise based on Chapter resource 10.1, Envirocar Project Team Scenario.

Option 2: Ask members of your study group to use Chapter resource 10.1, Envirocar Project Team Scenario, and practice team building skills.

Exercise 10.2   Project team exercise report

Project Team Report

If your instructor selects Option 1 of Exercise 10.1, review the results of your project team exercise and complete your project team report using the following format and outline headings.

Envirocar Project Team Report

Name _____(Your Name)_____

Team identification:

Team member names:

Your assigned scenario:

Team solution:

Major reasons for selection of team solution:

In what team activities would you be most effective? Give reasons for your choices.

How did you participate in each of the team building steps?

Forming:

Storming:

Conforming:

What would be your most effective contributions to this project during the performing stage?

Exercise 10.3   Personality trait self-evaluation
             Your instructor may assign this exercise or you can elect to complete
        it on your own. Use the self-evaluation form shown in Chapter resource 10.2,
        to determine your "*disp*osition" scores relating to a project team scenario.

Exercise 10.4   Project team report including application of personality trait evaluation
        results
             Use your personality trait self-evaluation results from Exercise 10.3 to
        consider how your traits were applied in the project team Exercise 10.1, and
        complete your project team report using the following format:

Envirocar Project Team Report

Name _____(Your Name)_____

Team solution:

Major reasons for selection of team solution:

Numerical subtotals of personality traits self-evaluation exercise:

   Driver

   Influencer

   Specialist

   Perfectionist

184 **CHAPTER 10** Team Building Skills

Based on your personality trait self-evaluation and skills, in what team activities would you be most effective? Give reasons for your choices.

How did you participate in each of the team building steps?

Forming:

Storming:

Conforming:

What would be your most effective contributions to this project during the performing stage?

END OF CHAPTER RESOURCES

Chapter resource 10.1

Envirocar Project Team Scenario

Contest overview: Your team goal is to design a race car that will achieve the highest total points in a 12-hour race. The car is to be constructed by students using school facilities and entered in a contest at a nearby Honda test track in which students from seven other universities will compete.

Contest details:

1. The race will be held in six months at a Honda Test Track from 10 AM to 10 PM.
2. Teams will be limited to eight people, including drivers.
3. Teams will be limited to a maximum of 20 gallons of regular unleaded gasoline.
4. Entries will be judged on a point system:
   - 500 points to complete the 12-hour contest.
   - Bonus of 1 point/mile completed.
   - Bonus points for lowest total car equipment, construction, and fuel cost:
     - 300 points for lowest cost of all contest cars.
     - 200 points for second lowest cost of all contest cars.
     - 100 points for third lowest cost of all contest cars.
   - Bonus points for environmental impacts:
     - 500 points for zero use of gasoline.
     - 300 points for maximum use of 10 gallons of gasoline.
     - 100 points for maximum use of 15 gallons of gasoline.

Race car designs are limited to the following:

1. Use an electric motor powered by solar photovoltaic cells on the car to charge batteries and interchange batteries as needed during pit stops.
2. Use an inexpensive internal combustion engine, aluminum body, 18-inch wheels, and high-pressure tires to obtain high fuel efficiency.
3. Use a new, experimental hybrid engine that is powered by gasoline and an electric motor powered by lead-acid batteries.

Team Building Exercise: Review assigned scenario details, prepare an outline of how to promote this scenario, meet with team, and follow the assignment steps.

Envirocar Scenario 1—Solar Car

Design details:

- Use photovoltaic cells located on the top of the car to charge nickel-metal hydride batteries.
- Use proven direct-current motor and simple speed control.
- Build car using fiberglass to reduce weight and steel for strength.
- Select body shape for maximum photovoltaic exposure and minimum air resistance.

Contest plans:

- Use small drivers to reduce weight.
- Change batteries as needed during pit stops.
- Provide battery charger and use existing track electrical outlets.

Potential advantages:

- Requires no use of gasoline so qualifies for 500 bonus points for zero environmental impact.
- Results in zero fuel cost during contest.
- Increases energy conservation and miles driven by low weight-to-power ratio.
- Provides opportunity to demonstrate engineering skills using futuristic systems and should enhance future job opportunities for team members.

Potential disadvantages:

- Estimated construction cost of $12,000 may be higher than other designs.
- Energy from photovoltaic cells will be reduced if weather is not sunny and will disappear after sunset a few hours before the end of the contest.
- The numerous electrical connections associated with photovoltaic cells increases construction time (600 hours) and could result in failures during the contest.
- Energy limitation of using only batteries after dark may limit ability to complete race.
- Top speed will be limited to 30 miles/hour.

Your role in this team exercise:

- Before meeting with your team,
    - Read outline of contest and details of this design scenario.
    - Outline your plan to discuss this design.
- During the forming process with your team,
    - Introduce yourself and record names of other team members.
    - Participate in selecting leader.
    - Offer ideas for ground rules.
- During the storming process with your team,
    - Briefly discuss this scenario and promote the advantages.
    - Be prepared to defend scenario when questions arise relating to potential disadvantages.
    - Listen to other scenario discussions and ask questions about potential disadvantages.
- During the conforming process with your team,
    - Compromise as needed to help team select final design.
    - Record advantages of final design so you can discuss with your team advisor.
- Complete the performing process.
    - Prepare a written report as assigned.

Envirocar Scenario 2—Aluminum Car

Design details:

- Use aluminum for car structure to keep weight low.
- Use large lawn mower internal combustion engine for low initial cost.
- Use 18-inch wheels and high-pressure tires for increased fuel efficiency.
- Keep car size very small to reduce energy consumption.

Contest plans:

- Use 20-gallon fuel tank to reduce number of pit stops.
- Select two small drivers and rotate to minimize fatigue.
- Limit top speed to 40 miles/hour to conserve fuel.

Potential advantages:

- High efficiency should support completion of contest and 500 points.
- Obtaining engine efficiency of over 40 miles/gallon may result in 100 point bonus.
- Total construction cost of $5,000 by using inexpensive engine and materials should increase cost bonus potential.
- Simple design should reduce construction time to 400 hours.
- Reduced pit stops should increase miles driven and bonus points.

Potential disadvantages:

- Making strong aluminum welds requires special skills.
- Most lawn mower engines are not designed to run at high speeds for 12 hours.
- Aluminum is more likely to be damaged if contact is made with cars or the track.
- Top speed of 40 miles/hour may limit bonus points for total miles driven.

Your role in this team exercise:

- Before meeting with your team,
    - Read outline of contest and details of this design scenario.
    - Outline your plan to discuss this design.
- During the forming process with your team,
    - Introduce yourself and record names of other team members.
    - Participate in selecting leader.
    - Offer ideas for ground rules.
- During the storming process with your team,
    - Briefly discuss this scenario and promote the advantages.
    - Be prepared to defend scenario when questions arise relating to potential disadvantages.
    - Listen to other scenario discussions and ask questions about potential disadvantages.
- During the conforming process with your team,
    - Compromise as needed to help team select final design.
    - Record advantages of final design so you can discuss with your team advisor.
- Complete the performing process.
    - Prepare a written report as assigned.

Envirocar Scenario 3—Hybrid Car

Design details:

- Use new experimental hybrid Honda system with gasoline engine and electric motor.
- Use standard lead-acid batteries to power electric motor.
- Design car with low air resistance for added fuel efficiency.
- Use automatic transmission to reduce driver fatigue.

Contest plans:

- Use 10-gallon fuel tank to reduce weight.
- Plan to run at top speeds of 50 miles/hour.
- Change batteries during pit stops.

Potential advantages:

- High average speeds should result in a large bonus for miles driven.
- Use of the hybrid engine will result in 300 bonus points.
- Use of Honda system builds relationship with company and may lead to job opportunities after graduation.
- University will receive goodwill by supporting new technology.

Potential disadvantages:

- Adapting new technology may result in problems during construction.
- The hybrid system will not be available until 2 months before contest—this may complicate construction estimated to be 300 hours for chassis and 200 for hybrid system.
- Untested new technology may limit miles driven and the ability to finish the competition.
- The high cost ($10,000) of this technology may minimize opportunity for cost bonus points.
- The frame to hold the engine, electric motor, and battery system needs to be very sturdy and may increase construction time.

Your role in this team exercise:

- Before meeting with your team,
    - Read outline of contest and details of this design scenario.
    - Outline your plan to discuss this design.
- During the forming process with your team,
    - Introduce yourself and record names of other team members.
    - Participate in selecting leader.
    - Offer ideas for ground rules.
- During the storming process with your team,
    - Briefly discuss this scenario and promote the advantages.
    - Be prepared to defend scenario when questions arise relating to potential disadvantages.
    - Listen to other scenario discussions and ask questions about potential disadvantages.
- During the conforming process with your team,
    - Compromise as needed to help team select final design.
    - Record advantages of final design so you can discuss with your team advisor.
- Complete the performing process.
    - Prepare a written report as assigned.

Chapter resource 10.2

Personality Trait Self-Evaluation

*Determining Your "**DISP**osition"*
in a Project Team Scenario

Place a "1" for all traits that represent **what you are good at** in a team or group situation.

Part "D"	Part "I"
_____ Making things happen	_____ Interacting with others
_____ Recognizing accomplishments	_____ Making good first impressions
_____ Accepting challenges	_____ Being comfortable in expressing ideas
_____ Making decisions	_____ Getting excited about a project
_____ Questioning the "status quo"	_____ Instilling enthusiasm
_____ Taking responsibility	_____ Entertaining people
_____ Causing trouble	_____ Helping others
_____ Solving problems	_____ Actively participating in a group
_____ Visualizing the future	_____ Talking more than listening
_____ Taking charge in difficult situations	_____ Not worrying about details

Part "S"	Part "P"
_____ Using established work procedure	_____ Following standards
_____ Staying in one physical place	_____ Concentrating on details
_____ Showing patience	_____ Being supervised by others
_____ Using specialized skills	_____ Being diplomatic
_____ Concentrating on your part of project	_____ Looking for accuracy
_____ Showing loyalty	_____ Accepting decisions
_____ Being a good listener	_____ Criticizing performance
_____ Calming excited people	_____ Thinking critically
_____ Being sincere and honest	_____ Liking familiar work situations
_____ Wanting to feel secure	_____ Receiving compliments for good work

SUMMARY OF YOUR DISPOSITION RESULTS: **TOTAL PART "D"** _____
TOTAL PART "I" _____
TOTAL PART "S" _____
TOTAL PART "P" _____

Chapter resource 10.3

Additional Information Relating to Personality Traits

Typical Characteristics of Personality Traits

Persons with strong **driver** traits:

May not be good at	Are motivated by	For success, need
Evaluating alternatives	Power and authority	Difficult assignments
Being careful	Prestige and challenge	To understand what others need
Working in a familiar setting	Accomplishments	To be practical
Completing research	Opportunities to advance	An occasional shock
Thinking before deciding	Direct answers	To identify with team members
Working in predictable setting	Variety of activities	To explain actions to others
Sacrificing self for others	Independence	An awareness of consequences
Patience and discipline	Diverse challenges	To relax more

Persons with strong **influencer** traits:

May not be good at	Are motivated by	For success, need
Discipline with their work	Social recognition	To use time more effectively
Gathering information	Public recognition of skills	Objectivity
Speaking directly	Freedom of expression	A democratic leader
Valuing honesty	People to talk to	Emotional control
Working independently	Nonwork group activities	A sense of urgency
Preferring things to people	Freedom from control	To be less ideological
Thinking about new ideas	Comfortable environments	To focus more on end products
Being patient	Chance to speak	To improve organizing skills

Persons with strong **specialist** traits:

May not be good at	Are motivated by	For success, need
Adapting to change	Security of situation	Conditioning prior to change
Taxing physical capacity	Stability	To use more shortcut methods
Different tasks at one time	Happy home life	To appreciate their value
Being opportunistic	Traditional procedures	Help with new tasks
Applying pressure	Sincerity by others	Supportive groups
Working in uncertain settings	Limited territory	Orders before acting
Being aggressive	Constant appreciation	Others to encourage creativity
Initiating new ideas	Identification with others	More self confidence

Persons with strong **perfectionist** traits:

May not be good at	Are motivated by	For success, need
Accepting control	Security assurances	Detailed work
Delegating work to others	Routine procedures	Careful planning
Making decisions	Safe work environment	Many explanations
Acting independently	Reassurance	Exact job descriptions
Standing their ground	Predictable circumstances	To spend less time on details
Taking unpopular stands	Being part of a group	Others to respect their value
Completing work quickly	Individual attention	Frequent feedback on progress
Initiating new ideas	Time for perfect results	To accept some imperfection

CHAPTER

11

Engineering Skills for Ethical Dilemmas

Turning Shades of Gray Situations into Black and White Solutions

Ethical Dilemma Scenario

"As engineering team leader, you are under pressure to deliver an innovative new design on time and on budget. You've developed the requirements, the design is progressing, and you are confident that the design will be a breakthrough in the market.

However, recent rumors of a competitor's new product make you doubt the superiority of the design. A colleague approaches you one day offering information that may help you gain advantage over the competitor. He has obtained a detailed presentation package that outlines the features and architecture of the competitor's emerging product. This data would allow you to revise your design to ensure it outperforms the competition.

After asking a few questions, you learn that the information was captured through questionable tactics. Furthermore, the material is marked Confidential and is covered by a Non-Disclosure Agreement executed between the competitor and one of their customers. What Will You Do?"

(James Peterman, Senior Product Manager, Strategic Projects—Tekelec)

Jim Peterman raises a very interesting question in this scenario. In our conversation with him at the end of this chapter, we will see how Jim resolved this ethical dilemma.

11.1 Introduction

Engineers impact the quality of life of others.

This case scenario introduces our topic for this chapter—ethics. Unlike many principles of engineering, ethics is difficult to structure and teach. Webster defines ethics as "pertaining to morals" and ethical as "in accordance with the rules or standards for right conduct or practice, especially the standards of a profession."

A profession is a learned occupation requiring systematic knowledge and training, and a commitment to a social good. Engineering is the creative art of applying science for the benefit of all mankind and is therefore a profession.

LEARNING OBJECTIVES

By using the information and exercises in this chapter you will be able to:

- Appreciate the need for ethical behavior.

- Recognize early signs and prepare for ethical dilemma situations.

- Use engineering tools and teams to solve ethical dilemmas.

- Evaluate potential impacts of making ethical decisions.

- Communicate recommended solutions to all stakeholders.

- Understand the impact of ethical decisions on your personal career.

Because engineering is a profession, we must consider the impact of ethics on our behavior. For example, we are ethical when we provide quality products and services. On the other hand, we are unethical if we knowingly endanger the lives of others by what we do. So, one of the most important qualities of professional engineers is to create a positive impact on the quality of life.

Ethics is especially important because what we do impacts the nontechnical world. Society has a high level of expectation for the performance and safety of our products and services. Because the general public often does not understand technology, they put their trust in engineers to design products that are safe and easy to use.

The fact that people trust us means that we have a greater responsibility to be ethical and assure personal safety and national security in all we do. Their trust also means we need to establish ethical conduct as a foundation of our career. In fact, engineering ethics is as important to good engineering practices as mathematics, physics, design skills, and other engineering fundamentals.

11.2 Preparing for Ethical Dilemmas

It is a good idea for you to start your study of ethics now. Because ethical situations and issues may appear rather quickly, the best way to be prepared to handle them is to build a foundation of ethical behavior in school, in your family, and in your community. Fortunately, you have many sources of information to help you develop this foundation.

11.2.1 Personal Code of Ethics

Your personal values are established throughout your life, starting with the impact of family and faith. Ethical values are formed when you observe actions of your parents and others. Your parents give you direction by telling and showing you what they believe is right and wrong. You learn other standards for behavior from your teachers in school and other adult models.

At first, little things may not seem to be important, but they set the stage for how you handle more important situations in your life and profession. For example, if someone gives you change for a $20 bill when you gave them $10, what do you do? The way you answer this question sets the pattern for how you may handle larger issues such as the scenario at the beginning of this chapter.

> *"The man of integrity walks securely, but he who takes crooked paths will be found out. Prov. 10:9*
>
> *These words, written over 2000 years ago, are still valid today. Whether they are applied to our personal life or our work life, the fact is that if we compromise our integrity and sacrifice our ethics, we are no longer someone to be trusted. We may be able to deceive some, but eventually our deception will be discovered. When we cultivate a life of integrity, we'll reap the trust of our family, friends and business associates."*
>
> (Kevin F. White, PE, Manager of Engineering and Operations, Northeast Missouri Electric Power Cooperative)

As indicated in Kevin White's comments, your ability to be trusted by others depends on your personal code of ethics. This code should be based on proven standards for life and your profession. Let's review sources of information to help you further develop your code of ethics.

11.2.2 National Society of Professional Engineers' Code of Ethics

The code of ethics established by the National Society of Professional Engineers is an excellent source of information to help you define the way to practice as an engineer. This is on the Internet at: http://www.nspe.org/Ethics/CodeofEthics/index.html. The July 2007 revision of this code is shown in Chapter resource 11.1.

The preamble to this code of ethics summarizes the content of this important professional guideline as follows:

> Engineering is an important and learned profession. As members of this profession, engineers are expected to exhibit the highest standards of honesty and integrity. Engineering has a direct and vital impact on the quality of life for all people. Accordingly, the services provided by engineers require honesty, impartiality, fairness, and equity, and must be dedicated to the protection of the public health, safety, and welfare. Engineers must perform under a standard of professional behavior that requires adherence to the highest principles of ethical conduct.

"A Professional Engineer does not receive his certificate in a particular engineering discipline. However, the Canons require him or her to only practice in an area in which s/he has acquired expertise. My area of expertise is combustion. I have several times consulted with law firms on disastrous fires, which have resulted in loss of life. In each case the plaintiff's lawyer has retained a professional engineer as an expert who only had minimal training in the field.

The so-called expert created ridiculous theories as to how the fire started and why the manufacturer of the device should be held responsible. In my opinion, these experts are misusing their licenses and should not have testified outside of their knowledge. The loss of life in each case was tragic, but was not an equipment malfunction and was actually due to negligence on the part of the individuals involved. It is tempting to want to blame another party, but it should always be resisted unless there is a good scientific reason."

(Dr. Richard Cohen, PE, Associate Professor
Mechanical Engineering, Temple University)

11.2.3 Professional Societies' Codes of Ethics

Throughout this book, we emphasize the value of active membership in professional organizations. An important benefit when you are a member of these organizations is the opportunity to use their codes of ethics as an additional guide for your ethical behavior.

The following quotation by Dr. Paul Bosela highlights some of the most important fundamental principles of the American Society of Civil Engineers Code of Ethics that were adopted on September 2, 1914 and amended on July 23, 2006.

"'The safety of the public must be the first and foremost concern in the practice of civil engineering.' The American Society of Civil Engineers Code of Ethics presents the fundamental principles and canons for the ethical practice of Civil Engineering, notably stating that 'Engineers shall hold paramount the safety, health and welfare of the public and shall comply with the principles of sustainable development in the performance of their professional duties . . .' Some of the major aspects for ethical practice include 'using their knowledge and skill for the enhancement of human welfare and the environment,' 'being honest and impartial,' 'performing services only in their areas of competency,' 'uphold the honor, integrity and dignity of the engineering profession,' with 'zero-tolerance for bribery, fraud, and corruption.'"

(Dr. Paul Bosela, PE, Professor of Civil & Environmental
Engineering at Cleveland State University)

Another example of codes of conduct is shown in Chapter resource 11.2 for the American Society of Mechanical Engineers. Uniform Resource Locators (URLs) for codes of conduct of some societies are shown in Figure 11.1.

Professional organization codes of ethics are similar to standards established by the Accreditation Board for Engineering and Technology (ABET). ABET's fundamental canons, listed in Figure 11.2, are a foundation for ethical development during your academic experiences.

American Institute of Chemical Engineers
http://www.chow.com/facts_6823508_code-american-institute-chemical-engineers.html

American Society of Civil Engineers
http://www.asce.org/Leadership-and-Management/Ethics/Code-of-Ethics/

American Society of Mechanical Engineers
http://files.asme.org/asmeorg/governance/3675.pdf

Association for Computing Machinery
http://courses.cs.vt.edu/cs3604/lib/WorldCodes/ACM.Code.1992.html

IEEE
http://www.ieee.org/about/corporate/governance/p7-8.html

Figure 11.1
Sample professional society codes of ethics.

ABET FUNDAMENTAL CANONS

1. Engineers shall hold paramount the safety, health, and welfare of the public in the performance of their professional duties

2. Engineers shall perform services only in the areas of their competence

3. Engineers shall issue public statements only in an objective and truthful manner

4. Engineers shall act in professional matters for each employer or client as faithful agents or trustees, and shall avoid conflicts of interest

5. Engineers shall build their professional reputation on the merit of their services and shall not compete unfairly with others

6. Engineers shall act in such a manner as to uphold and enhance the honor, integrity, and dignity of the profession

7. Engineers shall continue their professional development throughout their careers and shall provide opportunities for the professional development of those engineers under their supervision

Figure 11.2
ABET fundamental canons.

11.2.4 Corporate Codes of Ethics

Most corporations include ethical procedures in their formal or informal operating practices. These may be found in corporate objectives and policies, or they may be more informal in the established culture of the company. Figure 11.3 identifies typical topics in many corporate codes of ethics.

It is a good idea for you to discuss ethical attitudes of potential companies during job interviews. This can be accomplished by asking for a copy of their code of ethics or by asking questions that refer to their attitude about the impact of their product or service on customers.

To achieve ethical goals, many corporations establish procedures for employees to discuss ethical situations with higher management. This typically includes talking to your supervisor, or in some cases, higher levels of management. Some procedures may also include talking to an individual in the Human Resources Department or an outside consultant.

Following the established corporate code of ethics is important in all job situations. These help you define guidelines for making decisions about the quality of your work and your relationships to other employees and customers.

11.3 Recognizing Early Signs of Ethical Dilemmas

The third paragraph of the ethical scenario outlined at the start of this chapter indicates an ethical situation is likely involved. Some of these statements are red flags of unusual

> ### TYPICAL TOPICS
> ### IN CORPORATE CODES OF ETHICS
>
> ➤ Product quality
>
> ➤ Product support
>
> ➤ Customer relations
>
> ➤ Accountability with company funds
>
> ➤ Gifts from suppliers
>
> ➤ Trade secrets
>
> ➤ Environmental impacts
>
> ➤ Public health and safety
>
> ➤ International operations
>
> ➤ Travel and company representation
>
> ➤ Information relating to competitors

Figure 11.3
Corporate codes of ethics topics.

> ENGINEERING PROBLEM-SOLVING
> PROCESS
>
> 1. Define the problem
> 2. Determine objectives
> 3. Identify alternative solutions
> 4. Identify constraints
> 5. Select solution
> 6. Test solution for potential impacts
> 7. Document and communicate solution

Figure 11.4
Problem-solving process.

circumstances or activities that cause you to stop and consider if the suggestions of the colleague are ethical and should be used. There are often early signs when things are unethical and engineers have the responsibility to evaluate these signs.

> Look for early warning signs of unethical behavior.

When early signs of a potential ethical situation are noted, the next step is to record information. This builds a foundation on which you can decide if there is a problem, and if so, what you should do next. And this brings us to the most important part of handling ethical dilemmas—using engineering tools to solve them.

11.4 Using Engineering Tools for Ethical Dilemmas

As you investigate and document a potential ethical situation, you will discover that many of the issues are shades of gray with different impacts on different people. This makes your ability to find the right solution a little more challenging. Your goal in addressing an ethical dilemma should be to change these shades of gray situations to black and white solutions. So, how can you do that?

In many of your classes, you are learning how to solve engineering problems by following a step-by-step process shown in Figure 11.4. This same approach can be used to solve ethical problems. You can face an ethical situation with confidence because, with your engineering skills, you will know where to begin, how to proceed, and how to evaluate results of your solution.

11.4.1 Define the Problem

In solving a technical engineering problem, the most important step is for you to first identify all known quantities. This approach is also the most important step in addressing an ethical situation.

When something appears to be unethical based on comments from coworkers or casual observation, this is the time to look for facts. As you identify details of the situation, avoid stating or implying that this is unethical. It is risky to make hasty judgments about an ethical situation without first determining all the facts.

A decision about ethics should only be made after all information has been gathered. If you make false accusations, your reputation and career may be damaged.

Start your investigation of a potential unethical situation by obtaining quantitative information. You can do this by requesting information from others involved to ensure the situation is being properly assessed. Additional guidance can be solicited from friends and coworkers who can be trusted to keep the evaluation process confidential. Be sure to document detailed information.

11.4.2 Determine Objectives

When it appears something is unethical, based on the facts of early investigations, the next step is to determine if there is a reason for you to do something about it. The answer to that question is determined by the extent of the unethical act.

For example, is it important for you to disclose a student who is cheating in class? The answer may be yes if this is on a test and could impact your grade and the grades of other students. However, you might first discuss this privately with the student and suggest this is not in his or her best long-term interest.

If one of your laboratory team members is unethical and uses information from stolen laboratory reports, this might also reflect on you and other team members. In this case, you really should discuss this with your teammate and then with the instructor, if necessary.

> The decision to be involved in an ethical dilemma is based on codes of conduct.

As a student, your decision about becoming involved in ethical dilemmas can be determined by your personal code of ethics. You will be more successful in handling early ethical dilemmas if your personal code is based on professional codes. As a practicing engineer, decisions for involvement should always be based on professional and corporate codes of ethics.

An analysis, similar to the ones we discussed for student unethical situations, can be used when you consider getting involved in an ethical situation in your working career. Start by asking yourself how important is the ethical dilemma.

For example, are people taking pencils home for their children to use in school or are they giving trade secrets to a competitor? Does the unethical practice impact you, your company, or customers? Your decision about getting involved in ethical situations is usually based on potential impacts on you, your family, and your company.

The first step in most company ethical policies is to discuss situations with your supervisor. However, if your supervisor is involved in the unethical situation, you have a major challenge. The objective of your involvement in this case usually will be determined by weighing potential risks of talking to a third party or bypassing your supervisor and talking to someone in the next level of management.

11.4.3 Identify Alternative Solutions

When you decide to address an ethical dilemma, evaluate options for your approach to find a solution. If only one person is unethical, you might start by encouraging him or her to change. If many are involved, your objective may be to use the corporate process established to handle ethical problems.

For more complex ethical dilemmas, it is appropriate to form a team of associates to review as many options as possible and consider the consequences of each. Typically, this will reveal negative and positive impacts on various individuals or groups, and you can find the best solution for most stakeholders by a careful review of these options.

By using the process introduced in the chapter on team building, potential alternative solutions will be expanded because more team members will be contributing ideas. Group synergy can result in finding more options and selecting better final recommendations.

Another reason for using a team approach is that there is less personal risk when solving ethical dilemmas. The recommendations of several people are usually considered more viable than those offered by just one person. If recommendations are unpopular, the negative impact on individual team members is reduced when presented as a team solution.

11.4.4 Identify Constraints

Because alternative solutions include various constraints, it may be difficult to select the "best" solution. Ethical dilemmas are usually not black or white but different shades of gray. You can define some constraints by reviewing records made during the discovery process. Remember, your major objective is to change something that appears to be shades of gray to black and white options and then select a solution based on professional codes of ethics.

You can identify other constraints as you investigate the details of alternative solutions. As a student, if you suggest a laboratory team member should stop plagiarizing reports, you may not have the support of other team members. As a practicing engineer, you may be working for a company that has limited funds to cope with environmental impacts of a project. Most options have related constraints, so identify and include constraints in the evaluation process when seeking solutions.

11.4.5 Select Solution

And that brings us to the most difficult part of resolving ethical dilemmas—finding the right solution. You can select appropriate solutions by using documented facts, evaluating options and constraints, and holding discussions with advisors and team members.

Impacts on various stakeholders should also be part of the equation. Your ability to have others accept and support your decisions is often based on how it impacts them personally. In all cases, solutions should be based on personal, professional, and company ethical codes.

11.4.6 Test Solution for Potential Impacts

Before making suggested solutions public, it is a good idea to test potential impacts on all involved. This can be done within a team, by talking to trusted friends, and by discussing with supervision. Decisions have different impacts on different stakeholders. If one person is unethical, the implementation of a solution to correct the problem may hurt his or her career, but might save the careers of many others who work for the company.

> Test solutions for possible impacts before making final decisions.

Stakeholders include customers as well as the company. If a product is unsafe, it could injure those who use it. In addition to causing major injury to customers, this could also result in costly product recalls or lawsuits. This in turn could impact all employees.

Other important stakeholders are your family, as the discussion in Figure 11.5 shows. Although they are not directly involved in your work, they are impacted by what you do. To include their input, discuss potential impacts relating to ethical solutions with your family before finalizing your decisions.

11.4.7 Document and Communicate Solution

It is important to document information from start to finish when addressing an ethical dilemma. This provides facts on which you can make better decisions, and is an important resource when you communicate recommendations.

The final step in solving an engineering problem is to communicate the answer to your instructor or supervisor. The same holds true for solutions to ethical problems. Your effectiveness to communicate the solution, and the reasons for it, will greatly

Figure 11.5
Family discussions of ethical dilemma options.

dictate how others will accept and support it. So, time used in documenting and communicating your recommendations is a good investment and may be the difference in your solution being accepted or rejected.

11.5 Impact of Ethics on Career Success

As indicated in the introduction to this chapter, the nontechnical world relies on engineers to provide quality products and services. When this trust is violated by unethical conduct, there are consequences. Your company and your personal career can experience very negative impacts when ethics are not an integral part of everything you do.

11.5.1 Long-Term Consequences of Ethics

The consequences of some unethical activities may not at first appear to be harmful. Examples of taking a pencil home or using the company copy machine for personal reasons appear to be insignificant. After all, some people may think the company is big, has a lot of money, and no one will notice these actions.

But the difficulty with petty unethical actions is that they can develop into something much more significant. Then the consequences can be damaging to the company, to the person, and to his or her career. The idea of stealing a pencil is really just as unethical as stealing trade secrets to share with a competitor. In both cases, the property belongs to someone else.

Just as your career started the day you walked in the door as a freshman, your ethical attitude should also start early. A good way to establish ethical behavior is to incorporate the ABET Fundamental Canons and professional codes of ethics into your personal code of ethics.

Continue your focus on ethics by basing your behavior on professional codes as you start your working career. Because most companies desire a positive ethical image for long-term stability, you need to include ethical behavior when working for a company. Ethical behavior is one of the best methods to deliver quality work and products and to increase the potential level of your personal success.

Unethical behavior in an organization eventually will be discovered. If you are the one being unethical, this can interfere with your future opportunities within the company or result in termination, as indicated in Figure 11.6. Though it might not be apparent in the beginning, unethical behavior is risky and can result in negative impacts on your career.

11.5.2 Value of a Position of Strength

When you are involved in an ethical dilemma, you may experience personal risks, and you need to be prepared for possible results. Your recommendations may be perceived as "blowing the whistle" on an unethical situation, and could result in you being terminated by the company.

So, how can you prepare for possible negative impacts when facing an ethical dilemma? The best answer to this question is for you to operate from a position of strength. This starts with a history of your loyalty to the company and your quality

Figure 11.6
**Potential results of unethical
behavior.**

work. Your position becomes stronger when your supervisor and others are aware of your contributions to the company's success.

The second way to be in a strong position is to have a well-designed career plan that helps you anticipate potential detours and be ready to take advantage of unexpected opportunities. We will discuss career plans in detail in the chapter on career management.

To cope with potential negative impacts relating to solving an ethical problem, be proactive and not reactive. Then, you will be much more in control of your future, and can use detours to your advantage.

A CONVERSATION WITH JIM PETERMAN

Jim, how did you handle the ethical dilemma introduced in the beginning of this chapter?

Answer:

"Basic decision making and objective analysis is the key to addressing this dilemma. What are the pros and cons of using the data? While the benefits initially seem worth any price, the realization that the data is effectively stolen brings many more disadvantages. There could be legal repercussions to using the data including issues related to the NDA as well as potential violation of Intellectual Property Rights. Our personal integrity and that of our company were also at great risk. Communication and interpersonal skills were also required to discuss our decision with the colleague who offered the information and to explain our rationale for not accepting the data.

In summary, the project remained on-track without any design iterations and it was released on schedule. While competitor's products did emerge that were similar, our ability to meet schedules and demonstrate integrity helped mature and improve relationships with key customers that eventually led to long-term purchasing agreements."

What nontechnical skills did you use in this situation?

Answer:

"It is important to establish personal discipline to prevent reacting with rashness to unexpected situations. All decisions, especially nontechnical ones, require careful assessment, so you must exercise the discipline to make time to consider the situation. Knowing that difficult situations will arise, you should identify experienced individuals who demonstrate wisdom who can serve as trusted advisors and mentors. Select persons who reflect integrity in all situations."

What advice would you share with students?

Answer:

"Consider nontechnical skills that are required for your job and give equal energy to developing them. Understanding ethical issues prior to facing difficult dilemmas will help your preparation. Review IEEE's Code of Ethics and your company's Rules of Business Conduct. Also identify your company's ethics contacts, who usually offer anonymity for discussing or reporting ethical issues. Identify one or more trusted resources that you can use for advice and counsel. Finally, realize that your reputation for engineering excellence and ethical integrity is your greatest personal asset. Tarnishing it through a rush to judgment when an ethical dilemma arises may have lasting negative effects on your career."

(James Peterman, Senior Product Manager, Strategic Projects—Tekelec)

11.6 Conclusion

As we have discussed in this chapter, black and white solutions need to be developed for ethical situations that first appear to be shades of gray. In such dilemmas, engineers play a major role because they can use proven codes of ethics to find the best answer. In all cases, we need to ask if it should be done in addition to can it be done.

In making ethical decisions, we need to be sensitive to how our decisions will impact others. Many options will have different, but equally important, results. Various interest groups may be impacted in important ways.

Although ethical behavior is based on personal values, you need to use professional guidelines to help you make ethical decisions. These decisions may not be easy and the results can have negative impacts on your company, your career, and your family. Because others will be affected, you should discuss your options with them before making your final decision on what you will do when faced with an ethical decision.

In the competitive business world, there is often the temptation to focus on short-term profits. While profits are important for companies to stay in business, to be professional, you should accept the responsibility of ethical behavior and the relationship of your work to the overall society in which you live. The time for you to develop ethical attitudes and skills to handle future ethical situations is now.

END OF CHAPTER REVIEW QUIZ

Select the most appropriate answer to the following statements.

1. The best way to develop ethical behavior is to
   a. Ask your trusted friends how to handle an unethical situation.
   b. Read guidelines published by professional societies.
   c. Follow personal, professional, and company ethical guidelines.
   d. Be ethical in your work assignments.

2. You can usually see early signs of unethical behavior by
   a. Gathering facts and comparing them to ethical standards.
   b. Just using common sense.
   c. Asking people why they are doing something suspicious.
   d. Guilty looks on someone's face.

3. The most important guideline for being ethical is
   a. What your parents taught you about what is right and wrong.
   b. What the company you work for establishes as ethical codes.
   c. What your supervisor and peers tell you what is right.
   d. What professional organizations publish about ethics.

4. When a possible unethical dilemma is identified the first thing to do is
   a. Tell you instructor or supervisor there is a problem.
   b. Form a team and start looking for a solution.
   c. Gather and document as many facts as possible.
   d. Go to the local newspaper and ask them to investigate the situation.

5. The most important value of using a team to find a solution to an ethical problem is
   a. So you can blame other team members if people don't like the solution.
   b. To find more constraints to possible solutions.
   c. To delay making a decision and hope the problem will go away.
   d. To develop the best solution by using the synergy of group discussions.

6. Before making a final recommendation to an ethical dilemma, the best thing is to
   a. Document everything about the situation.
   b. Test possible impacts on all stakeholders.
   c. Determine the objective of your involvement in trying to find a solution.
   d. Ask your instructor or supervisor if they like your recommendation.

7. The greatest risk in getting involved in solving an ethical dilemma is
   a. You may lose your job and have a reputation for "whistle blowing."
   b. The unethical person may find a way to get even.
   c. You might waste a lot of your personal time.
   d. Your peers may never speak to you again.

8. The biggest problem in being unethical in small things is
   a. You might not get a promotion if someone knows what you did.
   b. You could develop a pattern that leads to much more serious unethical actions.
   c. You are taking a chance that someone will find out,
   d. None of the above.

9. A major potential long-term impact of being unethical is
   a. You will feel guilty and lose self-esteem.
   b. You might damage the reputation of your employer.
   c. You can be terminated by your employer.
   d. All of the above.

10. The best way to be prepared for potential impacts when solving an ethical dilemma is
    a. To have a career plan that prepares you for changing jobs if necessary.
    b. To have a strong friendship with your supervisor.
    c. To have family support in case you are terminated.
    d. Not having any debt so you don't lose your home in case you are terminated.

EXERCISES TO DEVELOP AND ENHANCE YOUR SKILL SET

Exercise 11.1   Ethical dilemma exercise

Select one of the three ethical dilemmas listed in Chapter resource 11.3, Ethical dilemma examples, and use the **ETHICAL DILEMMA REPORT** to answer questions and provide written comments and your recommended solution to the dilemma.

Include a paragraph under **ETHICAL DILEMMA EXERCISE ASSESSMENT** to report your evaluation of this exercise relating to this ethical dilemma.

Take your report to the university writing center and request their staff to review and comment on your writing skills. Then, add a final paragraph under **UNIVERSITY WRITING CENTER CONTACT AND EXPERIENCE ASSESSMENT** to report the name of the person who reviewed your report and discuss the experience of working with the center for this assignment.

The due date for your report will be established by your instructor. Hand in your written report at the start of class and send an electronic copy to your instructor on the due date.

Ethical Dilemma Report

By _____ (Your Name) _____

Ethical Dilemma Evaluation

1. **Ethical dilemma summary**

Summarize the major points of the dilemma in one paragraph.

2. **Solution options**

Develop various options for a solution to this dilemma and discuss them using one paragraph for each option.

3. **Potential impact of solution options**

Define potential positive and negative impacts for each solution option defined in the second part of this report and discuss them using one paragraph for each option.

4. **Recommended solution**

Select the solution you recommend and use one paragraph to discuss the reasons for recommending this solution.

Ethical Dilemma Exercise Assessment

Use one paragraph to discuss your experience in completing this assignment and your impression of the value of participating in this exercise.

University Writing Center Contact and Experience Assessment

Use one or more paragraphs to report the name of the person you contacted in the University Writing Center, your experience in working with the center and how this experience will help you in future writing assignments.

Exercise 11.2 Ethical dilemma team exercise

Review the ethical dilemma in Chapter resource 11.4, SAMPLE NSPE ETHICAL CASE STUDIES, assigned by your instructor. Conduct a team discussion as assigned and prepare your individual **ETHICAL DILEMMA REPORT** to answer questions, and provide written comments relating to the team discussion and team recommended solution to the dilemma.

Include a paragraph under **ETHICAL DILEMMA EXERCISE ASSESSMENT** to report your evaluation of this exercise relating to this ethical dilemma.

Take your report to the university writing center and request their staff to review and comment on your writing skills. Then, add a final paragraph under **UNIVERSITY WRITING CENTER CONTACT AND EXPERIENCE ASSESSMENT** to report the name of the person who reviewed your report and discuss the experience of working with the center for this assignment.

The due date for your report will be established by your instructor. Hand in your written report at the start of class and send an electronic copy to your instructor on the due date.

Ethical Dilemma Report

By _____ (Your Name) _____

Ethical Dilemma Evaluation

1. Ethical dilemma summary

Summarize the major points of the dilemma in one paragraph.

2. Solution options

Develop various options for a solution to this dilemma and discuss them using one paragraph for each option.

3. Potential impact of solution options

Define potential positive and negative impacts for each solution option defined in the second part of this report and discuss them using one paragraph for each option.

4. Recommended solution

Select the solution you recommend and use one paragraph to discuss the reasons for recommending this solution.

Ethical Dilemma Exercise Assessment

Use one paragraph to discuss your experience in completing this assignment and your impression of the value of participating in this exercise.

University Writing Center Contact and Experience Assessment

Use one or more paragraphs to report the name of the person you contacted in the University Writing Center, your experience in working with the center, and how this experience will help you in future writing assignments.

Exercise 11.3   Study group ethical dilemma discussion

If your instructor does not assign Exercise 11.2, you can enhance your team building and ethical skills by selecting one of the NSPE Ethical Cases from the Chapter resource 11.4 and discussing this case with a study group.

END OF CHAPTER RESOURCES

Chapter resource 11.1   National Society of Professional Engineers Code of Ethics for Engineers

National Society of Professional Engineers Code of Ethics for Engineers

As Revised July 2007

Preamble

Engineering is an important and learned profession. As members of this profession, engineers are expected to exhibit the highest standards of honesty and integrity. Engineering has a direct and vital impact on the quality of life for all people. Accordingly, the services provided by engineers require honesty, impartiality, fairness, and equity, and must be dedicated to the protection of the public health, safety, and welfare. Engineers must perform under a standard of professional behavior that requires adherence to the highest principles of ethical conduct.

I. Fundamental Canons

Engineers, in the fulfillment of their professional duties, shall:

1. Hold paramount the safety, health, and welfare of the public.
2. Perform services only in areas of their competence.
3. Issue public statements only in an objective and truthful manner.
4. Act for each employer or client as faithful agents or trustees.
5. Avoid deceptive acts.
6. Conduct themselves honorably, responsibly, ethically, and lawfully so as to enhance the honor, reputation, and usefulness of the profession.

II. Rules of Practice

1. Engineers shall hold paramount the safety, health, and welfare of the public.
   a. If engineers' judgment is overruled under circumstances that endanger life or property, they shall notify their employer or client and such other authority as may be appropriate.
   b. Engineers shall approve only those engineering documents that are in conformity with applicable standards.
   c. Engineers shall not reveal facts, data, or information without the prior consent of the client or employer except as authorized or required by law or this Code.
   d. Engineers shall not permit the use of their name or associate in business ventures with any person or firm that they believe is engaged in fraudulent or dishonest enterprise.
   e. Engineers shall not aid or abet the unlawful practice of engineering by a person or firm.
   f. Engineers having knowledge of any alleged violation of this Code shall report thereon to appropriate professional bodies and, when relevant, also to public authorities, and cooperate with the proper authorities in furnishing such information or assistance as may be required.

2. Engineers shall perform services only in the areas of their competence.

   a. Engineers shall undertake assignments only when qualified by education or experience in the specific technical fields involved.

   b. Engineers shall not affix their signatures to any plans or documents dealing with subject matter in which they lack competence, nor to any plan or document not prepared under their direction and control.

   c. Engineers may accept assignments and assume responsibility for coordination of an entire project and sign and seal the engineering documents for the entire project, provided that each technical segment is signed and sealed only by the qualified engineers who prepared the segment.

3. Engineers shall issue public statements only in an objective and truthful manner.

   a. Engineers shall be objective and truthful in professional reports, statements, or testimony. They shall include all relevant and pertinent information in such reports, statements, or testimony, which should bear the date indicating when it was current.

   b. Engineers may express publicly technical opinions that are founded upon knowledge of the facts and competence in the subject matter.

   c. Engineers shall issue no statements, criticisms, or arguments on technical matters that are inspired or paid for by interested parties, unless they have prefaced their comments by explicitly identifying the interested parties on whose behalf they are speaking, and by revealing the existence of any interest the engineers may have in the matters.

4. Engineers shall act for each employer or client as faithful agents or trustees.

   a. Engineers shall disclose all known or potential conflicts of interest that could influence or appear to influence their judgment or the quality of their services.

   b. Engineers shall not accept compensation, financial or otherwise, from more than one party for services on the same project, or for services pertaining to the same project, unless the circumstances are fully disclosed and agreed to by all interested parties.

   c. Engineers shall not solicit or accept financial or other valuable consideration, directly or indirectly, from outside agents in connection with the work for which they are responsible.

   d. Engineers in public service as members, advisors, or employees of a governmental or quasi-governmental body or department shall not participate in decisions with respect to services solicited or provided by them or their organizations in private or public engineering practice.

   e. Engineers shall not solicit or accept a contract from a governmental body on which a principal or officer of their organization serves as a member.

5. Engineers shall avoid deceptive acts.

   a. Engineers shall not falsify their qualifications or permit misrepresentation of their or their associates' qualifications. They shall not misrepresent or exaggerate their responsibility in or for the subject matter of prior assignments. Brochures or other presentations incident to the solicitation of employment shall not misrepresent pertinent facts concerning employers, employees, associates, joint ventures, or past accomplishments.

   b. Engineers shall not offer, give, solicit, or receive, either directly or indirectly, any contribution to influence the award of a contract by public authority, or which may be reasonably construed by the public as having the effect or intent of influencing the awarding of a contract. They shall not offer any gift or other valuable consideration in order to secure work. They shall not pay a commission, percentage, or brokerage fee in order to secure work, except to a bona fide employee or bona fide established commercial or marketing agencies retained by them.

III. Professional Obligations

1. Engineers shall be guided in all their relations by the highest standards of honesty and integrity.
    a. Engineers shall acknowledge their errors and shall not distort or alter the facts.
    b. Engineers shall advise their clients or employers when they believe a project will not be successful.
    c. Engineers shall not accept outside employment to the detriment of their regular work or interest. Before accepting any outside engineering employment, they will notify their employers.
    d. Engineers shall not attempt to attract an engineer from another employer by false or misleading pretenses.
    e. Engineers shall not promote their own interest at the expense of the dignity and integrity of the profession.

2. Engineers shall at all times strive to serve the public interest.
    a. Engineers are encouraged to participate in civic affairs; career guidance for youths; and work for the advancement of the safety, health, and well-being of their community.
    b. Engineers shall not complete, sign, or seal plans and/or specifications that are not in conformity with applicable engineering standards. If the client or employer insists on such unprofessional conduct, they shall notify the proper authorities and withdraw from further service on the project.
    c. Engineers are encouraged to extend public knowledge and appreciation of engineering and its achievements.
    d. Engineers are encouraged to adhere to the principles of sustainable development in order to protect the environment for future generations.

3. Engineers shall avoid all conduct or practice that deceives the public.
    a. Engineers shall avoid the use of statements containing a material misrepresentation of fact or omitting a material fact.
    b. Consistent with the foregoing, engineers may advertise for recruitment of personnel.
    c. Consistent with the foregoing, engineers may prepare articles for the lay or technical press, but such articles shall not imply credit to the author for work performed by others.

4. Engineers shall not disclose, without consent, confidential information concerning the business affairs or technical processes of any present or former client or employer, or public body on which they serve.
    a. Engineers shall not, without the consent of all interested parties, promote or arrange for new employment or practice in connection with a specific project for which the engineer has gained particular and specialized knowledge.
    b. Engineers shall not, without the consent of all interested parties, participate in or represent an adversary interest in connection with a specific project or proceeding in which the engineer has gained particular specialized knowledge on behalf of a former client or employer.

5. Engineers shall not be influenced in their professional duties by conflicting interests.
    a. Engineers shall not accept financial or other considerations, including free engineering designs, from material or equipment suppliers for specifying their product.
    b. Engineers shall not accept commissions or allowances, directly or indirectly, from contractors or other parties dealing with clients or employers of the engineer in connection with work for which the engineer is responsible.

6. Engineers shall not attempt to obtain employment or advancement or professional engagements by untruthfully criticizing other engineers, or by other improper or questionable methods.

   a. Engineers shall not request, propose, or accept a commission on a contingent basis under circumstances in which their judgment may be compromised.

   b. Engineers in salaried positions shall accept part-time engineering work only to the extent consistent with policies of the employer and in accordance with ethical considerations.

   c. Engineers shall not, without consent, use equipment, supplies, laboratory, or office facilities of an employer to carry on outside private practice.

7. Engineers shall not attempt to injure, maliciously or falsely, directly or indirectly, the professional reputation, prospects, practice, or employment of other engineers. Engineers who believe others are guilty of unethical or illegal practice shall present such information to the proper authority for action.

   a. Engineers in private practice shall not review the work of another engineer for the same client, except with the knowledge of such engineer, or unless the connection of such engineer with the work has been terminated.

   b. Engineers in governmental, industrial, or educational employ are entitled to review and evaluate the work of other engineers when so required by their employment duties.

   c. Engineers in sales or industrial employ are entitled to make engineering comparisons of represented products with products of other suppliers.

8. Engineers shall accept personal responsibility for their professional activities, provided, however, that engineers may seek indemnification for services arising out of their practice for other than gross negligence, where the engineer's interests cannot otherwise be protected.

   a. Engineers shall conform with state registration laws in the practice of engineering.

   b. Engineers shall not use association with a nonengineer, a corporation, or partnership as a "cloak" for unethical acts.

9. Engineers shall give credit for engineering work to those to whom credit is due, and will recognize the proprietary interests of others.

   a. Engineers shall, whenever possible, name the person or persons who may be individually responsible for designs, inventions, writings, or other accomplishments.

   b. Engineers using designs supplied by a client recognize that the designs remain the property of the client and may not be duplicated by the engineer for others without express permission.

   c. Engineers, before undertaking work for others in connection with which the engineer may make improvements, plans, designs, inventions, or other records that may justify copyrights or patents, should enter into a positive agreement regarding ownership.

   d. Engineers' designs, data, records, and notes referring exclusively to an employer's work are the employer's property. The employer should indemnify the engineer for use of the information for any purpose other than the original purpose.

   e. Engineers shall continue their professional development throughout their careers and should keep current in their specialty fields by engaging in professional practice, participating in continuing education courses, reading in the technical literature, and attending professional meetings and seminars.

Chapter resource 11.2   American Society of Mechanical Engineers Code of Ethics of Engineers

ASME Code of Ethics of Engineers

As Revised April 2009

ASME requires ethical practice by each of its members and has adopted the following Code of Ethics of Engineers as referenced in the ASME Constitution, Article C2.1.1.

The Fundamental Principles

Engineers uphold and advance the integrity, honor and dignity of the engineering profession by:

I. using their knowledge and skill for the enhancement of human welfare;

II. being honest and impartial, and serving with fidelity their clients (including their employers) and the public; and

III. striving to increase the competence and prestige of the engineering profession.

The Fundamental Canons

1. Engineers shall hold paramount the safety, health and welfare of the public in the performance of their professional duties.

2. Engineers shall perform services only in the areas of their competence; they shall build their professional reputation on the merit of their services and shall not compete unfairly with others.

3. Engineers shall continue their professional development throughout their careers and shall provide opportunities for the professional and ethical development of those engineers under their supervision.

4. Engineers shall act in professional matters for each employer or client as faithful agents or trustees, and shall avoid conflicts of interest or the appearance of conflicts of interest.

5. Engineers shall respect the proprietary information and intellectual property rights of others, including charitable organizations and professional societies in the engineering field.

6. Engineers shall associate only with reputable persons or organizations.

7. Engineers shall issue public statements only in an objective and truthful manner and shall avoid any conduct which brings discredit upon the profession.

8. Engineers shall consider environmental impact and sustainable development in the performance of their professional duties.

9. Engineers shall not seek ethical sanction against another engineer unless there is good reason to do so under the relevant codes, policies and procedures governing that engineer's ethical conduct.

10. Engineers who are members of the Society shall endeavor to abide by the Constitution, By-Laws and Policies of the Society, and they shall disclose knowledge of any matter involving another member's alleged violation of this Code of Ethics or the Society's Conflicts of Interest Policy in a prompt, complete and truthful manner to the chair of the Committee on Ethical Standards and Review.

Chapter resource 11.3   Ethical dilemma examples

Deciding What Belongs to a Company and What Belongs to You

During lunch breaks from work, you and one of your coworkers developed a new spreadsheet program on the computer in the office. It is powerful, yet easier to use than similar programs available to purchase. Because this program is so unique, your friend wants to market it.

This is a very attractive thought because you have many college loans to repay and you are confident this could result in a large profit for both of you. However, you developed this program using company equipment during time in the company office. What should you do?

Moving Software Design from One Company to Another

Upon graduation as a computer engineer, you worked for a small computer firm that specializes in developing software for management tasks. You were the primary contributor in designing an innovative software system for customer services.

Now, you are working for a much larger computer firm. You realize that by making a few minor changes in the innovative software system you designed at the small computer firm you could use this to simplify and significantly enhance your new tasks at the larger firm. Because you no longer work for the firm where you developed this software, should you use a slightly different version of this in your present position to help your employer by being more productive?

Dialysis Equipment for Different Economic Situations

As a design engineer for a company that supplies dialysis equipment for worldwide use, you know resources are limited for third-world countries compared to economically developed countries. Secondary infection is a risk in dialysis and patients with kidney disease could experience long-term injury and increased risk of death if infected. You have a choice between three designs:

- The first design will have a secondary infection rate of 1 in 1,000.
- The second design will have a secondary infection rate of 1 in 1,000,000 and cost 10 times as much as the first design.
- The third design will have a secondary infection rate of 1 in 5,000,000 but will cost 100 times the amount of the first design.

Questions? Which design will you choose? Would it make a difference if the design was primarily for the economically developed countries or for the third-world countries?

Chapter resource 11.4   Sample NSPE ethical case studies

The sources of information in this Chapter Resource are ethics cases listed on the website for the National Society of Professional Engineers http://www.niee.org/cases/.

This information is for educational purposes only. It may be reprinted without further permission provided that this statement is included before or after the text of the case AND that appropriate attribution is provided to the National Society of Professional Engineers' Board of Ethical Review.

CASE STUDY 1

Employment Information Gained from ABET Visitation

Case Scenario:

Engineer A is an engineering educator who serves as an evaluator on an Accreditation Board for Engineering and Technology (ABET) visitation team reviewing an engineering program at State X University. Because Engineer B is considering leaving State X University, State X University may have an opening in the position of chair of its chemical engineering department. State X University has not advertised or announced the opening.

Engineer A visits State X University with an ABET visitation team in October. During the ABET visit and interviews with the dean, department chairs, and engineering faculty, it becomes apparent to Engineer A that Engineer B might depart and a chemical engineering chair position at State X University might open.

Engineer A completes her evaluation and has no further influence on the report or the final action by ABET. In June, she formally learns of the chair position opening, applies for the position, is selected by a search committee, and accepts the appointment as chair of the State X University chemical engineering department.

Question:

Was it ethical for Engineer A to apply for the position of chair at State X University?

CASE STUDY 2

Use of Alleged Hazardous Material in a Processing Facility

Case Scenario:

Engineer A is a graduate engineer in a manufacturing facility that uses toxic chemicals in its processing operations. His job has nothing to do with the use and control of these materials.

A chemical called "MegaX" is used at the site. Recent stories in the news have reported alleged immediate and long-term human genetic hazards from inhalation of or other contact with MegaX. The news items are based on findings from laboratory experiments, which were done on mice, by a graduate student at a well-respected university's physiology department. Other scientists have neither confirmed nor refuted the experimental findings. Federal and local governments have not made official pronouncements on the subject.

Several colleagues outside of the company have approached Engineer A on the subject and ask Engineer A to "do something" to eliminate the use of MegaX at the processing facility.

Engineer A mentions this concern to her manager who tells Engineer A, "Don't worry, we have an Industrial Safety Specialist who handles that."

Two months elapse and MegaX is still used in the factory. The controversy in the press continues, but since there is no further scientific evidence pro or con in the matter, the issues remain unresolved. The use of the chemical in the processing facility has increased and now more workers are exposed daily to the substance than was the case two months ago.

Question:

Does Engineer A have an obligation to take further action under the facts and circumstances?

CASE STUDY 3

Offer of Employment by Vendor

Case Scenario:

Upon graduation from an ABET/EAC-accredited civil engineering program, Engineer A is employed by U&I Construction Co., which is owned and operated by Engineer B and Engineer C, both licensed professional engineers. Engineer A is soon delegated the responsibility of preparing bills of materials for construction designs that include appropriate allowance for waste and negotiations of material procurement with suppliers.

Engineer A negotiates quantity, schedule, specifications, and price, and then submits a recommendation to his highly experienced, nondegreed supervisor to arrange for appropriate company approval authority for the procurement contract if the financial commitment to a supplier on a project exceeds $250. After two years, Engineer A expresses concern to his supervisor that his job seems repetitive and lacks the variety of experiences and challenges that draw on the breadth of his education.

Engineer A is informed that he is providing an essential service to the company with exceptional proficiency, for which he seems very well paid, and that he will be considered for opportunities should they become available—if a replacement to cover his current activities can be found. Engineer A's financial authority is increased to $500 for any one supplier of the project.

Another year passes and Engineer A is still performing the same level of assignments. He has developed a highly respected reputation for knowledge, fairness, and integrity among the suppliers of U&I Construction Co. Engineer D, an employee of ACE Supplies, a frequent supplier to U&I, has developed a working relationship with Engineer A. When ACE has an opening for a civil engineer, Engineer D tells Engineer A about it. Engineer A interviews for the position and, after an evaluation period, Engineer A receives an offer of employment with ACE.

The offer letter states that ACE is "looking forward to having Engineer A on its team commencing on a mutually agreed upon date . . . that Engineer A is not an employee of ACE until Engineer A physically reports to work at ACE's facilities, executes patent and proprietary information agreements at that time, and that the employer's physician confirms that Engineer A has no preexisting health condition that would prevent Engineer A from performing the requirements of the position."

In a subsequent discussion with Engineer A, Engineer D mentions that the position was one that the ACE Vice President of Engineering has the prerogative of filling, but on occasion the ACE CEO has eliminated the position opening even with outstanding offers pending until business conditions improved or when a major customer had expressed displeasure with the hiring of one of its employees.

Engineer A submits his resignation with a customary two-week notice to U&I. Engineer A's supervisor, Engineer E, is disturbed by the resignation and expresses a desire that Engineer A stay with U&I, saying that if Engineer E could prevent his leaving he would. Engineer A insists that his decision is firm. Engineer A is not asked and does not believe it is in his interests to mention that he will be employed by ACE.

Engineer E requests that Engineer A should bring all of his work assignments to a point of completion that will facilitate his making an orderly transfer to other U&I employees and to conclude as many assignments as possible before departing. For the next two weeks before leaving U&I, Engineer A continues to negotiate and prepare recommendations on bids including those that had been submitted by ACE.

Questions:

1. Was it ethical for Engineer A not to volunteer to U&I the information that he would be employed by ACE within two weeks?
2. Was it ethical for Engineer D to entice Engineer A to consider employment with ACE?
3. Was it ethical for Engineer A to interview with a supplier of U&I without first advising U&I of his intent?
4. Was it ethical for the ACE Vice President of Engineering to offer employment to Engineer A without first divulging the risk that the offer might be withdrawn by the ACE CEO?
5. Would it have been ethical for U&I to have interfered in Engineer A's employment change had U&I become aware of the identity of the future employer and ACE's susceptibility to pressure from U&I?

CASE STUDY 4

Public Welfare—Bridge Structure

Case Scenario:

Engineer A, who works for a local government, learned about a critical situation involving a bridge 280 feet long, 30 feet above a stream. This bridge was a concrete deck on wood piles built in the 1950s by the state, and was part of the secondary roadway system given to counties.

In June 2000, Engineer A received a telephone call from the bridge inspector stating this bridge needed to be closed due to the large number of rotten piling. Engineer A had barricades and signs erected within the hour on a Friday afternoon. Residents in the area were required to take a 10-mile detour.

A detailed inspection report prepared, signed, and sealed by a consulting engineering firm, indicated seven pilings required replacement. Within three weeks, Engineer A obtained authorization for the bridge to be replaced. Several state and federal transportation departments needed to complete their reviews and tasks before the funds could be used.

A citizens' rally was held and a petition with approximately 200 signatures asking that the bridge be reopened to limited traffic was presented to the County Commission. Engineer A explained the extent of the damages and the efforts under way to replace the bridge. The County Commission decided not to reopen the bridge.

Preliminary site investigation studies were begun. Environmental, geological, right-of-way, and other studies were also performed. A decision was made to use a design build contract to avoid a lengthy analysis for the pile design.

A nonengineer public works director decided to have a retired bridge inspector, who was not an engineer, examine the bridge, and a decision was made to install two crutch piles under the bridge and to open the bridge with a 5-ton limit. No follow-up inspection was undertaken.

Engineer A observes that traffic is flowing and the movement of the bridge is frightening. Log trucks and tankers cross it on a regular basis. School buses go around it.

Question:

What is Engineer A's ethical obligation under these circumstances?

CASE STUDY 5

Misrepresentation of Education

Case Scenario:

Engineer A is a professional engineer who occasionally provides forensic engineering services as part of the litigation process. As part of a written submission during a legal proceeding, Engineer A indicates that he possesses a degree in electrical engineering and a doctoral degree in electrical engineering. In fact, Engineer A's baccalaureate degree was in engineering technology and his doctoral degree was an honorary degree bestowed upon him by an engineering school.

Engineer B, who knows Engineer A, learns of these misrepresentations in discussions with his colleague, Engineer C, who is serving as an expert witness for the side opposing Engineer A's client. Engineer C is unaware Engineer A is misrepresenting his educational credentials.

Question:

What is Engineer B's ethical obligation under the facts and circumstances of this case?

CASE STUDY 6

Former Consulting Engineer for Utility as Expert Witness for Utility Consumer Complaint Case

Case Scenario:

State Electric Light Company Inc. (SELCI) is a privately owned electric utility company that is part of a group of utility distribution companies. For several years, SELCI's parent company has hired an electrical engineer as a consultant to do several studies for SELCI. This consultant, Engineer B, has recently been asked to testify for Consumer X, a party that has filed a complaint to the State Public Utilities Commission (SPUC) against SELCI.

Question:

Is it ethical for Engineer B to testify for a party that has filed a complaint with the State Public Utilities Commission against SELCI?

CASE STUDY 7

Public Welfare—Duty of Government Engineer

Case Scenario:

Engineer A, an environmental engineer employed by the state environmental protection division, is ordered to draw up a construction permit for a power plant at a manufacturing facility. He is told by a superior to move expeditiously on the permit and "avoid any hang-ups" with respect to technical issues. Engineer A believes the plans as drafted are inadequate to meet the regulation requirements. This is because outside scrubbers to reduce sulfur dioxide emissions are necessary and without them the issuance of the permit would violate certain air pollution standards as mandated under the 1990 Clean Air Act.

His superior believes that plans that involve limestone mixed with coal in a fluidized boiler process would remove 90% of the dioxide and will meet the regulatory requirements. Engineer A contacts the state engineering registration board and is informed, based on the limited information provided to the board, that suspension or revocation of his engineering license was a possibility if he prepared a permit that violated environmental regulations.

Engineer A refused to issue the permit and submitted his findings to his superior. The department authorized the issuance of the permit. The case had received widespread publicity in the news media and is currently being investigated by state authorities.

Questions:

1. Would it have been ethical for Engineer A to withdraw from further work in this case?
2. Would it have been ethical for Engineer A to issue the permit?
3. Was it ethical for Engineer A to refuse to issue the permit?

CASE STUDY 8

Engineer's Duty to Report Data Relating to Research

Case Scenario:

Engineer A is performing graduate research at a major university. As part of the requirement for Engineer A to complete his graduate research and obtain his advanced degree, he is required to develop a research report.

In line with developing the report, Engineer A compiles data pertaining to the subject of his report. The vast majority of the data strongly supports Engineer A's conclusion as well as prior conclusions developed by others. However, a few aspects of the data are at variance and not fully consistent with the conclusions contained in Engineer A's report.

Convinced of the soundness of his report and concerned that inclusion of the ambiguous data will detract from and distort the essential thrust of the report, Engineer A decides to omit references to the ambiguous data in the report.

Question:

Was it unethical for Engineer A to fail to include reference to the ambiguous data in his report?

CASE STUDY 9

Engineer Misstating Professional Achievements on Resume

Case Scenario:

Engineer A is seeking employment with Employer Y. As an employee for Employer X, Engineer A was a staff engineer along with five other staff engineers of equal rank. This team of six was responsible for the design of certain products. While working for Employer X, Engineer A worked with five other engineers in his team and they were credited with the design of a series of patented products.

Engineer A submits his resume to Employer Y and on it implies that he personally was responsible for the design of products that were actually designed through a joint effort of the members of the team.

Question:

Was it ethical for Engineer A to imply on his resume that he was personally responsible for the design of the products that were actually designed through the joint efforts of the members of the design team?

CASE STUDY 10

Duty to Disclose Disciplinary Complaint to Client

Case Scenario:

Engineer A is retained by Client B to perform design services and provide a critical path method (CPM) schedule for a manufacturing facility. Engineer A prepares the plans and specifications and the CPM schedule.

During the rendering of services to Client B on this project, the state board of professional engineers contacts Engineer A regarding an ethics complaint filed against him by Client C relating to services provided on a project similar to the services being performed for Client B. Client C alleges that Engineer A lacked the competence to perform the services in question.

Engineer A does not believe it is necessary to notify Client B of the pending complaint. Later, through another party, Client B learns of the ethics complaint filed against Engineer A and tells Engineer A that he is upset by the allegations and that Engineer A should have brought the matter to Client B's attention.

Question:

Was it unethical for Engineer A to not report to Client B the ethics complaint filed against him by Client C?

CASE STUDY 11

Records Relating to Services to Former Client

Case Scenario:

Several years ago Engineer A, a mechanical engineer, consulted for Company A, a pressure vessel manufacturer, on a specific pressure vessel problem relating to the design of a boiler system. Engineer A's work focused on specific design and manufacturing defects that caused deterioration of the boiler system. Engineer A completed his work and was paid for his services.

Now, Engineer A was retained by Attorney X in a case involving a fatal explosion of a recently designed and manufactured pressure vessel at a facility previously owned by Engineer A's former client, Company A. The facility was sold to Company B seven years before the explosion.

The litigation does not involve any of the issues related to the services Engineer A provided to Company A ten years earlier. The defendant's attorney discovered through Engineer A's deposition and statements relating to his professional experience that Engineer A had worked for Company A on a pressure vessel problem.

Engineer A explains to the defendant's attorney that he is not relying on any of his prior work for Company A in this case. Nevertheless, the defendant's attorney requests that Engineer A provide his files from the previous work performed for Company A.

Question:

Would it be ethical for Engineer A to voluntarily release the files to defense counsel?

CASE STUDY 12

Specifying Equipment of Company Owned by Engineer

Case Scenario:

Engineer A is asked by a firm to prepare specifications for an air compression system. Engineer A made the firm aware that she is the president (and major shareholder) of a company that manufactures and sells air compression systems and that she has no problem with preparing a set of generic specifications. Engineer A also provides the firm with four other manufacturers that prepare air compression systems for bidding purposes, and Engineer A did not include her company as one of the four specified manufacturers.

The firm now wants to meet with Engineer A and a salesman from her company. Engineer A indicated to the firm that it might be a conflict of interest.

Question:

Would it be a conflict of interest for Engineer A to prepare a set of specifications for an air compression system and then have her company manufacture the air compression system under the facts?

CASE STUDY 13

Failure to Disclose Other Business Interest

Case Scenario:

Engineer A, a mining engineer, is retained by a company that owns land on which coal mines are located. Engineer A provides engineering services and surveys to determine the location of coal veins in the mine, assigns coal contractors to the locations in the mine, and performs other engineering services as required.

Engineer A also owns a laboratory that evaluates the quality of coal mined by coal contractors that contract with the coal mine owner. The quality and cost of mining the coal may vary.

Although Engineer A mentioned that he owns a laboratory, Engineer A never informs the coal mine owner about the size and the extent of his laboratory, which is substantial and employs several other engineers and technicians, nor about his clients who are mining the owner's coal.

Question:

Was it ethical for Engineer A to not fully disclose the size and extent of his laboratory and his clients to the coal mine owner?

CASE STUDY 14

Software Design Testing

Case Scenario:

Engineer A is employed by a software company and is involved in designing specialized software for the operations of facilities affecting the public health and safety. The design of this software includes extensive testing by Engineer A. Although tests demonstrate the software is safe to use under existing standards, Engineer A is aware of new draft standards that are about to be released by a standard setting organization—standards that the newly designed software may not meet.

Testing is extremely costly and the company's clients are eager to move forward. The software company wants to satisfy its clients, protect the software company's finances, and protect existing jobs; but the software company management wants to be sure that the software is safe to use.

A series of tests proposed by Engineer A should determine if the use of the software is safe. The tests are costly, will delay the software at least six months, will put the company at a competitive disadvantage, and cost them a significant amount of money. During the testing time, the state public service commission utility rates will rise significantly. The company requests Engineer A's recommendation concerning the need for additional software testing.

Question:

Under the code of ethics, does Engineer A have a professional obligation to inform his company of the reasons for needed additional testing and his recommendations that it be undertaken?

CHAPTER

SECTION III: CAREER SKILLS

13

Career Management Skills

Career Management—
An Incredible Personal Journey

"If you don't know where you are going, any road will take you there. However, you may not like the results. Floating through life without planning is the same as taking a long road trip without a map or sailing the seas without a compass."

—Jim Watson, PE, President, Watson Associates

CAREER MANAGEMENT SCENARIO

"Because your world is dynamic, your first career path might include some detours. If you are dissatisfied with your first job, should you consider making a career change? If so, what can you do to take advantage of new and different opportunities? How can you prepare for a major change in your work and life? How can you be proactive and take control of your future?"

(Kathryn Paine, PE, Mechanical Engineer and Director of Engineering & Inside Sales at Mechanical Products SW, Inc.)

These are excellent questions posed by Kathryn Paine. We will see how she successfully handled career changes in our discussion with her at the end of this chapter. To get us started, let's think about your career and how you can use career management to guide you through the many opportunities and challenges of your engineering experiences.

13.1 Introduction

By starting now to manage your career, you can prepare for future challenges and opportunities and enjoy an incredible journey. This chapter provides practical tools for you to develop and use a dynamic career management plan.

The engineering profession is a culture.

LEARNING OBJECTIVES

By using the information and exercises in this chapter you will be able to

- Understand why personal career management is so important to your success.

- Identify what is important in developing a career plan.

- Develop a professional and effective career plan.

- See why writing and implementing action plans are critical to success.

- Document and evaluate results for future planning.

- Control your career through career management.

Before discussing the details of career planning, let's think about how it relates to our profession. The engineering profession is actually a culture. It includes formal education, lifelong learning, experience, and a focus on helping people by solving problems. These are best accomplished by applying technology creatively, efficiently, and ethically to improve the quality of life.

For many years, industry and government have been seeking engineers who are technically competent. They also want engineers who have nontechnical skills and can work successfully with various levels of management while simultaneously serving as leaders and members of project teams. So, you need more than just technical knowledge and skills.

> *"While maintaining technical skills is of paramount importance—employability also depends on 'soft' skills and competencies. Time management, verbal and listening skills, written skills, and career management are of vital importance."*
>
> **(Comments from the IEEE Industry 2000 Conference)**

The challenge is to include the development of both technical and nontechnical skills in your career plan to secure better job opportunities. When you have a balance of these skills, you are also better prepared to take advantage of opportunities to advance in your career.

There is another reason to include nontechnical skills in your career plan. Although you may be familiar with technology, those in the nontechnical world do not share your knowledge or experience. Technology may be somewhat confusing to others including co-workers in nonengineering departments and the general public. When people do not understand what you do and why it is important, they may create negative impacts on your career.

To make sure others understand your contributions as an engineer, you need to write and speak clearly, and to use other nontechnical skills to make a positive impression on others. By using the career management concepts in this chapter, which include a balance of developing technical and nontechnical skills, you will be prepared to work in a nontechnical as well as a technical world.

13.2 Your Engineering Career

Your interest in engineering probably started long before you enrolled in engineering classes. You may have taken things apart to see what makes them "tick," and then put them back together just for the joy of accomplishment. You probably did well in mathematics and science in high school. And, based on your interests, you are now on your way to an engineering career.

Your career starts the moment you enter the door as a freshman.

You might think your career will start when you graduate from your engineering program. But your engineering career actually began when you started your freshman year in an engineering college or even before. Your early career decisions include selecting a specific type of engineering and then choosing elective courses that will complement your area of interest. You can maximize your educational experience by starting now to plan your career.

"There is no such thing as engineering job security. Jobs are controlled by others and that typically removes most forms of security. However, engineers can develop career security. So, to be successful, you need to plan and control your career."

**(Larry Dwon, PE, Electrical Engineer, retired,
American Electric Power Corporation)**

This quote, from a very knowledgeable and experienced engineer, Larry Dwon, is based on the more than sixty successful years of his engineering practice, and it is an important message to every engineer today.

When you graduate and start your working career, you will soon realize that all engineering positions include some risk. Technology or economic conditions can rapidly change, resulting in the elimination of jobs. If you work for others, they control your future. Even if you own your own company, your clients and your employees have a major impact on what you can do.

And, this raises an interesting question—when other people impact your work, how can you control your future? The answer is to be proactive and plan your career by using proven career management principles. This chapter focuses on showing you how to do this and giving you opportunities to put these principles to work in your life.

13.3 Your Career Plan

To establish a successful career plan, each part of the planning process should relate to the overall objectives of your personal life. Your plan starts by identifying your personal and professional visions. Then, you need to develop a strategy of goals and skill needs that relate to your visions.

The details of how you plan to accomplish your strategy are identified in an action plan. Your action plan is a valuable road map that will help you achieve goals and improve your skills. The important final steps are to implement your action plan, document and evaluate results, compare results to your visions, and revise your career plan when appropriate. An overview of the career plan process is shown in Figure 13.1.

At first glance, the career plan process in Figure 13.1 might appear to involve a lot of work and time investment. Career planning does take some time and effort, but it is not really that difficult and it is easy to apply this plan to your life. The key, which we discuss in this chapter, is to "engineer" your plan by using a logical approach and proven steps.

13.3.1 Personal Vision

Before writing a career plan, you should pause and ask yourself some very personal questions. What is important to you, personally? If you could design a perfect life, what would it include? How would it involve other people? What would create satisfaction and happiness for you?

More specifically, what type of lifestyle do you want? Is it to accomplish many things and have personal growth? Is your religious faith the foundation for your life? Is good health important? Would you like to have many friends, to enjoy a variety of recreational activities, and to have lots of fun?

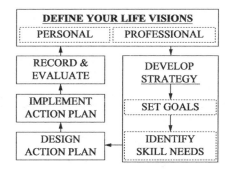

Figure 13.1
Career plan process.

Where would you like to physically live? If you could select any part of the world, what would be important to consider in that selection?

How important is your family? Are they less important than your career, equal to your career, more important than your career, or the most important part of your life?

How would you like to be involved in your local and professional communities? Do you want to avoid them, be informed, be somewhat involved, or be a leader? When you leave this world, how would you like to be remembered?

Your personal vision is what you want in life.

Your answers to these questions are the foundation for your personal vision, and to a great extent, they determine how you will invest time. You cannot add hours in a day, but you can use time more efficiently if you develop and use a time management system. You can manage your career better when you manage time by using proven principles of time management.

Many people think about what they want in life, but most people do not express what they want in a written vision statement. So, the first and very important step in preparing a career plan is for you to write a personal vision and keep it in focus as you develop the rest of the plan.

My personal vision is to develop a secure life for me and my future family, and have fun doing it. Although I want a job with a reasonable income, my family is really the most important part of my life. I want to participate in my community by being involved in my local schools.

Figure 13.2
Student personal vision example.

Notice how the personal vision example in Figure 13.2 includes the relationship of the person to his or her family and community. Vision statements can be short or long, but should identify what is really important. Examples of personal vision statements are shown in Chapter resource 13.2 and Chapter resource 13.3.

"Far better it is to dare mighty things, to win glorious triumphs even though check-ered by failure, than to rank with those poor spirits who neither enjoy nor suffer much because they live in the gray twilight that knows neither victory nor defeat."
(Theodore Roosevelt, 26th President of the United States of America)

Start by dreaming BIG even though you may have limitations and restrictions to the accomplishment of your dreams. For example, Jim Watson is 5'8" tall. If his "unrestricted" vision includes playing for a National Basketball Association team, his short height may prevent him from achieving that part of his vision. Can you picture him in a "dunk" contest?

As indicated by the quotation from Theodore Roosevelt, it is better to start with high expectations and fall a little short, than to never reach for the stars and to settle for much less. So, first think about what is important without limitations. Then, be realistic and consider possible restrictions as you complete your plan.

13.3.2 Professional Vision

Your professional vision is what you want to achieve.

Develop a professional vision by considering what you want as it relates to your work. What is your major professional focus? Is it to be a generalist or a specialist? Do you want to know a little about many areas of technology or as much as possible about only one or two areas?

Other questions to consider relate to your type of work. For example, are you interested in basic research for future product development? Or would you rather develop initial designs by computer modeling? Would you like to use your creativity and apply general concepts to specific products? Or, do you want to test new products and designs? Would you like to be involved in the production of products or in product sales?

In addition to traditional engineering jobs, you can consider other engineering-related career opportunities including management, consulting, entrepreneurship, and academia. Engineers often select these career opportunities after gaining experience in earlier job assignments.

The second area of your professional vision relates to your working environment. Where do you want to locate geographically? Do you want to work for a large or small corporation or do you want to own your own company? Are you interested in a job in government or private sector?

Other considerations relate to what you want to achieve. Is it respect, financial security, authority, expertise, or personal satisfaction of a job well done? Answers to these and the other questions relating to your professional vision provide direction to the development of your career plan.

Figure 13.3 is an example of one professional vision statement. Additional examples are included in Chapter resource 13.3.

My civil engineering focus is water resources. I want to develop efficient methods to use water for the production of electricity, for quenching the thirst of citizens in third-world countries, and for adding nutrients for agriculture. I desire to work in the field as well as in an office. My greatest accomplishment would be to use engineering skills to help others.

Figure 13.3
Student professional vision example.

Although you may find it difficult to define work activities early in your educational experience, you can investigate options now to form your professional vision. Remember, a career plan should be dynamic, so you can always make changes to reflect new ideas and opportunities.

When you have a clear vision, you are more likely to achieve higher levels of success, both personally and professionally. Let's consider the following example and see how it demonstrates why reaching a high level of success is beneficial for you.

Many electric utility companies have made substantial investments to increase the voltage (potential) of their transmission grid from 138 kV to 765 kV or higher. This is done because the amount of electric power that can be sent over a transmission line is directly proportional to the voltage. So, utilities use a higher transmission voltage to deliver more product (energy) at a lower cost and greater value for customers.

This example of increasing transmission voltage or potential can be easily related to your career. There are many benefits in achieving your highest potential accomplishments. When you deliver more results in your career, it is good for you, your family, the company for which you work or own, and the clients who use your product or service.

"My professional vision is to be constantly tackling challenging problems. I enjoy learning, and I want to be able to apply my knowledge to solve new and interesting real-world problems. I prefer dealing at the 'big-picture' level, because there's more scope for trying out various solutions. My career goals are to become technically proficient within my field of engineering, and leverage my business and people skills to be an effective problem trouble-shooter."

(Akshay Kashyap, Electrical Engineer, and Financial Technology Associate at Citadel Investment Group)

13.3.3 Strategy

Using your personal and professional vision statements as a foundation, your next step in your career plan is to develop a strategy to achieve results. As shown in Figure 13.1, this includes setting goals and identifying skill needs. Let's address the first part by focusing on the process and value of setting goals that relate directly to your vision.

Goals are targets of desired achievements.

Set Goals Goals should be specific, measurable, achievable, and relate directly to your visions. Examples in Figure 13.4 demonstrate the difference between weak and strong goal statements. Weak goals are typically too general to be measured.

```
┌─────────────────────────────────────────────────────────────┐
│                        SETTING GOALS                          │
│                                                               │
│        WEAK EXAMPLES                  STRONG EXAMPLES          │
│                                                               │
│  Get an "A" in physics          Learn basic principles of physics │
│                                                               │
│  Be rich                        Learn how to invest for profit │
│                                                               │
│  Have extra free time           Develop a time management system │
│                                                               │
│  Be healthy                     Exercise and control diet     │
│                                                               │
│  Have a coop job                Use resources to find a coop job │
│                                                               │
│  Retire when I am 55 years old  Make a career plan to retire early │
└─────────────────────────────────────────────────────────────┘
```

Figure 13.4
Weak and strong examples of goals.

As you define goals, review your visions and write goals that will help you achieve what you want. Be realistic, but don't be afraid to stretch a little. It is better to plan for high achievement and reach most of the way than to establish activities that are not challenging.

Three types of goals should be considered and established—long term, midterm, and short term.

Long term goals

■ Should focus on the big picture
■ Are based on what you want many years in the future
■ Should relate to your vision
■ May be more general than mid or short term goals

Midterm goals

■ Should focus on middle years of your career
■ Are easier to establish because you do not need to look as far into the future
■ Can be more structured than long term goals
■ Should support long term goals and visions

Short term goals

■ Should focus on your present situation
■ Are much easier to develop
■ Can be easier to achieve because the present is more stable and defined
■ Should support midterm and long term goals and visions

To expand our goal discussion, let's use Figure 13.5 to develop typical goals to support the personal vision in our example.

RELATIONSHIP OF GOALS TO PERSONAL VISION

Personal vision established in Figure 13.2:

My personal vision is to develop a secure life for me and my future family, and have fun doing it. Although I want a job with a reasonable income, my family is really the most important part of my life. I want to participate in my community by being involved in my local schools.

Related goal examples:

Long term:
◆ Establish a 401k account, and invest in long term securities
◆ Plan family trips for pleasure and to see new areas of the world
◆ Take an active role in the Parent-Teachers Association and schedule field trips for high school students to observe engineers at work

Midterm:
◆ Establish a savings plan for college expenses for my children
◆ Manage my time to reduce stress and to plan family activities
◆ Develop a plan and work with math and science teachers

Short term:
◆ Use a personal budget to balance financial needs
◆ Develop an effective time management system
◆ Establish a mentor program to help engineering students improve math and physics skills

---

Figure 13.5
Goals related to personal vision.

As you review the examples of goals in Figure 13.5, notice that they are identified as long term, midterm, and short term. Each goal has a direct connection to the personal vision.

A similar approach, shown in Figure 13.6, can be applied to the professional vision.

As in the case of goals for the personal vision, the goals in Figure 13.6 are listed as long term, midterm, and short term. Each goal has a direct connection to the professional vision. Additional examples of goals are included in Chapter resource 13.3.

Identify Skill Needs   The next step is to review your present skills and identify skills that you need to develop or improve. Start this process early in your educational experience because you have many choices during these years. Review your skills and identify what is needed to achieve your goals.

Skill needs will help you define what to improve to reach your goals.

RELATIONSHIP OF GOALS TO PROFESSIONAL VISION

Professional vision established in Figure 13.3:

My civil engineering focus is water nsounes. I want to develop efficient methods to use water for the production of electricity, for quenching the thirst of citizens in third-world countries, and for adding nutrients for agriculture. I desire to work in the field as well as in an office. My greatest accomplishment would be to use engineering skills to help others.

Related goal examples:

Long term:
- Attend local and international conferences on water resources
- Coordinate major projects that include design and implementation
- Develop leadership skills in ASCE international activities

Midterm:
- Find co-op positions with both indoor and outdoor assignments
- Obtain a master's degree in civil engineering
- Pass PE exam and practice as professional engineer

Short term:
- Select elective courses that nlate to water nsoUI'ce utilization
- Pass FE exam and prepare to take PE exam
- JoinASCE and be an active member

Figure 13.6
Goals related to professional vision.

Identifying skill needs is an integral part of planning and preparing for potential opportunities. To achieve your vision requires more than just being lucky. People who appear lucky usually are proactive and not reactive, as indicated by Thomas Jefferson. They plan and prepare for future opportunities by developing appropriate skills.

As we discussed earlier, skill needs are both technical and nontechnical. When establishing your career plan, identify skills in both areas. During the undergraduate education process, you have options for selecting your major area of study and elective courses. Select courses that help you develop the technical skills that you identified in your career plan.

> *"I'm a great believer in luck, and I find the harder I work the more I have of it."*
>
> **(Thomas Jefferson, 3rd President of the United States of America)**

Technical Skill Needs

To achieve the maximum benefit from each course, start by asking, what technical skills can I improve by actively participating in this class? How will this support my strategy and visions? What extra things can I do to maximize the value I receive from this course?

Prepare for class by reading the textbook and writing notes. Use notes to determine what information you need from class so you can ask appropriate questions. This approach will increase your technical knowledge and support your strategy of skill development. Asking questions in class is also a good way to build self-confidence and to learn how to communicate in a group environment.

Consider other technical skills that are more general but still relate directly to your goals. For example, you can use software for a time management system or Internet tools for financial investments. If you are involved in a co-op program or other work-related activities, look for opportunities to develop technical skills that help you be more productive and useful to your employer.

If one of your midterm goals is to become a registered, professional engineer, which we highly recommend, then you should identify specific skills to help you prepare for the Fundamentals of Engineering (FE) exam and PE exam. The opportunities to develop many of these skills will appear well before the date of the exams.

To achieve greater career success, we also recommend that you include earning a master's degree in engineering in your midterm goals. Then, use your present opportunities in laboratory classes to improve technical and nontechnical skills to prepare for future research projects associated with graduate degrees.

Nontechnical Skill Needs

This introduces the second type of skill needs—nontechnical. You will find many opportunities to improve nontechnical skills in your undergraduate education experience. You can improve your communication skills when you ask questions in classes and participate in study groups. You can improve your interpersonal skills by learning to effectively interact with people who are from diverse backgrounds and who may have different ideas.

> "As engineers, one of the motivations to which our human mechanism responds to is to correctly communicate technical information—no matter what the culture may be. Today, one of the most basic of human needs—verbal communication— remains vital to success, and the successful engineer should have a working knowledge of various languages, and an understanding of the world's cultures. A thirty-eight year career with a world leading hot and cold forging machinery manufacturer taught me that an engineer's success depends upon a basic knowledge of the customers' language and culture."
>
> **(Gary Stroup, Mechanical Engineer)**

The classroom is an excellent place to apply ethics, another important nontechnical skill. You are being ethical by studying for exams and not using copies of previous exams (unless this is suggested by the instructor as a study aid). If you use information prepared by others, give proper credit. Cheating is inappropriate and very unprofessional.

Professional organizations offer another great way for you to develop nontechnical skills. These inexpensive "laboratories" offer outstanding opportunities to practice many nontechnical skills in a comfortable environment. When you volunteer to participate in activities, organizations will welcome your involvement.

In addition to listing membership in organizations on your resume, become an active member. This will give you many opportunities to improve important skills such as written and oral communications, teamwork, project management, time management, and ethics. Then, expand your resume with a list of activities to show how you were involved in professional organizations. This often is one of the most important discussion items in job interviews.

Review your present nontechnical skills. Are you comfortable working with other people? Can you write clearly and concisely? Are you confident to stand before an audience and give a presentation? Have you developed effective leadership skills, or do you have experience in project management? Are you a good team member? If the answer to any of these questions is no, then you can add these skill needs to your career plan.

Although we tend to focus on technical skill needs, in reality, nontechnical skills have a greater impact on career success. So, identify important nontechnical skills that you need and target them for short term, midterm, and long term enhancement.

Typical skill needs for goals in the personal vision example are shown in Figure 13.7. Additional skill needs, listed in Figure 13.8, will help reach professional vision goals.

The examples in Figures 13.7 and 13.8 show how to connect skill needs with goals that relate to your personal and professional visions. Additional examples of skill needs are shown in Chapter resource 13.3. Keep these examples in mind as you define your skill needs and make sure they have a direct connection to your goals and visions.

13.3.4 Action Plan

So far we have discussed how you can define what you want in life, what you would like to achieve, and how you set goals and identify skill needs. This is a good start, but it is not a complete plan. As Figure 13.1 indicates, there is more to be done, and the next step is to design an action plan to make your strategy become reality.

> Your action plan brings everything together and includes what, when, and how you plan to achieve results.

An action plan provides details of what, when, and how you control your career. It includes specific activities that relate directly to your strategy. Without an effective action plan, you may not achieve your visions. To be effective, design your action plan to be a road map for the journey you selected when you developed your vision statements.

Start with short term goals and skills that can be developed in the next few weeks and months. Outline activities and define details of what to do, and put target dates

SKILL NEEDS FOR ESTABLISHED GOALS

<u>Goals established in Figure 13.5 relating to personal vision:</u>

Long term goals:
- Establish a 401k account, and invest in long-term securities.
- Plan family trips for pleasure and to see new areas of the world
- Take an active role in the Parent-Teachers Association and schedule field trips for high school students to observe engineers at work

Midterm goals:
- Establish a savings plan for college expenses for my children
- Manage my time to reduce stress and to plan family activities
- Develop a plan and work with math and science teachers

Short term goals:
- Establish a personal budget
- Develop an effective time management system
- Establish a mentor program to help engineering students improve math and physics skills

<u>Skill needs examples:</u>

Technical skills
- Gain experience using Internet tools for investments
- Learn how to use an electronic time management system
- Expand math and physics knowledge

Nontechnical skills
- Learn how to balance expenses and savings
- Learn how to become more organized
- Learn how to work as part of a team

Figure 13.7
Skill needs for personal vision goals.

on each activity. Your action plans should be achievable and measurable and should include a process to record results.

Break up long term activities into smaller steps that you can complete in a reasonable amount of time. Then, you can pat yourself on the back after each successful activity. This may sound insignificant, but it helps you maintain interest in your career management process.

Good-poor examples of action plan items

Good: Schedule 8 PM–9 PM on Monday to read Chapter 3 of the textbook and solve homework problems in Sections 3, 4, and 5 for the statics class.

Poor: Study for the statics class. (Should be more specific and measurable)

Good: Join a study group and spend at least 1 hour three times per week with the group to solve homework problems in calculus.

Poor: Get a good grade in calculus class. (What is a "good" grade and what will you do to achieve it?)

SKILL NEEDS FOR ESTABLISHED GOALS

Goals established in Figure 13.6 relating to professional vision:

Long term goals:
◆ Attend local and international conferences on water resources
◆ Coordinate major projects that include design and implementation
◆ Develop leadership skills in international ASCE volunteer activities

Midterm goals:
◆ Find co-op positions with both indoor and outdoor assignments
◆ Obtain a master's degree in civil engineering
◆ Pass PE exam and practice as professional engineer

Short term goals:
◆ Select elective courses that relate to water resource utilization
◆ Pass FE exam and prepare to take PE exam
◆ Join ASCE and be an active member

Skill needs examples:

Technical skills
➢ Expand knowledge of fundamentals of fluid mechanics
➢ Increase basic understanding of hydroelectric generation systems
➢ Stay current with changes in water management technology

Nontechnical skills
➢ Develop methods to obtain the maximum benefit from classes
➢ Develop leadership skills
➢ Learn to structure and deliver professional presentations

Figure 13.8
Skill needs for professional vision goals.

When developing action plans, it is important to understand the difference between an action plan item and a goal. A goal is something you want to obtain or achieve and an action plan item is what you will do to make that happen.

We can demonstrate the relationship between a goal and action plans to achieve that goal by using an example from one short term goal established for the professional vision. This is shown in Figure 13.9.

An efficient way to develop action plan items is to start with short term goals. Action plans for these are typically easier to establish because you will be implementing them first. Decide what you can do, how you can do it, and when you need to do it to reach your first short term goal. Continue with other short term goals. Then, move to midterm goals and complete the process with long term goals.

After determining action plans for goals, use a similar approach to define action plans to develop new skills identified in your list of skill needs. Examples of action plans for one technical skill and one nontechnical skill associated with the professional vision are shown in Figure 13.10.

ACTION PLAN FOR ONE SAMPLE GOAL

Short term goal to achieve professional vision in Figure 13.8:

Short term goal:
◆   Select elective courses that relate to water resource utilization

Sample action plans for this goal:

Action plan items:
➢   Meet with advisor to review course options
➢   Prepare schedule to include classes associated with water resources
➢   Focus on gaining information and improving skills in each course

Figure 13.9
Sample action plan items for goals.

The examples in Figures 13.9 and 13.10 illustrate the difference between action plan items and goals and skill needs. These action plans are specific, measurable, and have a direct relationship with each goal or skill need. Additional examples are shown in Chapter resource 13.3.

Let's summarize the process used to create action plans based on your strategy. Action plans are developed after you establish what you want to do by designing the details of how to do it, as shown in Figure 13.11.

You have a variety of sources of information and activities to help you decide what to include in your action plans. Many of these are associated with classes. You can expand your options by using other resources outside of your classes. If, for example, you need to improve your math skills, join a math study group or use a tutor. If your writing skills are weak, visit the university writing center and request help from their staff.

We associate technical skill development with classes and labs. However, when preparing your action plan, you can also include the development of nontechnical skills in these classes. A good opportunity to build teamwork and interpersonal skills is available when you work with your laboratory team. Other opportunities to enhance nontechnical skills are in classroom exercises relating to ABET accreditation, which we discussed in the chapter on developing your skill set.

"Try out the opportunities your school has to offer. Do an internship. Join a technical student society (preferably the ones that design real projects or participate in professional competitions). Attend corporate recruiting events and talk to the students who interned with the company. Take an undergrad research course with a professor. The most interesting stuff happens outside the classroom; one of the best things you can do for yourself is to find those opportunities and figure out what they mean to you."

(Akshay Kashyap, Electrical Engineer,
and Financial Technology Associate at Citadel Investment Group)

ACTION PLAN EXAMPLES FOR SKILL NEEDS

Technical skill to achieve professional vision in Figure 13.8:

Technical skill
◆ Expand knowledge of fundamentals of fluid mechanics

Sample action plans for this skill need:

➤ Select and complete fluid mechanics and dynamics courses
➤ Attend conferences, seminars, and presentations on these topics
➤ Join students in study group and work homework problems
➤ Select senior design project that relates to these topics

Nontechnical skill to achieve professional vision in Figure 13.8:

Nontechnical skill
◆ Develop methods to obtain the maximum benefit from classes

Sample action plans for this skill need:

➤ Talk to the instructor to establish a personal network
➤ Make a list of what I can learn in this class relating to my vision
➤ Establish time schedule and read textbook before each class session
➤ Write notes as I read and identify information I do not understand
➤ Listen carefully to the class lecture and take effective class notes
➤ Use my text notes to ask appropriate questions for clarification
➤ Add instructor's answers to questions to class notes

Figure 13.10
Sample action plans for skill development.

We identified how you can improve nontechnical skills by active involvement in professional student organizations. In addition to improving your communication, interpersonal, project management, and teamwork skills, volunteer activities help build self-confidence and add important experiences to your resume. So, think about how you can use these organizations when you develop your action plan.

13.3.5 Action Plan Implementation

"Genius is one percent inspiration and ninety-nine percent perspiration."
(Thomas Edison, Famous American inventor)

```
┌─────────────────────────────────────────────────┐
│                                                   │
│      PROCESS LEADING TO DEVELOPMENT OF ACTION PLAN│
│                                                   │
│  ESTABLISH WHAT TO DO                             │
│                                                   │
│  Strategy to achieve personal and professional visions│
│                                                   │
│        Set goals                                  │
│                                                   │
│             Long term                             │
│                                                   │
│             Midterm                               │
│                                                   │
│             Short term                            │
│                                                   │
│        Determine skill needs                      │
│                                                   │
│             Technical                             │
│                                                   │
│             Nontechnical                          │
│                                                   │
│  DESIGN DETAILS OF HOW TO DO IT                   │
│                                                   │
│  Action plans to achieve strategy                 │
│                                                   │
│        Action plan items for goals                │
│                                                   │
│             Short term                            │
│                                                   │
│             Midterm                               │
│                                                   │
│             Long term                             │
│                                                   │
│        Action plan items for skill development    │
│                                                   │
│             Technical                             │
│                                                   │
│             Nontechnical                          │
│                                                   │
└─────────────────────────────────────────────────┘
```

Figure 13.11
Action plan development summary.

Up to this point we have reviewed sample personal and professional visions, developed a strategy that includes some goals and skill needs, and combined some of this into an action plan. These are important steps but we are not finished.

Action plans are like the story of three frogs sitting on a log in the middle of a pond. Their names are Bud, Wise, and Ur. A fly landed on a lily pad. Ur did not have an action plan, and so did not know how to catch the fly.

Bud had an action plan and decided to jump off the log to catch the fly. So, how many frogs were left on the log? The logical answer would be two. Sorry, but that answer is incorrect. Bud *decided* to jump, but he did *not implement* his action plan and jump!

Wise, as you might expect from his name, was much more successful. He had an action plan and when he saw the fly he decided to implement his action plan by jumping off the log and eating the fly. The moral of this story is—be wise, have an action plan for potential opportunities, and implement the plan when opportunities arrive.

Action plans are useless without implementation.

The most useless action plan is the one not implemented! Implementing an action plan requires your time investment. When and how you schedule activities has a major impact on how successfully you can complete them on time. So, use time-management to plan, schedule, and complete activities.

13.3.6 Documentation and Analysis of Results

Three additional important steps are needed to complete your plan—documenting results, evaluating results, and fine-tuning your plan. In this section, we will discuss the value of documentation and how recorded results can be used to enhance future success.

Documentation   Your action plan should identify the process you will use to document results of the goals you achieve and your success in improving skills. As demonstrated by the student in Figure 13.12, you can establish your documentation process

Figure 13.12
Documentation of career plan results.

now and start recording your accomplishments in classes, laboratories, professional organization projects, and jobs.

It is best to record results soon after you complete each major part of your action plan so you can remember details. Documentation is an important resource for career management because it provides the basis for evaluating results and is a record of accomplishments for future reference.

Documentation of activities relating to work experiences is especially important and useful. If you are fortunate to be involved in co-op or intern positions while in school, experiences gained in these jobs will be some of the best examples of your skill development and accomplishments. Add these to your portfolio, and you will have a more effective story to tell future employers.

Documentation becomes even more important in your future working career. You will probably have many different work positions and may work for many different companies in your career. The best way to demonstrate your skills to a future employer is to use the record of what you achieved in past positions.

Evaluation   Your action plan should also include a systematic process of analyzing results. By evaluating what you did, you can determine if you reached goals and developed desired skills that are defined in your strategy to accomplish your visions. This provides the foundation for career plan revisions and helps to determine areas that need additional refinement or changes.

As you evaluate results, you will see that many of your goals were successfully met. Enjoying success is good, but you can learn even more from failure.

In developing your career plan, include some reasonable risks. The key word is reasonable. Then, don't be afraid to fail. You will fail from time to time like everyone else. But remember, failure is not a bad thing, as long as it is not too severe.

So, don't be discouraged when some results fall short of your expectations. Failure is a wonderful teacher that can lead you to greater success. Most successful people fail part of the time, and almost all good products experienced some level of failure in their development process.

By the way, failure is not in falling down—failure is not in getting back up after falling. Review the process that led to failure and learn how you can use this experience to enhance your career. Look back to learn from the past, and then focus more on the future and how your experiences can make you more successful.

Fine-Tune Career Plan   This brings our discussion to the last part of the career plan process. Make appropriate changes in future planning based on the results of your action plan implementation. Notice how Figure 13.1 shows a closed loop between evaluation and your visions. You should fine-tune your visions to take advantage of changing conditions and new opportunities.

Even if your vision is still valid, you may want to revise your strategy and subsequent action plans. Many new professional opportunities require new or enhanced skills. You will be more successful in taking advantage of unexpected opportunities when you are proactive and develop skills for possible situations before they appear.

A CONVERSATION WITH KATHRYN PAINE

Kathryn, you raised some very interesting questions at the start of this chapter. How have you managed your career?

Answer:

"Career management and success is typically a lifelong pursuit. I have had three major experiences where I decided to shift the focus of my career.

The first was a major change in career. I had a degree in accounting and came to the conclusion I needed something more challenging. Having lived with an electrical engineer for 10 years, I decided turn-about was fair play. I went back to school and obtained a mechanical engineering degree.

Upon graduating with the engineering degree, I had hoped to pursue work in the field of HVAC. The job market was difficult and I ended up estimating for a tool and die company in NE Ohio. It was still interesting to see how that company functioned and gave me background for a future shift in my career within engineering. Never underestimate the opportunity to learn from what may appear to be a setback.

It did not take long to explore avenues in the HVAC arena and shift my career into consulting engineering. After nearly 5 years with a small firm designing HVAC/plumbing systems for commercial buildings, the opportunity presented itself for the spouse to make a move from the Midwest to the Southwest. At the same time, I had decided I needed to narrow my focus with respect to building systems engineering.

After settling in the Southwest, I managed to secure a position with a manufacturer's representative for HVAC equipment. This third shift was indeed a much more narrow focus by concentrating on particular types of equipment with particular factories. Sales engineering as a profession is perhaps not as technically challenging, but certainly beneficial in many other respects."

How did you decide to make career path changes?

Answer:

"All three major decisions were opportunities that I initiated. In each case, I performed research and took action required to accomplish the goal. I explored college programs available and made various changes in employment for 5 years to accommodate engineering college coursework. To find a position in HVAC consulting, I joined the local chapter of the associated professional organization, ASHRAE (American Society of Heating, Refrigerating and Air-Conditioning Engineers), having been a student member while in college.

It's never too early to start building a professional network. As it happened, it was at a local chapter meeting where I first met my future employer in the consulting world. To secure employment in a new geographic location, I used the relationships I had built while in the consulting business to make contacts with similar professionals in my new town."

What nontechnical skills did you use in managing your career?

Answer:

"Nontechnical skills required for any career management involve research, study, good writing skills as well as people skills and self-promotion. It also requires nontechnical, nonengineering tasks such as self-examination and soul searching in an attempt to learn what you think you desire and recognize the areas where you excel. You also need the ability to revisit and reexamine those same subjects throughout your career in case some adjustment is required.

In all three situations, the career change was a positive experience, filled with the benefits of learning new skills, making new professional contacts, and progressively increased monetary rewards. Each prior experience benefited the succeeding career position."

What advice would you share with students?

Answer:

"A majority of technically inclined individuals such as engineering students tend to view the world in terms of black or white issues, see questions as having yes or no answers, and believe everything should be very clear-cut and well-defined. Math and science have those tendencies.

However, I am of the opinion that you will enjoy greater success in your professional and personal life if you can learn to expand your horizons, view and consider the larger picture as well as maintain an open mind to consider many options. It's important to remember that every experience, whether it's viewed at the time (or even in retrospect) as good or bad, is a learning experience."

(Kathryn Paine, PE, Mechanical Engineer and Director of Engineering & Inside Sales at Mechanical Products SW, Inc.)

13.4 Conclusion

As Kathryn has demonstrated with her personal example of career management, successful careers are the result of taking a personal, active role in planning, controlling, evaluating, and revising what we want to accomplish and then taking steps to be prepared for unexpected opportunities well before they happen.

Although you cannot prevent changes caused by business or other economic situations, you can initiate desired changes if you prepare for new opportunities as described by Kathryn. Do this by reviewing your career status, by setting goals and developing skills, and by being prepared to initiate career changes when the timing is right. In other words, don't knock on that door of opportunity until you have developed the proper skills to be successful in a new career position.

So, who is responsible for your career management? Look in a mirror. When should you start planning and controlling your career? Now! When can you relax and stop controlling your career? Perhaps never, but certainly not before you have achieved your professional vision or retire. Even then, you need to focus on your personal vision for the balance of your life.

END OF CHAPTER REVIEW QUIZ

Select the most appropriate answer to the following statements.

1. The most important thing you can do to achieve greater career success is
   a. Work hard in school and earn a GPA of 3.8 or higher.
   b. Join a professional society and participate in activities.
   c. Balance technical skill development with many nontechnical skills.
   d. Interview for new job openings as soon as they become available.

2. The first step in preparing a career plan is to
   a. Write short-term goals because these can be accomplished quickly.
   b. Develop an action plan so you can start using the process early.
   c. Determine how you will document and evaluate results.
   d. Write personal and professional vision statements.

3. The most important consideration when preparing a personal vision is
   a. What you want to accomplish.
   b. To first decide what you want personally, and then determine the role that your family and community will play in your life.
   c. To think about what you want your life to be like when you are 60 years old.
   d. Ask your parents and friends what you should do in your life.

4. Professional visions statements are most effective when they include
   a. What type of work you want, where you would like to live and work, and what you would like to accomplish.
   b. A lifelong learning plan.
   c. A statement of what kind of work you would like to do and if you want to own your own company or work for a corporation.
   d. Details of work activities and how you will be able to retire at an early age.

5. To be most effective, goals should be developed to
   a. Make sure you do not waste time on unimportant tasks.
   b. Help you achieve your personal and professional visions.
   c. Help you learn new technical and nontechnical skills.
   d. Give you information for discussion with your supervisor so you are working on the correct assignments.

6. When preparing a list of skill needs, you should
   a. Select skills that support your goals and help achieve professional and personal visions.
   b. List skills that you did not learn in previous classes but can be obtained in elective courses during your undergraduate experience.
   c. Identify skills that you feel will be easy so you can enjoy learning them.
   d. Learn skills that will prepare you to own your own company.

7. The most important purpose of an action plan is to
   a. Help you remember your goals and skill needs.
   b. Provide details of your professional vision.
   c. Structure your time-management plan to ensure you complete tasks effectively.
   d. Identify how, when, where, and what you will do to achieve your goals and enhance your skills to realize your personal and professional visions.

8. The greatest value of documenting results is to
   a. Provide a database of information for review and to use in fine-tuning future goals and skill need statements,
   b. Keep a record of your accomplishments to use when you ask for a raise at work or to show your instructor how much you did in class.
   c. Have as a resource in case you would like to write an autobiography.
   d. Find ways to reduce work when using future versions of your career plan.

9. To achieve success in career planning, the most important step is to
   a. Define clear personal and professional visions.
   b. Select a strategy of appropriate goals and skill needs.
   c. Develop, implement, and document an action plan that will help to achieve your skill needs, goals, and visions.
   d. Accomplish all of the above.

10. The greatest value of career planning is to
    a. Achieve a good grade in this class.
    b. Be in control of your life and career, and be prepared to take advantage of unexpected opportunities.
    c. Be organized so you do not waste time.
    d. Accomplish all of the above.

EXERCISES TO DEVELOP
AND ENHANCE YOUR SKILL SET

Exercise 13.1   Vision statements

The exercises that follow are designed to help you develop a successful career plan. Complete the following statements as a foundation for developing your visions:

My definition of personal success is _____

_____

_____

In relation to my career, my family is _____

_____

My desired role in my community is _____

_____

In my personal life, I would like to be remembered by _____

_____

_____

My definition of professional success is _____

_____

_____

My first choice for location to live would be _____

_____

The work environment most desirable for me would be _____

_____

In my professional life, I would like to be remembered by _____

_____

_____

Exercise 13.2   Career plan assignment
The following is designed to help you develop an initial career plan.

STEP 1

Use the Career Plan Format in Chapter resource 13.1 to develop an initial career plan.

Review your Career Plan Exercise 13.1 results. Develop your personal vision in paragraph format. Start with what is important to you personally. Then, add a paragraph relating to your family and a paragraph relating to your community.

Review the sample professional visions and write three paragraphs relating to three areas of your professional vision: initial career focus, desired working environment, and overall achievements.

STEP 2

Visualize your life when you are 55 years old. Then, consider what could make that vision come true. Don't be too detailed, but select one general goal that supports the vision of your life at age 55. Express this as a bullet point under long-term goals.

Add bullet points for two midterm goals for the next 5 to 10 years. Repeat the process with bullets for three short-term goals for the next 1 to 5 years.

Review your visions and goals, and select at least two technical skills that will help you achieve them. Add these as bullets under Technical Skills.

Repeat the process for least two nontechnical skills as bullets under Nontechnical Skills.

STEP 3

Develop your action plan by reviewing the first short-term goal. Write one or more action plan bullets to accomplish that goal. Continue this process for each of the other subtopics, ending with an action plan for your Nontechnical Skill Needs. Make sure your action plan items are measurable and that they will help you accomplish your goals, skill needs, and visions.

Complete your action plan by identifying how you will document results. This should be a structured plan that includes periodic documentation and one that can easily be used to review results and to revise future career management plans. Save the file with title of "Your name Career Plan YYMMDD" (year, month, day).

STEP 4

Hand in a printed copy of your career management plan at the start of class on the day established by your instructor and provide an electronic copy to your instructor that day.

STEP 5

Review evaluation and make appropriate revisions to your career plan. For maximum benefits, keep your career management plan dynamic with appropriate changes.

END OF CHAPTER RESOURCES

Chapter resource 13.1

Career plan format

CAREER PLAN

Prepared by _____(Your Name)_____

Personal Vision

(Three paragraphs relating to you, your family, and your local/professional communities)

Professional Vision

(Three paragraphs relating to your initial career focus, desired working environment, and desired achievements)

Strategy

Goals

   Long term

   ✓

   Midterm

   ✓

   Short term

   ✓

Skill Needs

   Technical

   ✓

   Nontechnical

   ✓

Action Plan

To Reach Short-Term Goals

✓

To Reach Midterm Goals

✓

To Reach Long-Term Goals

✓

To Enhance Technical Skills

✓

To Enhance Nontechnical Skills

✓

Documentation Plan

(Three paragraphs to discuss: [1] how you will document results; [2] how you will evaluate results; [3] how you plan to keep your career plan dynamic and effective.)

Chapter resource 13.2

Outstanding Career Plan Example

by James Sadey

Personal Vision

When I think about my future I never worry about being financially stable, I think about having a family and a wonderful, fulfilling life. This tells me that I will always put my family before my profession. I do not want to be the father who is at work seven days a week and unable to be a part of my children's personal activities. My parents always made time for my interests and that is exactly what I plan to do. By correctly planning my career, I can be the loving father who balances out his profession with his personal life.

Family, in my mind, is the most important part of a person's life. They are the closest people to you and at the end of the day they are all you need. People have wants that they can live without, but living without a family seems like an impossible feat to me. I was raised in an environment where family meant everything. Wants, hobbies, and friends were all a distant second to spending time with each other.

This is what my mindset is when it comes to having my own family someday. I want to be a role model for my children and a loving husband as well. I cannot wait for the opportunity to be the person who my family needs, looks up to, and loves unconditionally. Having a career that I enjoy will satisfy my professional needs, allow me to provide for my family, and empower me to be the person I want to be.

When it comes to my community I have a very simple plan: to display more positive actions than negative. I want a safe environment to raise my family and that might not be an option unless I become an active participant. When it comes to my professional community, I feel the same way. I would love to be involved by displaying positive and ethical practices. I believe by making positive contributions the end result will be constructive.

Professional Vision

My initial career focus is a vague one at this point in time because I have yet to explore the countless areas of electrical engineering. I know for a fact that my passion is in the electrical engineering field but I have not yet decided specifically where I am headed. I am currently interested in designing energy sources because I have always been fascinated with creating new things. The energy field is a popular one at the moment and I am interested in the endless possibilities that can arise in this area.

My desired work environment is outside in the fresh air. I am not someone who likes to be stuck inside for extended periods of time and cannot sit still for very long. I feel like I must always be doing something and being able to work outside would be very enjoyable for me. That being said, if I am focused on something such as building or creating a new idea I can spend hours or maybe days without leaving my work area. Creating things excites me and while being inside is almost a necessity when it comes to our profession, I would love the opportunity to be an active, outdoor electrical engineer.

When thinking about what I would like to achieve in my career, a few things come to mind. Most importantly, I want to learn all that I can about electrical engineering. Obtaining more knowledge will not only help me professionally, but it is actually more of a personal goal. Life is short and I would like to learn as much as possible in the time that I have.

I also have a specific goal that I would like to achieve that I have not mentioned before: My father and brother are both very knowledgeable when dealing with electrical systems and I hope that one day we can all start our own business or company. Working with family in a field that I love would be a dream come true. I dream of being hired by several different companies or industries where we are the people who can provide them a service. Being hired to design electrical systems by possibly a zoo or a company that is outside would be the ultimate high for me because it is a combination of all of my favorite things. I hope one day I can make this dream a reality.

Goals

Long term

- Have a job outside designing electrical systems.
- Own an engineering company with my father and brother.

- Design and create new energy sources.
- Obtain as much knowledge in the electrical engineering field as possible; read theories as well as new technology that is being produced.
- Raise and spend time with my family in a respectable community.

Midterm

- Graduate college with at least a master's degree in electrical engineering.
- Have a few years of experience working at local engineering companies.
- Start saving money toward a car and possibly a house.
- Further knowledge in electrical systems and look into job opportunities in an outdoor environment.
- Create a daily exercise habit to keep health an important factor in my life.

Short term

- Retain a 4.0 grade point average this semester as well as the spring semester.
- Get a summer internship at a local engineering company.
- Join and become an active member in IEEE.
- Create a study group rather than studying alone.
- Ask more questions in class and during office hours.
- Continue to get exercise on a daily basis.

Skill Needs

Technical

- To actually understand and learn new material, rather than just remember it.
- To transition all of my knowledge into the work field, where I can physically apply it.

Nontechnical

- Learn how to trust others and not feel the need to correct them.
- Try to eliminate the need to do all of the work myself.
- Learn how to manage my time efficiently and plan ahead so I can finish work with enough time to enjoy other activities.

Action Plan

To reach short term goals

- Continue to ask daily questions in class to further understand the material.
- Plan ahead to study at least an hour per day for each class outside of school with a study group of friends.
- Read theories behind the material to understand why and how things work.
- Create a solid resume and apply to several companies to obtain a summer internship.
- Participate in announced IEEE activities whenever time is allowed.
- Wake up an hour earlier each day to make time for a run around the neighborhood.

To reach midterm goals

- Integrate master's courses into my senior year so I can graduate with a master's degree in 2015.
- Continually work summer internships during my years at college to further my experience in the engineering field.
- Start saving at least 50% of my paycheck while living at home.
- Travel to companies around the area and ask about possible job openings in the future, and what I can do to increase my chances of obtaining a job from them.
- Work at local engineering firms until I gain the expertise of running my own business.
- Workout for an hour when I come home from work and make time for recreational activities on the weekend.

To reach long term goals

- Research all of the crucial aspects of running a company and start looking for a potential building location.
- Start spreading the word about my company to local businesses and on the East Coast of the country for possible job opportunities.
- Start a family and find an appropriate house and neighborhood to live in.
- Start a college fund for my children and save enough money to fund their expenses.
- Create a weekly planner to figure out an appropriate balance to spend time at work and with my family.

To enhance technical skills

- Instead of doing numerical problems, actually read the theory behind what I am computing and how it works.
- Find online sources about the material I am reading to see another perspective on the material.
- Build objects at home or at work that apply the material in a hands-on fashion.

To enhance nontechnical skills

- Get to know people on a more personal note to build trust between each other.
- Start working at least twice a week with a study group to build friendship together.
- Complete homework as soon as it is assigned and complete projects in the same manner.

Documentation Plan

To document the results of my career plan I have decided the best way to do this is once every week, electronically. Documenting my results every day would be too excessive and it might be impossible to remember details if documentation occurred only once per month. If I set an hour or so every Sunday to document the results of the past week I believe I can properly set myself up for evaluation.

Evaluating my results is an action that I will complete every three months. I should have a good idea of what needs to be completed each year, but to make sure I am on the right track, I will compare my documentation to my original action plan in this continuous interval.

Nothing drastic can happen over three months, to the point that my career plan can no longer be related to, but it is a sufficient amount of time that I can make minor changes as I move along in my career.

My career plan will always be changing. There is no way that I have predicted my entire career at the age of nineteen. But, it is a great starting point to which I can always refer back. I have listed the most important aspects of what will truly make me happy and if I can follow these simple plans, my life will be successful. On that note, I will consistently alter my plan as my needs change as I grow both personally and professionally.

(James Sadey, Electrical Engineering Student, Fenn College of Engineering, Cleveland State University)

Let us give you a few observations, make sure that your goals are things you can control. James said one of his goals is to maintain a 4.0, which we are sure he will. However, grades are controlled by faculty members, so James would have been better off stating his goal is to do those things that will maximize the likelihood of his earning a 4.0.

Chapter resource 13.3

Additional Career Plan Examples

SAMPLE CAREER PLAN #1

VISION

Personal

Enjoy a lifestyle that brings happiness to me and my family, and makes a positive impact on my local and professional communities. Establish the ability to care for my family and take advantage of many opportunities with no regrets on decisions.

Professional

Focus my career on mechanical engineering as it relates to vehicles. More specifically, apply a variety of mechanical functions to create one great product. In addition, research the conversion of energy in vehicles and apply new ideas for energy conservation.

Enter the automotive industry and join a team of designers with a goal of finding a more environmentally friendly car. Then, secure a management position in research and make decisions to benefit the economy and the country.

Play a major role in the production of a new product and make enough money to support myself and my family and to give back to the community.

Strategy

Goals

Long term
- Develop a lifestyle to bring success and happiness for all members of my family.
- Be financially independent and debt free.
- Be a leader in my church, community, and school system and use my mechanical engineering skills to enhance the secondary education system.

- Provide for the education of my children and help them start their careers.
- Have a management position with a positive impact on my career and profession.
- Prepare for an enjoyable and successful retirement.

Midterm

- Start a family and become active in my church and local community.
- Expand professional networks by membership in engineering societies.
- Plan time with family to develop quality time and enhance the enjoyment of life.
- Establish a budget and savings plan as a financial foundation for my vision.
- Finish school with a bachelor's degree in mechanical engineering.
- Complete graduate school with a master's degree in mechanical engineering.
- Gain industry experience while in school.
- Start working career in automotive industry.
- Become a licensed professional engineer.

Short term

- Learn to balance time for school, work, and leisure.
- Build a personal network of friends and classmates.
- Develop effective study habits to obtain maximum benefits from classes.
- Evaluate the mechanical engineering profession and decide what elective classes will provide the best method to achieve my professional vision.
- Establish an initial GPA of at least 3.80 and develop a process to maintain a high GPA for entry to graduate school.
- Research different engineering colleges and determine if the present curricula is appropriate to prepare me for my vision.

Skill Needs

Technical

- Gain proficiency in calculus and differential equations.
- Increase knowledge and application of engineering software.
- Enhance "hands-on" experience in car maintenance.
- Learn how to apply the principles of thermodynamics and heat transfer.

Nontechnical

- Develop library and other information research skills.
- Improve grammar and writing skills.
- Develop oral presentation skills.
- Learn how to work with other people.

Action Plan

Short term

- Develop a time-management system and learn how to balance time between school, professional societies, and part-time work.
- Join the student chapter of SAE and work on the Baja Car Project.

- Analyze each class to determine how it helps to prepare for my desired work focus and work to obtain a maximum benefit from each class.
- Join a study group and to learn how to work with other students.
- Meet with advisor and review class options to plan my undergraduate class schedule.
- Allocate 30 hours/week for textbook review, homework problems, and test preparation.
- Attend all classes and spend extra time in preparation for exams to receive high scores and grades to support a high GPA.
- Use the library and Internet to research various university engineering programs for direction in completing undergraduate and graduate degrees.
- Establish a tutor for calculus and increase time to practice solving problems when involved in the Differential Equations class.
- Use the University Writing Center for suggestions to improve writing skills.
- Be an officer in SAE and practice leadership, interpersonal, and communication skills.
- Apply for a co-op position in the automotive or related industry.

Midterm

- Get married and start a family.
- Participate in community activities when my children start school by working with science teachers to encourage students to consider engineering careers.
- Be an active member of my church and develop a religious foundation for my family.
- Be an active member of SAE and ASME and participate in activities relating to the automotive industry.
- Work with my spouse and establish quality time for all family members.
- Plan a family budget and use of funds that will provide the desired lifestyle and build a savings foundation for future use.
- Use vacation time to plan and enjoy travel and other activities that will educate and provide recreation for all family members.
- Establish a physical fitness routine to maintain good personal health.
- Continue to develop and use efficient time management and study skills to maintain a high GPA and to gain the most from each class.
- Expand personal and professional networks by active membership in my community and my professional societies.
- Complete FE exam during senior year in preparation for registration.
- Select university for graduate school.
- Complete undergraduate and graduate school.
- Secure my first position in the automotive industry.
- Complete PE exam to become registered as a professional engineer.

Long term

- Work with my family to plan activities and quality time together.
- Support my spouse's career and other activities to build a solid marriage.
- Work with my spouse to review and make successful investments and take advantage of other financial tools such as the 401k program to build security for retirement.

- Consider being a school board member or using volunteer opportunities to improve the secondary school system in my community for my children and other students.
- Develop a plan to help my children review career opportunities and select their life work.
- Provide partial or full financial support of higher education opportunities for my children.
- Develop a lifelong learning program that includes preparation for management and other career positions.
- Seek and secure career related positions of authority and leadership to contribute to long-term goals and professional vision.
- Continue a physical fitness routine to support quality of life and extend retirement years enjoyment.

SAMPLE CAREER PLAN #2

VISION

Personal

The primary focus of my personal vision is on my family. I would like to provide financial support so my wife can be a full-time mother. In addition, it is important that I have the opportunity to be at home and spend quality time with our children.

I would like to have a career that supports a reasonable lifestyle but money is not the most important thing for me. It is much more important to enjoy a happy and successful family and not be concerned about having a lot of expensive gadgets.

Professional

Initially, I want to teach in an undergraduate civil engineering program at a well-known university. I am willing to work hard and learn about the engineering education process because I would like to eventually be a dean of engineering.

My desired working environment is one that includes the association with many groups of people. I enjoy using my communicating and socializing skills to work in teams and enjoy the benefits of different ideas and viewpoints of others.

I would be happy if my career accomplishments include working on projects to improve or save lives. This would give me satisfaction by making a positive impact on my world.

It is important to make enough money to care for my family, help my community, and contribute to the well-being of other people in this world in a similar way that others have helped me.

Strategy

Goals

Long term
- Enjoy life and activities associated with my family.
- Work with my children to help them do well in secondary school and to prepare for their vocations.

- Spend quality time with my family.
- Expand my professional network and practice leadership skills in preparation for seeking a position as dean of engineering.
- Learn how to use financial resources efficiently and to be satisfied with a reasonable lifestyle.
- Find opportunities to be involved in my community and to participate in various activities that provide positive impacts on the community.
- Be a dean of engineering and encourage students to do well in their preparation for their career.
- Be prepared for retirement and help my children enjoy successful lives.

Midterm

- Find a wife, get married, and start our family.
- Develop a balance between school and family activities.
- Establish a good time management system to reduce stress and improve my ability to have extra time for my family.
- Complete my bachelor's degree in engineering and prepare for graduate school.
- Determine the main focus of my career and how I can incorporate helping other people in research associated with teaching in a university.
- Complete a master's degree in engineering.
- Learn how to work efficiently with other people and become a leader.
- Obtain a doctorial degree and become a teacher.

Short term

- Learn how to be a successful student and make the most of class opportunities.
- Obtain good grades in all classes and keep a GPA of 3.75 or better.
- Learn more about academia and what is involved in teaching and becoming a dean of engineering.
- Develop a personal network and learn how to work better with other students.
- Research various engineering fields and make the final selection of the type of engineering to study and receive a bachelor's degree.

Skill Needs

Technical

- Learn how to use computers and software.
- Increase knowledge in math and science theory.
- Enhance my skills in solving problems.

Nontechnical

- Develop leadership skills.
- Improve communication skills.
- Learn how to influence other people.

Action Plan

Short term

- ◼ ·Attend all classes, read the textbook before class and ask questions in class to obtain clarification or additional information.
- ◼ Be optimistic and spend at least 2 hours to prepare for each exam.
- ◼ Spend time in the library and with other resources to learn more about academia and what is involved in teaching and administration.
- ◼ Talk to the dean of engineering and instructors and find out what they do on a daily basis and what they did to prepare for their present positions.
- ◼ Form a study group and work with other students a minimum of 5 hours each week.
- ◼ Join a student professional society and volunteer for a few projects.

Midterm

- ◼ Expand my personal network and share many activities with friends so I can find the love of my life, get married, and start a family.
- ◼ Improve my time management system to be more efficient and have more time for my family as well as the balance of my education.
- ◼ Work hard, plan daily activities, and maintain a high GPA so I can graduate and enter the graduate school of my choice.
- ◼ Select the area of interest and complete a master's degree in engineering
- ◼ Continue active membership in my engineering professional organization and expand my professional network and leadership skills.
- ◼ Complete my doctorial degree and prepare for academia.
- ◼ Learn how to handle failure and build success from experience.

Long term

- ◼ Work with my wife and plan activities that will be enjoyed by the entire family including trips and other vacations.
- ◼ Discuss career opportunities with my children and be involved in their secondary educational activities to encourage them to be prepared to make good career choices.
- ◼ Take advantage of opportunities for leadership positions in my professional society and expand my professional networks.
- ◼ Develop a family budget and prepare for future expenses such as college for my children and retirement.
- ◼ Review research opportunities and select those that will make a positive impact on society to fulfill my professional vision.
- ◼ Prepare and seek opportunities to be a dean of engineering.
- ◼ If successful in securing a position as dean of engineering, use my vision to encourage faculty to provide a quality educational environment and students to prepare for and compete a successful career experience.

SAMPLE CAREER PLAN #3

VISION

Personal

The most important part of my personal vision is to provide financial and personal support to my family. My desired lifestyle is to focus first on my family, then my work, and finally, on my community. So, I want to plan and control my career to enjoy a good balance between work and a personal and family life.

I would like to be a wife and mother who is respected and loved. Enjoying a close family is very important and I want to have a home environment that will make that possible. This includes spending time every day with my family and using vacation to introduce my children to new ideas and experiences.

Because I am also interested in my community and society in general, I would like to make positive contributions through my profession. This includes becoming a professional engineer and being ethical in all that I do.

It is important that I maintain good health so I can be successful at work and be a good support for my family needs. I would like to retire in good health so this part of life will also be enjoyable.

Professional

My primary area of interest is chemical engineering and environmental related equipment for buildings. I would like to start my working career with a mid to large size consulting firm where I would get the chance to work on a variety of different projects such as healthcare, educational, industrial facilities, and the like.

My desired work environment is to spend at least 40% of the time in the field and participate in the application of my design projects. I would not be happy in an office all the time.

In addition to obtaining a broad range of work experience, I want to build a large professional network with others in the industry. This will be an important resource for me to be successful the second part of my career.

I want to work for an existing company for about 10–15 years in order to develop the necessary skills and experience to start and run my own business. My long-range plans include establishing my own engineering consulting firm where I would specialize in the design of environmentally friendly systems for major commercial buildings.

Goals

Long term
- Initiate the process of starting my own engineering consulting firm.
- Specialize in environmental related systems for commercial facilities.
- Assume leadership roles in local AIChE and other industry-related organizations.
- Start with light commercial system designs and progress to larger-scale projects.
- Provide financial support for my children's education and my future retirement.
- Balance time between family and business and enjoy vacations with my family.

Midterm

- Be employed by an engineering firm, working on my 4 years of work experience needed in order to take the PE exam.
- Complete payment of all student loans.
- Be active in AIChE and expand my personal and professional networks.
- Develop a business plan before my 35th birthday and start preparations for owning a consulting company.
- Establish a solid personal financial plan to support my family needs and to prepare for company ownership.
- Continue my personal exercise program to maintain good health.

Short term

- Have an outstanding spring semester in order to improve my GPA and postgraduation marketability.
- Complete a successful Senior Design Project and graduate before my 25th birthday.
- Increase my activities in the student branch of ASME, build a personal network of peers, and practice leadership and interpersonal skills.
- Pass the Fundamentals of Engineering exam before graduation.
- Take the PE exam and become a professional engineer before my 30th birthday.
- Develop a personal exercise program.

Skill Needs

Technical

- Increase my ability to process complicated information more efficiently.
- Stay up to date with the most current technologies necessary to be competitive.

Nontechnical

- Learn to balance my work and personal life in order to maintain an adequate level efficiency.
- Learn to utilize the available resources that I have taken for granted in the past (i.e., Careers Services, AIChE contacts, etc.).
- Find a business associate with marketing skills and contacts to help establish and maintain a successful consulting company.

Action Plan

Short term

- Use time wisely and efficiently by expanding my time-management system and reviewing results on a daily basis.
- Learn to say "NO" to extra activities that would interfere with my primary objectives.
- Organize a senior design team and select a project that can be successfully completed within the time allocated.
- Attend monthly meeting of AIChE and volunteer for a limited number of activities in which I can expand my network and practice communication and leadership skills.
- Prepare for the FE exam by allocating 3 hours/week to study exam topics.

- Document projects continue a learning program that will prepare me to successfully pass the PE exam.
- Establish an exercise program that includes running at least three times/week at Bally's or on the streets in my neighborhood.

Midterm

- Increase my marketability by utilizing the contacts and resources made available (Career Services, Engineering Networking Events, etc.).
- Work hard on my initial job position after graduation to establish a solid foundation of expertise.
- Expand my knowledge of the overall operations of a consulting firm by talking to several departments in the company.
- Control finances responsibly to pay off my student debt and increase my net assets.
- Join AIChE and volunteer for leadership opportunities to further expand my professional networks and project management skills.
- Use SCORE seminars and develop a financial plan for my consulting company.

Long term

- Research opportunities for location and type of consulting services to make successful decisions on starting my company.
- Develop adequate knowledge about risks and liabilities involved with owning a business by contacts in AIChE and by conversations with other consulting engineers.
- Initiate the development of a solid financial backing and support from my family and from financial institutions by completing and discussing a business plan.
- Establish a part-time business and explore opportunities for expansion of my consulting business while working for my employer.
- Find at least three to five potential clients who are willing to sign contracts with my company and complete designs of their projects.
- Review results of early operations for my company and decide if I should leave my employer and operate my own business on a full-time basis.
- Use time management to develop a balance between my business and family.
- Provide at least 75% of the expenses for a 4-year undergraduate education for each of my children and help them decide on schools and career paths.

SAMPLE CAREER PLAN #4

VISION

Personal

The most important part of my personal vision is first to be successful in my academic career. I want to make my family proud, especially my dad who is sacrificing so much for me to be in college.

After obtaining a bachelor's degree in electrical engineering, the next step is to find a job in America that will provide experience in the communications field. This work experience will be important in developing skills and in building a good resume so I can return home to Kenya and continue my career. In addition to desiring a successful career, it is important that

I live close to my parents and start my own family. As all this unfolds, I want to develop as a man and make the right decisions in my life.

I will dedicate all my knowledge acquired in college to help the company I find myself working for while at the same time investing in my father's real estate business in Kenya.

A healthy physical, social, and financial state is also another priority. I want to be a healthy man for as long as I live. I know this is hard, but I want to eat right and exercise enough. It would be nice to be wealthy, but being financially stable is good enough for me. Socially, I'd like to make good new friends and keep in touch with current friends.

Professional

My major career focus is communication systems. As an electrical engineer, I'd like to work for a company involved with communications, such as Ericsson, Samsung, and NASA. Working for this type of company would provide important hands-on experience. Because there is a lack of efficient mobile communication systems and Internet availability in my homeland, I would like to start my own company to compete with the few that monopolize this industry in Kenya.

Initially, the most desirable work environment would be a large corporation. Then, after gaining experience, I will move to Kenya and work to establish my own company.

If successful in establishing my own company, it will be important for it to grow so I can provide excellent services and make a positive contribution to society by developing and advancing communication technology.

Strategy

Goals

Long term
- Have a successful business of my own in Kenya.
- Enjoy a simple life without worry or stress by building financial security.
- Help my children obtain a college education.
- Financially support my children and help them start their own careers.
- Take an active role in IEEE and my community and help my neighbors improve their lifestyle through the application of technology.
- Retire and enjoy spending time with my grandchildren.

Midterm
- Complete classes and receive a bachelor's degree in electrical engineering.
- Obtain a position in an American-based company in communications.
- Establish my family and spend quality time with them.
- Minimize stress and enjoy a balance of work and family.
- Take care of my parents in their older years.
- Develop a healthy lifestyle to minimize health problems.
- Move to Kenya and start my own communications business.
- Establish an IEEE Section in my community in Kenya.
- Provide employment opportunities for people in my community.
- Be a silent partner in my father's real estate business.

Short term

- Take personal responsibility for my activities and learn to manage time.
- Complete all tasks in my time-management plan to be more successful.
- Expand personal networks and search for a future wife.
- Join IEEE and be active in projects to learn how to work with others.
- Start a physical fitness program and exercise on a routine basis.
- Increase my ability to obtain more technical knowledge from each class.
- Find part-time work and add work experience to prepare a good resume.

Skill Needs

Technical

- Learn how to apply mathematics to each engineering class.
- Improve my ability to solve homework and test problems.
- Learn the principles associated with wireless communication systems.

Nontechnical

- Learn how to be more effective in preparing for classes.
- Learn how to manage time and to minimize stress of time schedules.
- Be physically fit.
- Strengthen my religious faith.
- Learn how to be patient and to work with others who have different ideas.

Action Plan

Short term

- Develop a time-management system and revise it at the start of each day.
- Review textbook material and attend all classes.
- Write questions when reading textbooks and ask them in class to better understand the technical material.
- Join a study group and learn how to work with others in solving problems.
- Walk four miles on Monday, Wednesday, and Saturday each week.
- Apply for a part-time job in the University Student Center.
- Attend church every Sunday.
- Join IEEE this semester.

Midterm

- Schedule conferences with my advisor and select elective classes to prepare to work in the communications field.
- Write a brief summary of what I can obtain from each class and improve my technical skills by working homework problems with my study group.
- Learn how to work in a laboratory team and how to use equipment to conduct successful experiments.
- Volunteer for leadership opportunities in IEEE and learn how to lead committees and manage projects.

- Start my working career in a company in America.
- Increase my activities in church and expand my personal network so I can search for a future wife.
- Work with a personal trainer and expand my physical fitness program.
- Send money to my father so he can invest this in his real estate business.
- Focus on obtaining experience in the application of communication technology in preparation for relocating to Kenya.
- Get married and start a family.
- Start my own wireless communication company in Kenya.
- Work with my parents and help them plan for retirement years.

Long term

- Use good business principles and operate my company so that it is successful and provides a good living for my employees.
- Develop a budget and establish a saving plan for expenses for my children's college.
- Be a leader by volunteering in community activities and by helping the schools improve their math and science classes.
- Establish a management team that can continue successful operations of my company and provide retirement benefits to me and others in retirement.
- Help my children start their careers and plan time with my grandchildren.
- Encourage young people to improve their overall lifestyle for our community by offering to tutor them in math and science subjects in high school.

Index

APPENDIXES

APPENDIX A

UNIT CONVERSION FACTORS

A.1   PLANE ANGLE

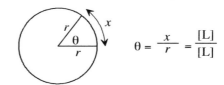

$$\theta = \frac{x}{r} = \frac{[L]}{[L]}$$

TABLE A.1
Plane angle conversion factors (Reference)

	°	′	″	rad	rev
1 degree =	1	60	3600	$\pi/180$	1/360
1 minute =	1/60	1	60	$\pi/10,800$	1/21,600
1 second =	1/3600	1/60	1	$\pi/648,000$	1/1,296,000
1 radian =	$180/\pi$	$10,800/\pi$	$648,000/\pi$	1	$1/(2\pi)$
1 revolution =	360	21,600	1,296,000	2π	1

90° = 100 grade [a] = 100^g = 100 gon   90° = 1000 angular mil [b]

[a] All grade subdivisions are indicated with decimals, so there are no equivalent units of minutes or seconds. This system is not widely used except in France.

[b] During World War II, the U.S. artillery divided a right angle into 1000 parts called *angular mil*.

An angle θ is defined by

$$\theta \equiv \frac{x}{r} \tag{A-1}$$

where the angle is measured in radians. Because the perimeter around a circle is $2\pi r$, one complete revolution is

$$\theta = \frac{2\pi r}{r} = 2\pi\left(\frac{r}{r}\right) = 2\pi \text{ rad} \tag{A-2}$$

The perimeter may also be divided into 360 equally spaced divisions called *degrees.* Therefore,

$$2\pi \text{ rad} = 360° \tag{A-3}$$

The degree may be further subdivided into 60 divisions called *minutes,* and the minutes may be subdivided into 60 divisions called *seconds.* This is a fractional system of measuring angles that dates back to the Babylonians.

A.2 SOLID ANGLE

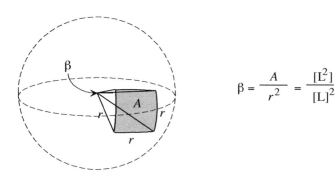

$$\beta = \frac{A}{r^2} = \frac{[L^2]}{[L]^2}$$

TABLE A.2
Solid angle conversion factors (Reference)

	Square Degree	Square Minute	Square Second	Steradian	Sphere
1 square degree =	1	$(60)^2$	$(3600)^2$	$(\pi/180)^2$	$(\pi/4)(180)^{-2}$
1 square minute =	$(1/60)^2$	1	$(60)^2$	$(\pi/10,800)^2$	$(\pi/4)(10,800)^{-2}$
1 square second =	$(1/3600)^2$	$(1/60)^2$	1	$(\pi/648,000)^2$	$(\pi/4)(648,000)^{-2}$
1 steradian =	$(180/\pi)^2$	$(10,800/\pi)^2$	$(648,000/\pi)^2$	1	$(4\pi)^{-1}$
1 sphere =	$(4/\pi)(180)^2$	$(4/\pi)(10,800)^2$	$(4/\pi)(648,000)^2$	4π	1

1 sphere = 2 hemisphere	1 sphere = 8 spherical right angles

A solid angle β is defined as the surface area on the sphere A divided by the radius r squared:

$$\beta \equiv \frac{A}{r^2} \tag{A-4}$$

The surface can be defined by projecting four radii from the center of a sphere and connecting the ends of adjacent radii with circumference segments. If the angle between adjacent radii is one radian, then a square is defined on the sphere surface that has circumference segments of length r. This solid angle is a *steradian,* given by the formula

$$\beta = \frac{A}{r^2} = \frac{r^2}{r^2} = 1 \text{ steradian} \tag{A-5}$$

APPENDIX A   UNIT CONVERSION FACTORS   **263**

If the angle between adjacent radii is 1 degree, then the solid angle is a *square degree*; if the angle between adjacent radii is 1 minute, then the solid angle is a *square minute*; and if the angle between adjacent radii is 1 second, then the solid angle is a *square second*. Table A.2 shows the relationship between these various solid angle measurements.

If a sphere is divided into two parts, then the solid angle is a *hemisphere*. If a hemisphere is divided into four equal parts, the solid angle formed is a *spherical right angle*.

A.3   LENGTH

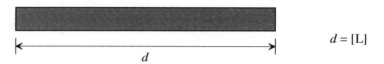

$$d = [L]$$

TABLE A.3
Length conversion factors (Reference)

	cm	m	km	in	ft	mi [e]
1 centimeter =	1	0.01	1.0000 E–05	0.3937	0.03281	6.214 E–06
1 meter =	100	1	0.001	39.37	3.281	6.214 E–04
1 kilometer =	1.00 E+05	1000	1	3.937 E+04	3281	0.6214
1 inch [b] =	2.54000	0.02540	2.540 E–05	1	0.08333	1.578 E–05
1 foot [a] =	30.48000	0.304800	3.048 E–04	12	1	1.894 E–04
1 U.S. statute mile =	1.609 E+05	1609	1.609	6.336 E+04	5280	1

1 nautical mile (n. mile) [f]=1852 m=1.151 mi=6076 ft	1 rod (rd) = 1 pole = 1 perch = 16.5 ft	1 fermi (fm) [j] = 1.00 E–15 m
1 ångström (Å) [k] = 1.00 E–10 m	1 yard (yd) = 3 ft	1 micron (μ) [l] = 1.00 E–06 m
1 light-year (ly) [g] = 9.4606 E+12 km	1 bolt of cloth = 120 ft	1 printer's pica = 0.16604 in
1 parsec (pc) [h] = 3.086 E+13 km	1 mil [d] = 1 thou = 0.001 in	1 printer's pica = 12 points
1 astronomical unit (i) = 1.496 E+08 km	1 pace = 30 in	1 fathom (fath) [c] = 6 ft
1 statute league = 2640 fathoms	1 cable [m] = 120 fathoms	1 cubit = 18 in
1 chain (ch) = 66 ft = 100 Gunter's links (li)	1 palm = 3 in	1 span = 9 in
1 furlong (fur) = 660 ft = 1/8 mi	1 hand = 4 in	1 skein = 360 ft

[a] The *foot* has been used in England for over 1000 years and is approximately equal to the length of a man's foot.
[b] The *inch* is derived from "ynce," the Anglo-Saxon word for twelfth part.
[c] A *fathom* is used to describe the depth of the sea. It is approximately the distance between the hands when the arms are out-stretched; its name is derived from the Anglo-Saxon word for "embrace."
[d] The *mil* is equal to one thousandth of an inch and is not to be confused with the millimeter. It is commonly used in metal machining.
[e] The *mile* traces to the Romans and is about equal to 1000 double paces (about 5 ft).
[f] The *nautical mile* is the average meridian length of 1 minute of latitude, a definition that makes navigation easier.
[g] The *light-year* is the distance light travels in 1 year.
[h] The *parsec* is the height of an isosceles triangle of which the base is equal to the diameter of the earth's orbit around the sun, and the angle opposite that base is 1".
[i] An *astronomical unit* is approximately equal to the mean distance from the earth to the sun.
[j] The *fermi* is used to measure nuclear distances.
[k] The *ångström* is used to measure atomic distances (a hydrogen atom is approximately 1 Å).
[l] The *micron* is slang for "micrometer" and is not SI.
[m] The *cable* is used to measure lengths at sea and dates back to the middle of the 16th century.

A.4 AREA

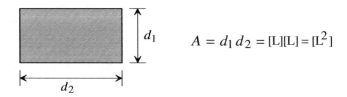

$$A = d_1 d_2 = [L][L] = [L^2]$$

TABLE A.4
Area conversion factors (Reference)

	m^2	cm^2	ft^2	in^2
1 square meter =	1	1.000 E+04	10.76	1550
1 square centimeter =	1.000 E–04	1	0.001076	0.1550
1 square foot =	0.09290	929.0	1	144
1 square inch =	6.452 E–04	6.452	0.006944	1

1 square mile = 2.788 E+07 ft^2 = 640 acres	1 are (a) [a] = 100 m^2
1 yd^2 = 9 ft^2	1 hectare (ha) [a] = 100 are = 10,000 m^2 = 2.471 acres
1 square rod = 30.25 yd^2 = 272.25 ft^2	1 barn (b) [d] = 1.0000 E–28 m^2
1 rood = 40 square rod	1 circular mil (cir mils) [c] = (0.001 in)$^2\pi$/4 = 7.854 E–07 in^2
1 acre [b] = 4 roods = 160 square rods = 43,560 ft^2	1 U.S. township = 36 mi^2 = 36 sections

[a] An area 10 m on a side is an *are* and an area 100 m on a side is a *hectare* (i.e., 100 are). Both the are and hectare are used in international agriculture to measure land area.
[b] The *acre,* which has been in existence since about 1300, is the approximate area that a yoke of oxen could plow in a day.
[c] A *circular mil* is the cross-sectional area of a circle that is 1 mil (0.001 in) in diameter. It was first used to measure the cross-sectional area of wire.
[d] The *barn* is used to measure the effective target area of atomic nuclei when bombarded with particles. The unit was invented in 1942 as Manhattan Project code; it probably derives from the expression "I bet you couldn't hit the broadside of a barn."

A.5 VOLUME

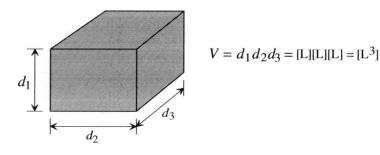

$$V = d_1 d_2 d_3 = [L][L][L] = [L^3]$$

APPENDIX A   UNIT CONVERSION FACTORS   **265**

TABLE A.5
Volume conversion factors (Reference)

	m³	cm³	L	ft³	in³
1 cubic meter =	1	1.000 E+06	1000	35.31	6.102 E+04
1 cubic centimeter =	1.000 E–06	1	0.001	3.531 E–05	0.06102
1 liter =	0.001000	1000	1	0.03531	61.02
1 cubic foot =	0.02832	2.832 E+04	28.32	1	1728
1 cubic inch =	1.639 E–05	16.39	1.639 E–02	5.787 E–04	1

1 acre-foot [d] = 43,560 ft³	1 stere (st) [a] = 1 m³	1 λ = 1 μL [b]
1 board-foot (fbm or bd-ft) [e] = 144 in³	1 yd³ = 27 ft³	1 cord (wood) [f] = 128 ft³
1 barrel (bbl) [h] = 42 gal	1 masonry perch = 24.75 ft³	1 cord-foot [g] = 16 ft³
1 U.K. gallon = 1 Imperial gallon = 1.2009 U.S gallon [c]		1 ft³ = 7.4805195 U.S. gallon (liq)

[a] The *stere* is no longer recommended.
[b] 1 μL is sometimes called 1 λ, but the use of this unit is not recommended.
[c] The *gallon* was first mentioned in 1342 and was given legal status in 1602. The U.S. gallon originated with the old English wine gallon in Colonial times. The *Imperial gallon* (which is about 20% larger than the U.S. gallon) is defined by a 1963 British law as the volume occupied by 10 lb$_m$ of distilled water provided the water has a density of 0.998859 g/mL weighed in air with a density of 0.001217 g/mL against weights with a density of 8.136 g/mL.
[d] An *acre-foot* is the volume when one acre is covered by water with 1 ft depth. This unit is commonly used in agricultural irrigation.
[e] A *board-foot* corresponds to the volume occupied by a board that is 1 ft × 1 ft × 1 in.
[f] The *cord* describes the volume of a wood stack that measures 4 ft × 4 ft × 8 ft.
[g] A *cord-foot* describes the volume of a wood stack that measures 4 ft × 4 ft × 1 ft.
[h] U.S. petroleum barrel.

TABLE A.6
Customary units of volume (Reference)

United Kingdom (Liquids and Solids)		
20 minims (min)	= 1 scruple	= 1.1838 E–06 m³
3 scruples	= 1 fluid drachm	= 3.5515 E–06 m³
8 fluid drachms	= 1 fluid ounce (fl oz)	= 2.8413 E–05 m³
5 fluid ounces	= 1 gill or noggin	= 1.4207 E–04 m³
4 gills	= 1 pint (pt)	= 5.6825 E–04 m³
2 pints	= 1 quart (qt)	= 1.1365 E–03 m³
2 quarts	= 1 pottle or quartern (dry)	= 2.2730 E–03 m³
2 quarterns (dry)	= 1 gallon (gal)	= 4.5461 E–03 m³
2 gallons	= 1 peck (pk)	= 9.0919 E–03 m³
4 pecks	= 1 bushel (bu)	= 3.6368 E–02 m³
9 gallons	= 1 firkin	= 4.0914 E–02 m³
9 pecks	= 1 kilderkins	= 8.1830 E–02 m³
3 bushels	= 1 sack or bag	= 1.0910 E–01 m³
36 gallons	= 1 barrel (bbl)	= 1.6365 E–01 m³
8 bushels	= 1 quarter or seam	= 2.9094 E–01 m³
640 gallons	= 1 lasts	= 2.9094 m³

United States (Liquid)		
60 minims (min)	= 1 fluid dram (fl dr)	= 3.6967 E–06 m³
3 teaspoons (t or tsp)	= 1 tablespoon (T or Tbsp)	= 1.4787 E–05 m³
2 tablespoons	= 1 fluid ounce (fl oz)	= 2.9574 E–05 m³
8 fluid drams	= 1 fluid ounce (fl oz)	= 2.9574 E–05 m³
4 fluid ounces	= 1 gill	= 1.1829 E–04 m³
2 gills	= 1 cup	= 2.3659 E–04 m³
2 cups	= 1 liquid pint (pt)	= 4.7318 E–04 m³
2 liquid pints	= 1 liquid quart (qt)	= 9.4635 E–04 m³
4 liquid quarts	= 1 gallon (gal)	= 3.7854 E–03 m³
9 gallons	= 1 firkin	= 3.4068 E–02 m³
31.5 gallons	= 1 barrel (bbl)*	= 1.1924 E–01 m³
63 gallons	= 1 hogshead (hhd)	= 2.3847 E–01 m³
84 gallons	= 1 puncheon	= 3.1797 E–01 m³
126 gallons	= 1 U.K. butt	= 4.7696 E–01 m³
252 gallons	= 1 tun	= 9.5392 E–01 m³

United States (Dry)		
2 dry pints	= 1 dry quart (qt)	= 1.1012 E–03 m³
4 dry quarts	= 1 dry gallon (gal)	= 4.4049 E–03 m³
2 dry gallons	= 1 peck (pk)	= 8.8098 E–03 m³
4 pecks	= 1 bushel (bu)	= 3.5239 E–02 m³
105 dry quarts	= 1 dry barrel (bbl)*	= 1.1563 E–01 m³

*Not to be confused with a U.S. petroleum barrel.

A.6   MASS

 [M]

TABLE A.7
Mass unit conversions (Reference)

	g	kg	lb$_m$	slug
1 gram-mass =	1	0.001	0.002205	6.852 E–05
1 kilogram-mass =	1000	1	2.205	0.06852
1 pound-mass [c] =	453.6	0.4536	1	0.03108
1 slug =	1.4594 E+04	14.594	32.174	1

1 grain [b] = 6.479891 E–05 kg
1 short hundred weight = 100 lb$_m$
1 short ton = 2000 lb$_m$
1 tonne (t) = 1 metric ton = 1000 kg
1 metric carat [d] = 2.000 E–04 kg
1 point = 0.01 metric carat
1 γ [a] = 1 μg = 1.000 E–09 kg

1 glug = 980.665 g = 0.980665 kg
1 mug = 1 metric slug = 1 par = 1 TME = 9.80665 kg
1 unified atomic mass unit (u) [e] = 1 dalton = 1.6605402 E–27 kg
1 atomic mass unit, chem. (amu) [e] = 1.66024 E–27 kg
1 atomic mass unit, phys. (amu) [e] = 1.65979 E–27 kg
1 eV of equivalent mass [f] = 1.7827 E–36 kg

[a] The symbol "γ" is used to represent 1 μg, but its use is discouraged.
[b] The *grain* dates back to the 16th century and is thought to be equal to the weight of a wheat grain.
[c] The *pound* originated with the Roman Libra (327 g). The Imperial Standard Pound was defined in 1855 as the mass of platinum with given dimensions. In 1963, the pound was defined as 0.45359237 kg exactly, a number chosen because it is evenly divided by seven to ease the conversion from grains to grams.
[d] Precious stones are measured in *metric carats,* which correspond to 200 mg.
[e] The *atomic mass unit* was originally intended to be the mass of a single hydrogen atom, the lightest element. In 1885, it was suggested that more elements would have integer numbers for their atomic weights if the atomic mass unit were defined using 1/16 the mass of oxygen. Chemists used oxygen in its natural abundance (2480:5:1 $^{16}O{:}^{18}O{:}^{17}O$) whereas physicists used isotopically pure ^{16}O for their standard. Thus, there was a slight discrepancy between the scales used by chemists and physicists (272 parts per million). It was later found that expressing the atomic mass unit as 1/12th the mass of a single carbon-12 atom allowed even more elements to have masses that were integer numbers. Thus, the *unified atomic mass unit* was established, which had the added benefit of eliminating the discrepancy between the chemist and physicist scales.
[f] The famous Einstein relationship $E=mc^2$ showed that when mass is destroyed, energy is produced (and vice versa). The amount of energy E is found by multiplying the destroyed mass m by the speed of light c squared. Thus, physicists and nuclear engineers sometimes express mass in energy units, such as electron volts (eV).

APPENDIX A   UNIT CONVERSION FACTORS   **267**

TABLE A.8
Customary units of mass (Reference)

Avoirdupois Weights		Apothecaries Weights [b]		Troy Weights [c]	
1 pound (lb avdp) [a]		**1 pound (lb ap)**		**1 pound (lb t)**	
= 7000 grains [d]		**= 5760 grains [d]**		**= 5760 grains [d]**	
16 drams (dr avdp)	= 1 ounce (oz)	20 grains	= 1 scruple (s ap)	24 grains	= penny weight (dwt)
16 ounces	= 1 pound (lb avdp)	3 scruples	= 1 U.K. drachm (dr ap)	20 penny weights	= 1 ounce (oz t)
14 pounds	= 1 stone	3 scruples	= 1 U.S. dram (dr ap)	12 ounce (oz t)	= 1 pound (lb t)
28 pounds	= 1 quarter	8 drachm or dram	= 1 ounce (oz ap)		
112 pounds	= 1 long hundred weight (cwt)	12 ounce (oz ap)	= 1 pound (lb ap)		
252 pounds	= 1 wey				
2240 pounds	= 1 long ton				

[a] The common pound with which we are familiar (and the pound indicated by the symbol "lb_m") is the avoirdupois pound.
[b] The apothecary scale is not used anymore.
[c] The troy scale is used in the United States for weighing precious metals.
[d] The grain is the same in all systems.

A.7 DENSITY

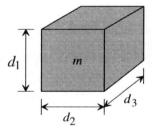

$$\rho = \frac{m}{d_1 \, d_2 \, d_3} = \frac{[M]}{[L][L][L]} = \frac{[M]}{[L^3]}$$

TABLE A.9
Density conversion factors (Reference)

	g/cm³	kg/m³	lb_m/ft³	lb_m/in³	slug/ft³
1 gram per cubic centimeter =	1	1000	62.43	0.03613	1.940
1 kilogram per cubic meter =	0.001	1	0.06243	3.613 E–05	0.001940
1 pound-mass per cubic foot =	0.01602	16.02	1	5.787 E–04	0.03108
1 pound-mass per cubic inch =	27.68	2.768 E+04	1728	1	53.71
1 slug per cubic foot =	0.5154	515.4	32.174	0.01862	1

Density can also be expressed by *specific gravity* SG, a dimensionless number formed by dividing the density of substance A ρ_A by the density of a reference substance ρ_R:

$$SG = \frac{\rho_A}{\rho_R} \tag{A-6}$$

Although any reference may be used, the most common reference substance is water at its maximum density (4°C, 1.000 g/cm³).

A.8 TIME

TABLE A.10
Time conversion factors (Reference)

	yr	d	h	min	s
1 year [a] =	1	365.24	8.766 E+03	5.259 E+05	3.1557 E+07
1 day [c] =	2.738 E–03	1	24	1440	8.640 E+04
1 hour [d] =	1.141 E–04	4.167 E–02	1	60	3600
1 minute [e] =	1.901 E–06	6.944 E–04	1.667 E–02	1	60
1 second [e] =	3.169 E–08	1.157 E–05	2.778 E–04	1.667 E–02	1

1 year = 365.24 solar days [c]	1 year = 366.24 sidereal days [b]	1 week = 7 days
1 mean solar day [c] = 86,400 s	1 sidereal day [b] = 86,164 s	1 fortnight = 2 weeks

[a] A *year* is the time required for the earth to return to a given position as it orbits the sun. Our calendar is adjusted to the *tropical year*, the time it takes for the earth to orbit the sun between successive vernal equinoxes (March 21, the spring date in which light and dark are equal).

[b] A *sidereal day* is the mean time taken for the earth to complete one revolution as determined by comparing the earth's position to distant stars.

[c] A *solar day* is the mean time required for the sun to return to a fixed position (e.g., overhead) in the sky. The solar day and sidereal day differ. The solar day is slightly longer because the sun is viewed from a different position as the earth orbits the sun. In common parlance, we refer to a solar day, not a sidereal day. It has been known since the Egyptians and Babylonians that there are $365\frac{1}{4}$ solar days per year.

[d] In ancient times, the day was divided into 24 time fractions which we call *hours*. Light and darkness were each divided into 12 equal time fractions regardless of the time of year. According to the season, the length of the dark-hour differed from the light-hour. When mechanical clocks were invented, the length of the hour was standardized. In England, each community kept its own local time; each community was completely independent of the others. In 1880, Greenwich mean time was established as the official time throughout England. Today, most of the world has agreed to standardize on Greenwich mean time.

[e] The *minute* and *second* of time trace to the Babylonians, who used units of 60. Efforts to decimalize time have proved unsuccessful.

APPENDIX A   UNIT CONVERSION FACTORS   **269**

A.9   SPEED/VELOCITY

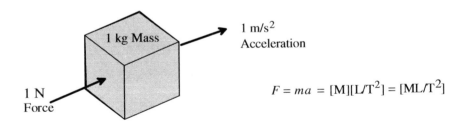

$$\text{Speed, Velocity} = \frac{d}{t_2 - t_1} = \frac{[L]}{[T]} = [L/T]$$

TABLE A.11
Speed/velocity conversion factors (Reference)

	m/s	cm/s	ft/s	km/h	mi/h (mph)	knot
1 meter per second =	1	100	3.281	3.6	2.237	1.944
1 centimeter per second =	0.01	1	0.03281	0.036	0.02237	0.01944
1 foot per second =	0.3048	30.48	1	1.097	0.6818	0.5925
1 kilometer per hour =	0.2778	27.78	0.9113	1	0.6214	0.5400
1 mile per hour =	0.4470	44.70	1.467	1.609	1	0.8690
1 nautical mile per hour =	0.5144	51.44	1.688	1.852	1.151	1

1 knot = 1 nautical mile per hour	1 mi/min = 88.00 ft/s = 60.00 mi/h

A.10   FORCE

1 kg Mass

1 m/s² Acceleration

1 N Force

$$F = ma = [M][L/T^2] = [ML/T^2]$$

TABLE A.12
Force conversion factors (Reference)

	N	dyne	pdl	kg_f	g_f	lb_f
1 newton =	1	1.00 E+05	7.233	0.1020	102.0	0.2248
1 dyne =	1.00 E-05	1	7.233 E-05	1.020 E-06	0.001020	2.248 E-06
1 poundal =	0.1383	1.383 E+04	1	0.01410	14.10	0.03108
1 kilogram-force =	9.807	9.807 E+05	70.93	1	1000	2.205
1 gram-force =	0.009807	980.7	0.07093	0.001	1	0.002205
1 pound-force =	4.448	4.448 E+05	32.174	0.4536	453.6	1

1 pound-force = 16 ounce-force	1 kilopond [b] = 1 kg_f	1 kip [a] = 1000 lb_f
1 ton-force = 2000 lb_f	1 fors [c] = 1 g_f	

[a] The *kip* (for *Kilo Imperial Pound*) is sometimes used to describe the load on a structure.
[b] The *kilopond* is used in Germany for "kilogram-force."
[c] The *fors* (Latin for "force") was proposed in 1956 as an alternate name for "gram-force."

A.11   PRESSURE

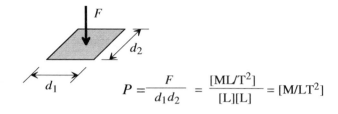

$$P = \frac{F}{d_1 d_2} = \frac{[ML/T^2]}{[L][L]} = [M/LT^2]$$

TABLE A.13
Pressure conversion factors (Reference)

	Pa	dyne/cm²	lb$_f$/ft²	lb$_f$/in² (psi)	atm	cm-Hg	in-H$_2$O
1 newton per square meter =	1	10	0.02089	1.450 E–04	9.869 E–06	7.501 E–04	0.004015
1 dyne per square centimeter =	0.1	1	0.002089	1.450 E–05	9.869 E–07	7.501 E–05	4.015 E–04
1 pound-force per square foot =	47.88	478.8	1	0.006944	4.725 E–04	0.03591	0.1922
1 pound-force per square inch =	6895	6.895 E+04	144	1	0.06805	5.171	27.68
1 standard atmosphere [c] =	1.013 E+05	1.013 E+06	2116	14.696	1	76	406.8
1 centimeter [d] of mercury at 0°C =	1333	1.333 E+04	27.84	0.1934	0.01316	1	5.353
1 inch [d] of water at 4°C =	249.1	2491	5.202	0.03613	0.002458	0.1868	1

1 kg$_f$/m² = 9.806650 Pa
1 atm = 2.493 ft-Hg = 33.90 ft-H$_2$O = 27,714 ft-air (1 atm, 60°F) [d]
1 bar [a] = 1 barye = 1.00 E+06 dyne/cm² = 0.1 MPa = 100 kPa ≈ 1 atm
1 millibar (mb) = 1.00 E+03 dyne/cm² = 1000 microbar (μb) [b]
1 torr [e] = (101325/760) Pa ≈ 1 μm-Hg = 0.1 cm-Hg

1 kip/in² (ksi) = 1000 lb$_f$/in²
1 technical atmosphere [c] = 1 kg$_f$/cm²
1 micron pressure = 1 μm-Hg [d]
1 g$_f$/cm² = 980.665 dyne/cm²

[a] The bar is most commonly employed in meteorology because it is approximately equal to the atmospheric pressure on earth. Although the bar is not properly SI, its use is temporarily tolerated because it is so widespread. The *barye* was the original name given to this unit of pressure in 1900, but it has been shortened to "bar."

[b] Although there is no proper abbreviation for the bar, the *millibar* (mb) and *microbar* (μb) abbreviations are sometimes used.

[c] Because the atmospheric pressure changes (in fact, meteorologists measure it to predict weather changes), a *standard atmosphere* P° has been defined as 101,325.0 Pa. The *technical atmosphere* is defined as 1 kg$_f$/cm². Unless otherwise specified, an "atmosphere" is generally the "standard atmosphere." The use of *atmosphere* for pressure measurements is discouraged by SI, but its use will probably continue because it is easily visualized.

[d] The simplest way to measure pressure is with a *manometer*, a U-shaped tube filled with liquid. Differences in pressure acting on each liquid column change the liquid levels, which are then easily read using a meterstick. For accurate work, the conversion factors in Table A.13 may be used only if the temperature of the liquid is controlled [4°C for water, 0°C for mercury (Hg)]. (Alternatively, tables listing the liquid density as a function of temperature may be used to correct the reading, provided the manometer temperature is known.) Also, the local acceleration due to gravity (*g*) affects the reading. The values given in Table A.13 use the standard acceleration due to gravity (*g°*).

[e] The *torr* differs from a mm-Hg by less than 1 part in 7 million. The use of *torr* is discouraged by SI.

APPENDIX A   UNIT CONVERSION FACTORS   **271**

A.12 ENERGY

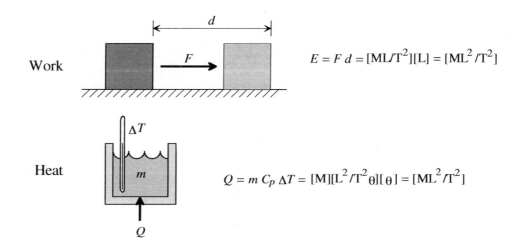

Work

$$E = F d = [ML/T^2][L] = [ML^2/T^2]$$

Heat

$$Q = m\, C_p\, \Delta T = [M][L^2/T^2\theta][\theta] = [ML^2/T^2]$$

TABLE A.14
Energy conversion factors (Reference)

	J	erg	ft·lb$_f$	cal	Btu	kW·h	hp·h
1 joule =	1	1.000 E+07	0.7376	0.2390	9.485 E–04	2.778 E–07	3.725 E–07
1 erg =	1.000 E–07	1	7.376 E–08	2.390 E–08	9.485 E–11	2.778 E–14	3.725 E–14
1 foot pound$_f$ =	1.356	1.356 E+07	1	0.3240	0.001286	3.766 E–07	5.051 E–07
1 calorie [b] =	4.184	4.184 E+07	3.086	1	0.003968	1.162 E–06	1.559 E–06
1 Brit. thermal unit [c] =	1054	1.054 E+10	777.6	252.0	1	2.929 E–04	3.928 E–04
1 kilowatt hour [d] =	3.600 E+06	3.600 E+13	2.655 E+06	8.606 E+05	3414	1	1.341
1 horsepower hour [d] =	2.685 E+06	2.685 E+13	1.980 E+06	6.414 E+05	2545	0.7457	1

1 electron volt (eV) [f] = 1.60217733 E–19 J   1 kcal [a] = 1 calorie (kg)   1 W·h = 3600 J [d]
1 kg$_f$·m = 9.806650 J   1 g$_f$·cm = 980.6650 erg   1 W·s = 1 J [d]
1 V·C = 1 J   1 V·A·s = 1 J   1 Pa·m^3 = 1 J [e]
1 (dyne/cm^2)·cm^3 = 1 erg [e]   1 atm·L = 101.3 J [e]   1 atm·cm^3 = 0.1013 J [e]
1 atm·ft^3 = 2116 ft·lb$_f$ [e]   1 psia·ft^3 = 144 ft·lb$_f$ [e]   1 bar·cm^3 = 0.1 J [e]
1 ton (nuclear equivalent TNT) = 4.184 E+09 J

[a] *Kilocalorie* is the heat required to raise 1 kg water by 1 K. Because the heat capacity of water is not constant, a variety of kilocalories are defined. This is the *thermochemical* kilocalorie, the most commonly used.
[b] *Calorie* is the heat required to raise 1 g water by 1 K. In diet books, the energy content in food is usually expressed in *calories*, but actually *kilocalories* are meant. Sometimes dietitians use *Calorie* to mean *kilocalorie*. Because the heat capacity of water is not constant, a variety of calories are defined. This is the *thermochemical* calorie, the most commonly used.
[c] *British thermal unit* is the heat required to raise 1 lb$_m$ water by 1 F°. Because the heat capacity of water is not constant, a variety of Btus are defined. This is the *thermochemical* Btu, the most commonly used.
[d] Energy = power × time. These units can be visualized as answering the question "how much energy is expended if a 1-kW (1-hp) motor operates for 1 hour?"
[e] Energy = pressure × volume
[f] The energy required to move a single electron through a vacuum with 1 volt of potential is an *electron volt*.

A.13   POWER

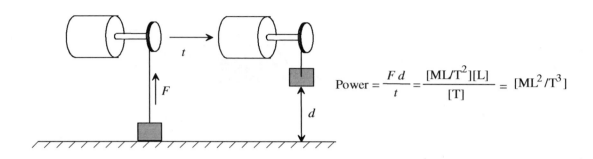

$$\text{Power} = \frac{F\,d}{t} = \frac{[ML/T^2][L]}{[T]} = [ML^2/T^3]$$

TABLE A.15
Power conversion factors (Reference)

	W	kW	ft·lb$_f$/s	hp	cal/s	Btu/h
1 watt [a] =	1	0.001	0.7376	0.001341	0.2390	3.414
1 kilowatt =	1000	1	737.6	1.341	239.0	3414
1 foot-pound$_f$ per second =	1.356	0.001356	1	0.001818	0.3240	4.629
1 horsepower [b] =	745.7	0.7457	550	1	178.2	2546
1 calorie per second =	4.184	0.004184	3.086	0.005611	1	14.29
1 British thermal unit per hour =	0.2929	2.929 E–04	0.2160	3.928 E–04	0.07000	1

1 W = 1.00 E+07 erg/s   1 ft·lb$_f$/s = 60 ft·lb$_f$/min = 3600 ft·lb$_f$/h   1 hp = 33,000 ft·lb$_f$/min = 550 ft·lb$_f$/s
1 hp (electric) ≡ 746 W   1 ton of refrigeration [d] = 12,000 Btu/h
1 hp = 0.0760181 hp (boiler) = 0.999598 hp (electric) = 1.01387 hp (metric) = 0.999540 hp (water) [c]

[a] A *watt* is a J/s.
[b] In 1782, James Watt (1736–1819) devised the *horsepower* to help him sell steam engines. He assumed a horse could pull with a force of 180 lb$_f$ and, when harnessed to a capstan, would walk a 24-ft diameter circle $2\frac{1}{2}$ times each minute. This was a work expenditure of 32,400 ft·lb$_f$/min, which he rounded to 33,000 ft·lb$_f$/min (550 ft·lb$_f$/s). Engines are often rated in *brake horsepower* (bhp) or *shaft horsepower*, which is the power available at the turning drive shaft.
[c] A *boiler horsepower* (bhp) is the amount of heat needed to evaporate 34.5 lb$_m$/h of water at 212°F. A *metric horsepower* is the power required to raise 75 kg 1 meter per second.
[d] A *ton of refrigeration* is a U.S. term that describes the amount of refrigeration required to freeze 1 ton (2000 lb$_m$) per day of water at 32°F.

A.14   AMOUNT OF SUBSTANCE

The *mole* is the number of atoms in 0.012 kg (12 g) of carbon-12. This number is given special recognition as *Avogadro's constant* N_A, which is

$$N_A = 6.0221367 \times 10^{23} \text{ atoms/mol} \tag{A-7}$$

The *coulomb* C is the number of electrons that flow in a 1-ampere current in 1 second. The number of electrons in a coulomb N_C is

$$N_C = 6.24150636 \times 10^{18} \text{ electrons/C} \tag{A-8}$$